MW00615939

Searching for ORDER IN the COMPLEXITY of Evolving Worlds

THE SANTA FE INSTITUTE is the world headquarters for complexity science, operated as an independent, nonprofit research and education center located in Santa Fe, New Mexico. Our researchers endeavor to understand and unify the underlying, shared patterns in complex physical, biological, social, cultural, technological, and even possible astrobiological worlds. Our global research network of scholars spans borders, departments, and disciplines, bringing together curious minds steeped in rigorous logical, mathematical, and computational reasoning. As we reveal the unseen mechanisms and processes that shape these evolving worlds, we seek to use this understanding to promote the well-being of humankind and of life on earth.

ACKNOWLEDGMENTS

The SFI Press would not exist without Andrew Feldstein,
Feldstein Program on History, Regulation, & Law,
William H. Miller, Miller Omega Program,
and Alana Levinson-LaBrosse.

[HISTORY, BIG HISTORY, & METAHISTORY]

DAVID C. KRAKAUER, JOHN LEWIS GADDIS,
& KENNETH POMERANZ, EDS.

THE SANTA FE INSTITUTE PRESS

1399 Hyde Park Road
Santa Fe, New Mexico 87501

History, Big History, & Metahistory
ISBN (PAPERBACK): 978-1-947864-02-3

The SFI Press is supported by the
Feldstein Program on History, Regulation, & Law,
the Miller Omega Program, and
Alana Levinson-LaBrosse.

SEMINAR SERIES

New findings emerging from the Institute's ongoing
working groups and research projects, for an audience
of interdisciplinary scholars and practitioners.

Chapters previously appeared in
*Cliodynamics: The Journal of Quantitative History
and Cultural Evolution*, Vol. 2, no. 1 (2011).

In them there was talk of algebraic series and benzol rings, the materialist philosophy of history and the universalist one as well, bridge-piles, the evolution of music, the spirit of the motor-car, Hata 606, the theory of relativity, Bohr's atomic theory, autogenous welding, the flora of the Himalayas, psychoanalysis, individual psychology, experimental psychology, physiological psychology, social psychology, and all the other achievements that prevent a time that has been enriched by them from producing good, whole, integral human beings.

— ROBERT MUSIL
The Man Without Qualities, Vol. 1, Chapter 54
Translated by Eithne Wilkins & Ernst Kaiser

CONTRIBUTORS

EDITORS & AUTHORS
John Lewis Gaddis *Yale University*
David C. Krakauer *Santa Fe Institute*
Kenneth Pomeranz *University of Chicago*

AUTHORS
David Christian *Macquarie University*
Douglas H. Erwin *National Museum of Natural History*
Murray Gell-Mann *Santa Fe Institute*
Geoffrey G. Harpham *National Humanities Center*
J. R. McNeill *Georgetown University*
Fred Spier *University of Amsterdam*
Peter Turchin *University of Connecticut*
Geerat J. Vermeij *University of California, Davis*
Geoffrey B. West *Santa Fe Institute*

TABLE OF CONTENTS

Introduction: An Inquiry into History,
Big History, & Metahistory
David C. Krakauer, John Lewis Gaddis, & Kenneth Pomeranz . . *i*

1: A Single Historical Continuum
David Christian 1

2: A Paleontological Look at History
Douglas H. Erwin 39

3: War, Peace, & Everything: Thoughts on Tolstoy
John Lewis Gaddis 57

4: Regularities in Human Affairs
Murray Gell-Mann 73

5: Metahistory's Dangerous Dream
Geoffrey G. Harpham .101

6: The Star Gazer and the Flesh Eater: Elements of
a Theory of Metahistory
David C. Krakauer .117

7: Homogeneity, Heterogeneity, Pigs & Pandas
in Human History
J. R. McNeill 151

8: Labeling and Analyzing Historical Phenomena:
Some Preliminary Challenges
Kenneth Pomeranz .173

9: Complexity in Big History
Fred Spier 205

10: Toward Cliodynamics — an Analytical,
Predictive Science of History
Peter Turchin 235

11: A Historical Conspiracy: Competition, Opportunity,
& the Emergence of Direction in History
Geerat J. Vermeij .261

12: Can there be a Quantitative Theory for the
History of Life & Society?
Geoffrey B. West .289

INTRODUCTION:
AN INQUIRY INTO HISTORY,
BIG HISTORY, & METAHISTORY

David C. Krakauer, Santa Fe Institute
John Lewis Gaddis, Yale University
Kenneth Pomeranz, University of Chicago

WHAT IS HISTORY ANYWAY? Most people would say it's what happened in the past, but how far back does the past extend? To the first written sources? To what other forms of evidence reveal about pre-literate civilizations? What does that term mean—an empire, a nation, a city, a village, a family, a lonely hermit somewhere? Why stop with people: shouldn't history also comprise the environment in which they exist, and if so, on what scale and how far back? And as long as we're headed in that direction, why stop with Earth and the solar system? Why not go all the way back to the Big Bang itself?

There's obviously no consensus on how to answer these questions, but even asking them raises another set of questions about history: who should be doing it? Traditionally trained historians, for whom archives are the only significant source? Historians willing to go beyond archives, who must therefore rely on, and to some extent themselves become, psychologists, sociologists, anthropologists, archaeologists? But if they're also going to take environments into account, don't they also have to know something about climatology, biology, paleontology, geology, and even astronomy? And how can they do that without knowing some basic physics, chemistry, and mathematics?

You see where this is going: history, by this capacious definition, includes everything that has happened up until the present moment—and because the present moment has already become the past by the time you've finished reading this sentence, history must also provide a basis (what other one could there be?) for anticipating the future.

What is to prevent history, then, from being the study of "life, the Universe, and everything," as the late Douglas Adams proposed in his *The Hitchhiker's Guide to the Galaxy*? Nothing in principle, but there is a problem in *practice*, which is that no one person, or academic department, or professional discipline, or method of inquiry, can do it all. Students of this kind of Very Big History have for very good reasons divided themselves into fields, sub-fields, and even micro-fields, knowing that things rarely get simpler the more closely you look at them.

Much good has come of this. Our knowledge of this capaciously defined past has expanded exponentially over the past several hundred years. We now have a much clearer sense of who we are and where we came from than was available to, say, Copernicus, when he first ventured the suggestion that the Universe did not revolve around us.

Some bad has come of this process as well, however. For if the volume of information in relation to time looks like a hockey stick as it approaches our era, rapidly accelerating in the production of contemporary knowledge—then it is a laminated hockey stick, the parts of which define a trajectory without interacting with one another. How much do we really know, therefore, about where we came from, who we are — and where we may be going—if the disciplines we've divided ourselves into have lost the languages that would allow them to speak to anyone apart from themselves?

Moreover, it seems likely that the disciplines themselves develop less than optimally when they lack ready access to each other's insights and methods. Indeed, it seems likely that history suffers most of all from such segmentation. At least to some extent, history, more than the study of literature, or economics, or political science (though perhaps not much more than anthropology or sociology) aims to integrate the understanding of how human social arrangements, technologies, interactions with the larger biosphere, intellectual creations, and even our habitual cognitive and emotional responses to the world around us have changed over a given period of time: no matter what s/he emphasizes as a researcher, the person who teaches a history of 19th century England knows it cannot omit dramatic changes in birth and death rates, the expansion of suffrage, the publication of *The Origin of Species*, the expansion of overseas possessions, or the environmental consequences of industrialization. So despite what has sometimes seemed a strong allergy to "theory" (of various sorts) in history departments, historians may have the most to gain by opening more lines of communication to people studying change over time in various phenomena and on various timescales.

This volume has grown out of a series of conversations and meetings, sponsored by the Santa Fe Institute, on how we might recover such languages. It proceeds from the proposition that if generalization is necessary within particular disciplines — how could it not be? — then it should also be useful across all the disciplines that take, as the subject of their inquiries, Very Big History. It pursues the possibility of taking what one of our contributors, Murray Gell-Mann, has called "a crude look at the whole." It explores the possibility that the science of complexity and its many tributary fields and concepts pioneered at Santa Fe, may provide new methods, or minimally metaphors, by which to do this. It is premised on the notion that curiosity — the foundation of all knowledge — requires the ability to be both a specialist and a generalist at the same time — and that this simultaneity of perspective is in need of new transdisciplinary approaches and ideas.

· ·

HOW MUCH DO WE REALLY KNOW, THEREFORE, ABOUT WHERE WE CAME FROM, WHO WE ARE — AND WHERE WE MAY BE GOING — IF THE DISCIPLINES WE'VE DIVIDED OURSELVES INTO HAVE LOST THE LANGUAGES THAT WOULD ALLOW THEM TO SPEAK TO ANYONE APART FROM THEMSELVES?

· ·

Our title, *History, Big History and Metahistory*, requires a brief explanation. By "history," we mean the study, chiefly, of written records, extending from the most ancient cuneiform tablet through the most recent e-mails and tweets. By "Big History," we mean all reconstructions of the past that do not rely on written materials. By "metahistory," we mean the patterns that emerge from both modes of inquiry which make generalization, and hence analysis, possible. We do not mean to imply by this sequence of terms that moving to the method and scale of "Big History" is the only way to search for meaningful patterns. We are, however, confident that juxtaposing types of inquiry developed to deal with change in literate societies with those developed to deal with a much longer record of change has proved to be one very useful way of exposing important, often neglected questions, about both what it makes sense to look for in the always-incomplete records of the past and how to do the looking.

As in any good discussion, our contributors do not all agree with one another. Some insist that there are unifying principles, or laws, to which both human and biological history are subject. Others seek ideas, tools, and perhaps standards of truth from dynamical systems, evolution, and statistics that could augment traditional approaches to history, but do not necessarily see such borrowings as requiring that history and Big History become a single discipline. One contributor sees any attempt at unification in the humanities as dangerous, citing as precedents the extent to which social Darwinism was used to

....

WE ARE CONFIDENT THAT JUXTAPOSING TYPES OF INQUIRY DEVELOPED TO DEAL WITH CHANGE IN LITERATE SOCIETIES AND THOSE DEVELOPED TO DEAL WITH A MUCH LONGER RECORD OF CHANGE HAS PROVED TO BE ONE VERY USEFUL WAY OF EXPOSING IMPORTANT, OFTEN NEGLECTED QUESTIONS.

....

abuse less powerful people and societies. All do share the view, however, that history is too important—and too encompassing—to be analyzed exclusively through the methods of qualitative text-based narratives. We have arranged our contributors alphabetically, for no better reason than to shuffle their ideas and to avoid enforcing on this volume's readers the editor's conclusions.

We start with **David Christian,** who discusses the chronometric revolution, and how this has led to a single historical continuum stretching all the way back to the Big Bang, allowing for what he calls Grand Unified Stories.

Douglas Erwin explores how paleontologists deal with the vagaries of preservation, how statistical techniques developed in biology and have been applied to textual evidence, and the complexities of nonuniform trends leading to convergent and parallel events.

John Lewis Gaddis shows that several 19th century searches for a science of history—those of Leo Tolstoy, Carl von Clausewitz, and Henry Adams—grasped key concepts of complexity theory, but lacked the means of visualizing and verifying it that are available today.

Murray Gell-Mann discusses the nature of empirical regularities, and their relationship to measures of complexity, and illustrates how apparently complex histories and patterns can sometimes be organized using simple models of growth and scaling.

Geoffrey Harpham discusses the possible limitations and abuses of unified frameworks of explanation, using the history of philology as a case study. Unchecked, scientific trajectories in a social matrix can lead to unjustified inferences.

David Krakauer introduces a range of concepts from nonlinear dynamics, statistical physics, and evolutionary biology, which he argues should be of use to all students of history. Using examples from traditional historicism, he shows how history often uses analogs of concepts and tools expressed quantitatively in the natural sciences.

John McNeill explores parallels between cultural and biological evolution, exploring patterns of increasing cultural heterogeneity through time, and the role that specialist (pandas) and generalist (pigs) societies and states have played in explaining these patterns.

Ken Pomeranz describes the ways in which naming historical phenomena influences how we then analyze them. Arguing that many of the classification schemes that are conventional among historians serve some other purposes well but are not very conducive to seeking meaningful generalizations or engaging in dialogue with scientists. He suggests other approaches while also giving reasons why they are far more likely to complement than displace currently popular taxonomies.

Fred Spier, speaking as an historian, explores how Big History might be brought within a reductive framework of physics, using the concept of free energy rate density, as a means of organizing major transitions, from the abiotic to the biotic and cultural domains.

Peter Turchin explores the value of general quantitative theory in areas where prediction is limited and comparative data and retrodiction need to be explored. The transformation of natural history into quantitative biology is used as possible precedent and model for a transformation of qualitative history.

Geerat Vermeij considers a grand, economic theory of history, in which biology and culture might both be subsumed. Concepts of competition, feedback, and power provide potential unifying historical concepts.

Geoffrey West argues for quantitative approaches to history through a suitable choice of coarse-grained variables. He proposes that it is unlikely that we shall discern common patterns at the level of individuals, but that if we allow ourselves to study collective phenomena, such as urban systems, then we might make surprising new discoveries.

No reader is likely to find all of these contributions persuasive, or perhaps even congenial. Nonetheless, we think that

....

... THESE EFFORTS SHOULD GIVE READERS WHAT THE

MEETINGS FROM WHICH THEY SPRANG GAVE TO THEIR

PARTICIPANTS: A BETTER SENSE OF THE RANGE OF CON-

VERSATIONS WE MIGHT JOIN.

....

most will gain more from engaging with them in their current diversity than they would gain from any superficial consensus we could wring from them. Readers may think of some of these chapters as introducing them to new tools, potentially useful for their current inquiries or for others they had previously deemed impossible. Other chapters stand as arguments about what sorts of inquiries should be attempted; still others as preliminary reports from lines of inquiry (in various historical disciplines) that it would be good for a wider range of scholars to know about. Each of these, of course, bears on the others, at least indirectly: what we should ask, what tools we have for answering new and old questions, and what people have found by asking unusual questions or using unusual tools are obviously overlapping issues.

The overlaps on display here are not nearly large enough to let us suggest a single, unified agenda for further work; they are, however, sufficiently numerous to suggest many places where more focused interdisciplinary projects might take root and prove fruitful. Perhaps even more important, these efforts should give readers what the meetings from which they sprang gave to their participants: a better sense of the range of conversations we might join, the opportunities and problems in those discussions, and some ways in which joining new conversations will give us new ways of analyzing our common past. ❧

ↄﻝ

A SINGLE HISTORICAL CONTINUUM

David Christian, Macquarie University

*"In our own generation we have been able to visualize our past
as human beings in the context of geological time and the prehistoric basis of our recorded history."*
—Grahame Clark,
Space, Time and Man: A Prehistorian's View [1]

IN THE MIDDLE OF THE TWENTIETH CENTURY, our
understanding of the past underwent a quiet revolution
whose full implications have yet to be integrated into
modern historical scholarship. At the heart of the revolution were new chronometric techniques, new ways
of dating past events.[1] For the first time, these techniques allowed the construction of reliable chronologies extending back before the first written documents,
before even the appearance of the first humans, back to
the early days of our planet and even to the birth of the
Universe as a whole. This expanded timeline provided
the foundation for the "Single Historical Continuum"
of my title. This chapter describes the chronometric
revolution and the creation of a single historical continuum. It then discusses some of the implications of
these changes for our understanding of "history." I am
a historian by training, so that, despite an enduring
amateur interest in the sciences, my account of the
chronometric revolution reflects the somewhat intu-
itive pattern-seeking methodologies of my discipline,
rather than the often more rigorous, and more mathematical methods of the natural sciences. I will argue
that the chronometric revolution requires a fundamental rethinking of what we understand by "history."

---

[1] Parts of this chapter are based on an earlier paper about the chronometric
revolution: "Historia, complejidad y revolución cronométrica" ["History,
Complexity and the Chronometric Revolution"] [2].

History Before the Chronometric Revolution

Historical scholarship has traditionally been confined to the study of human societies. There were many reasons for this bias. One that is often ignored is the technical fact that until very recently the only way to reliably date past events or objects was by using written documents generated by our human ancestors. Though often taken for granted by historians, good timelines are fundamental to historical scholarship because without them events cannot be ranked chronologically, and there can be no serious discussion of sequence or causality. History fades into myth. So the use of written records to create reliable timelines was fundamental to historical scholarship. Yet it also limited what historians could study, for it meant that good timelines were available only for the history of literate human societies. The result? History as a serious scholarly discipline came to mean human history rather than the study of the past as a whole.

Reliance on written records set chronological as well as topical limits. "History cannot discuss the origin of society," wrote Ranke in the 1860s, "for the art of writing, which is the basis of historical knowledge, is a comparatively late invention. ... The province of History is limited by the means at her command, and the historian would be over-bold who should venture to unveil the mystery of the primeval world, the relation of mankind to God and nature."[2] When pushed to their limits, written records could take scholars back, at most, 5,000 years, for that was when writing first appeared.[3] Beyond this chronological barrier, there could be no serious history. Of course, lack of chronological evidence did not prevent speculation. Christian tradition argued on the basis of biblical genealogies that God had created the earth about 6,000 years ago. Some traditions

---

[2] Cited in Dan Smail [3, p.1350].

[3] And even then, the evidence is often indirect. For example, evidence such as the Egyptian dynastic records carved on the famous Palermo stone (dating to about 2,500 BCE), can be used to generate plausible timelines reaching back another 500 years or so, but only on the assumption that they, in turn, used earlier written records.

imagined even older Universes.[4] But none of these chronologies could claim the objectivity, the precision, or the fixity of those based on written records.

It is a remarkable, and often ignored, fact, that the 5,000-year chronometric barrier was finally crossed only in the mid-twentieth century. Until then, even archaeologists had to rely for absolute dates on the written record. As Renfrew and Bahn write: "Before World War II, for much of archaeology, virtually the only reliable absolute dates were historical ones — Tutankhamun reigned in the fourteenth century BC, Caesar invaded Britain in 55 BC" [5, p.101]. These chronometric limitations help explain why even today the "history" taught in modern universities is essentially the history of literate human societies during the last 5,000 years. However, the research that would eventually break the chronometric barrier had its roots in the era of the scientific revolution.

In seventeenth century Europe, growing interest in geology and in fossils encouraged the idea that Earth had to be more than 6,000 years old. Nils Steensen, usually known as Steno, found fossils of what appeared to be marine organisms in rocks high in the hills of Tuscany. In his *Prodromus*, published in 1671, he argued that marine fossils could appear in mountains only if the rocks containing them had once been beneath the sea. Though Steno resisted the idea that such changes must imply an Earth older than the biblical 6,000 years, others were less cautious. The eighteenth-century naturalist, Buffon, argued that it might be possible to date events by using the natural world as a sort of historical archive:

> *Just as in civil history we consult warrants, study medallions, and decipher ancient inscriptions, in order to determine the epochs of the human revolutions and fix the dates of moral events, so in natural history one must dig through the*

---

[4] "Suppose, O Monks—said the Buddha—there was a huge rock of one solid mass, one mile long, one mile wide, one mile high, without split or flaw. And at the end of every hundred years a man should come and rub against it once with a silken cloth. Then that huge rock would wear off and disappear quicker than a world-period [kalpa]. But of such world-periods, O Monks, many have passed away, many hundreds, many thousands, many hundred thousands." Cited from Mahathera [4].

archives of the world, extract ancient relics from the bowels
of the earth, gather together their fragments, and assemble
again in a single body of proofs all those indications of the
physical changes which can carry us back to the different
Ages of Nature. This is the only way of fixing certain points
in the immensity of space, and of placing a number of mile-
stones on the eternal path of time [6, p.144].

Just before the French Revolution, using an idea already
suggested by Newton (only to be immediately rejected), Buffon
tried to date the earth itself by assuming it was a cooling body
that had once been molten [6, pp.146-147]. His calculations suggested that it must be at least 100,000 years old, and perhaps
much older. His contemporary, James Hutton, went further.
Writing in 1788, he described an Earth shaped by endless cycles
of erosion and uplift and concluded that there could be found:
"no vestige of a beginning—no prospect of an end" [6, p.157].
In the nineteenth century, the emergence of thermodynamics
revived interest in the idea that the Sun and Earth were both
cooling bodies. Lord Kelvin estimated that the Sun had to be at
least 500 million years old, but that on a rapidly cooling Earth,
life could not have existed for more than a few million years
[6, p.223]. Though speculative, his conclusions carried enough
weight to embarrass Darwinians. But the truth was that at the
end of the nineteenth century it was still impossible to assign
reliable absolute dates to any events before the appearance of
the first written records.

Meanwhile, geologists had made significant progress with
the task of constructing *relative* timelines. They did so by identifying and ranking different geological strata, and correlating
them according to the fossils they contained, a technique pioneered by an English surveyor, William Smith, early in the
nineteenth century. But without absolute dates, no one could
tell, within several orders of magnitude, when these geological
strata had been laid down.

What the pioneers of modern chronometry did show was
that time was deep. There had been plenty of history before
the appearance of the first written records, and even before the

appearance of the first human beings. This implied that it should be possible to imagine a single historical continuum extending back to the origins of time itself, uniting human history with the history of the natural world. Toulmin and Goodfield [6, p.130] describe Kant's *General History of Nature and Theory of the Heavens* (1755) as "the first systematic attempt to give an evolutionary account of cosmic history . . . ." Kant imagined an infinite and infinitely old Universe in which gravity would gradually clump matter into more and more ordered regions until the entire Universe collapsed in a "big crunch" which would scatter matter once more through the Universe, allowing the entire process to repeat. In his *Ideas towards a Philosophy of the History of Man*, Herder tried to integrate human history into the larger story of cosmic evolution. In the nineteenth century, the notion of a single historical continuum would shape the work of many social and historical thinkers, including Hegel and Marx. To the pioneering British archaeologist, John Lubbock, whose *Prehistoric Times* was published in 1865, it already seemed natural to treat human prehistory as part of a larger story that embraced geology and even astronomy. As Clark puts it, Lubbock "discussed human biological and cultural evolution in universal terms" [1, p.121].

~5~

However, nineteenth-century attempts to construct a single historical continuum were highly speculative, and without the chronological mooring of absolute dates, they drifted helplessly in relative time. This may help explain why, late in the nineteenth century, historians lost interest in the idea of a single historical continuum. As historical scholarship became more "scientific" historians retreated from such large speculative matters, and returned to human history and the documents that recorded it. The modest work of building up a reliable database of dateable information about the recorded past—that was the way to ensure that history maintained its scientific credibility. Henri Houssaye thundered at the opening session of the First International Congress of Historians in 1900: "We want nothing more to do with the approximations of hypotheses, useless systems, theories as brilliant as they are deceptive, superfluous moralities. Facts, facts, facts—which carry within themselves their lesson and their philosophy. The truth, all the truth, nothing but the truth" [7, pp.37-38]. Houssaye's naive inductionism became the dominant methodological slogan of historical scholarship in the early twentieth century. In their *Introduction to the Study of History* of 1898, Langlois and Seignobos wrote: "The historian works with documents. Documents are the traces which have been left by the thoughts and actions of men of former times. . . . No documents, no history" [3, pp.1350-1351].

~6~

In this climate, the few historians who persisted in the search for larger historical patterns invited the scorn of their colleagues. The English historian, Hugh Trevor-Roper, wrote of Toynbee's *Study of History*, that "as a dollar earner ... it ranks second only to whiskey" [8, p.108]. Toynbee himself was confident that eventually he would be vindicated. Early in the 1960s, in an interview with Ved Mehta:

> . . . he comforted himself with the thought that the days of the microscope historians were probably numbered. They, whether they admitted it or not, had sacrificed all generalizations for patchwork, relative knowledge, and they thought of human experience as incomprehensible chaos. But in the perspective of historiography, they were in the minority, and Toynbee, in company with St. Augustine — he felt most akin to him — Polybius, Roger Bacon, and Ibn Khaldun, was in the majority [8, p.143].

At the time, Toynbee's hopes seemed utterly Utopian.

As the scope of respectable historical scholarship narrowed once more, some concluded that there was a fundamental epistemological divide between history and the natural sciences. The great English historiographer, R.G. Collingwood, explicitly raised the notion of a single historical continuum only to dismiss it.

> The methods of historical research have, no doubt, been developed in application to the history of human affairs; but is that the limit of their applicability? They have already before now undergone important extensions: for example, at one time historians had worked out their methods of critical interpretation only as applied to written sources containing narrative

material, and it was a new thing when they learnt to apply them to the unwritten data provided by archaeology. Might not a similar but even more revolutionary extension sweep into the historian's net the entire world of nature? In other words, are not natural processes really historical processes, and is not the being of nature an historical being? [9, p.210]

Collingwood did not fall for the already outdated notion that history dealt with unpredictable, contingent processes while the natural sciences dealt with processes that were more regular, law-abiding, and predictable. "With Darwin," he wrote, "the scientific point of view capitulated to the historical, and both now agreed in conceiving their subject matter as progressive" [9, p.129]. What really distinguished historical scholarship in his view was that it dealt with an unpredictable world of conscious acts rather than merely with events. "The events of nature are mere events, not the acts of agents whose thought the scientist [i.e., historian] endeavors to trace" [9, p.214]. The historian's goal, therefore, was not to seek general laws, but to "penetrate" the thoughts that motivated past actions. That was why historians seemed to occupy a different epistemological Universe from natural scientists.

The Chronometric Revolution and the Creation of a Single Historical Continuum

Dropping the idea of a single historical continuum made sense given the limitations of nineteenth-century dating techniques. Over the next century, historians would make great progress in the more manageable project of documenting human history as thoroughly as possible using written evidence. Indeed, so absorbing was this challenge that few historians noticed when, in the middle of the twentieth century, it suddenly became possible to construct reliable timelines extending back to the origins of time itself.[5]

---

[5] You will find no references to radiometric dating and its significance in standard surveys such as Georg Iggers [10] or Joyce Appleby, Lynn Hunt and Margaret Jacob [11].

In the two decades after World War II, the notion of deep historical time acquired a firm scientific foundation as a result of breakthroughs in biology, geology, and cosmology. Discovery of the genetic role of DNA in 1953 put evolutionary theory on an entirely new footing; discovering and unraveling the meaning of deep ocean trenches helped clinch the new theory of plate tectonics; and the discovery of the cosmic background radiation in 1964 provided empirical evidence for Big Bang cosmology. Each of these breakthroughs assumed the reality of deep time and of long-term historical change. This story is too well known to be described in more detail here.[6]

Less well appreciated is the significance of what I have called the chronometric revolution. This provided the dating techniques needed to revive the idea of a single historical continuum. Ironically, the crucial breakthrough was the discovery of radioactivity by Henri Becquerel and Marie and Pierre Curie in the last decade of the nineteenth century, just as historians began to turn away from the idea of a single historical continuum. Radioactivity explained why the calculations of Buffon and Kelvin could be wrong by so many orders of magnitude. Earth was indeed a cooling body; but it also contained an internal source of heat previously unknown to science. In the first decade of the twentieth century, Ernest Rutherford showed that radioactive materials decayed with such regularity that they could provide the natural clocks that Buffon had searched for in vain. Armed with knowledge of an element's half-life (the time in which half its mass decays), it should be possible to calculate when a lump of matter containing that element had originally formed by determining what proportion of it had decayed. Rutherford demonstrated his idea as early as 1905 by calculating that a piece of pitchblende (an ore of uranium) must have been formed about 500

~8~

---

[6] A brief account written by a historian for historians is William H. McNeill [12].

million years ago.[7] The technique Rutherford pioneered has come to be known as radiometric dating.[8]

However, many difficulties had to be overcome before radiometric dating could be used routinely to determine absolute dates. So the revolutionary implications of this demonstration would not become apparent until after World War II. During the war, Willard F. Libby of the University of Chicago had worked on the Manhattan project, developing precise methods for separating different isotopes of uranium. This was the crucial skill needed to measure precisely the extent of decay of radioactive materials. After the war, Libby developed similar techniques for measuring the proportion of carbon-14, a rare and unstable isotope of carbon, in samples of organic material. Because all living organisms take in carbon dioxide while alive, this is an ideal technique for dating organic remains. The relatively short half-life of carbon-14 (about 5,600 years) also makes it highly suitable for archaeology, because it can be used to determine dates from a few centuries to about 50,000 years, and the technique of accelerator mass spectrometry can extend that range to close to 80,000 years. Other radiometric techniques were soon developed. For example, thermoluminescence dating and electron spin resonance, though less precise than radiocarbon dating, can be used over several hundred thousand years, and in this way they can fill in the eras beyond the reach of carbon-14 dating but below the reach of other techniques using materials with much longer half-lives. Potassium/argon dating depends on the breakdown of potassium-40 to argon-40, and because the half-life of potassium-40 is 1.25 billion years, it can be used for scales from 100,000 years up to the age of Earth. Similar techniques, based on the radioactive breakdown of uranium in meteorites, were used in 1953 by Clair Patterson to determine

~9~

---

[7] His demonstration immediately challenged the shorter chronology championed by Lord Kelvin.

[8] There are many good, brief discussions of radiometric dating techniques. I have relied, in part, on Neil Roberts [15, pp.9-26]. Colin Renfrew and Paul Bahn [14, ch. 4] offers a good survey of modern dating techniques from the perspective of archaeology.

the first accurate date for the formation of the earth (ca. 4.5 billion years).

Improvements in the accuracy and reliability of radiometric techniques stimulated the development of new, non-radiometric dating techniques. In 1965, Hans Suess showed that the relative amounts of different isotopes of carbon in the atmosphere were not constant, as Libby had assumed, and these changes could distort carbon-14 dates, sometimes by thousands of years. So alternative dating methods had to be developed to calibrate carbon-14 dates in different eras. Of these, the most important was "dendrochronology," a non-radiometric technique based on the counting of tree-rings. The idea of using such techniques is very old, but as a practical dating technique it was developed by A.E. Douglass (1867-1962) in the American Southwest. Analogous techniques have been developed using patterns of annual sedimentation in lakes (varve analysis, a technique pioneered by a Swedish geologist, Baron Gerard de Geer, in the late nineteenth century), or the annual sequences in which ice is laid down in ancient ice sheets.

Meanwhile, genetic dating techniques helped put evolutionary biology on a firmer chronological footing. They depend on the realization that much genetic change (for example in mitochondrial DNA or in so-called "junk" genes) is effectively random. This means that alterations in gene frequencies can be used (after careful calibration) to estimate the evolutionary distance between different species. Techniques such as these have revolutionized understanding of human evolution, by showing that the human and ape lines diverged approximately 7 million years ago. Dating the age of the Universe became a viable challenge with the rise of Big Bang cosmology. Since Edwin Hubble first proposed that the Universe was expanding, there have been attempts to estimate the age of the Universe by measuring the rate at which it is expanding today, the so-called "Hubble constant." The practical difficulties of determining the Hubble constant are immense, primarily because of the difficulty of establishing the distance of remote galaxies. However, present estimates, combined with alternative methods of dating the Big Bang, are converging on a date of about 13.7 billion years.[9]

History after the Chronometric Revolution

The armory of new dating techniques developed during the chronometric revolution made it possible for the first time to construct an objective, scientifically rigorous and increasingly detailed timeline for the entire past. The techniques are now so familiar that it is easy to take them for granted. Yet the full implications of the chronometric revolution have still not been incorporated within modern historical scholarship. The rest of this chapter will describe some of these implications. Though I will focus on the implications for the History discipline, the discussion is really about the possibility of a grand unification of historical research within the framework of a single historical continuum.

Redefining History

If there is, indeed, a single historical continuum, it ought to follow that there is an underlying unity to all forms of historical research. All the disciplines that make up the continuum describe and explain change in the past, even if they work on different parts of the continuum, operate at different scales, use different methods and paradigms, and focus on very different types of objects. The single historical continuum does indeed appear, as Collingwood put it, to "sweep into the historian's net the entire world of nature." This ought to mean that scholars in these disciplines have much to learn from each other, and students have much to learn from understanding what links different parts of the historical continuum. Indeed, the existence of a single historical continuum makes it anachronistic to describe as "History" a scholarly discipline that concerns itself only

---

[9] Current estimates put the Hubble Constant at about 71 kilometers per second per megaparsec, which implies that the Universe is about 14 million years old; this estimate is remarkably close to estimates based on radiometric dating of the ages of the oldest stars, and on detailed analysis of tiny variations in the temperature and density of the cosmic background radiation.

with part of the past of our own species. Logically, we should apply the label to all disciplines researching the past. Though such rearrangements would encounter significant resistance, it would make pedagogical sense, for example, if universities were to group all the historical sciences within a single "college" or "school" of historical sciences. In such a context, the discipline traditionally called "History" would presumably have to be re-badged as "Human History." (However, in this chapter I will continue to refer to it as *History* with a capital *H*.)

Within the natural sciences the assumption of an underlying unity between different disciplines is taken for granted. As E.O. Wilson puts it: "The Natural Sciences have constructed a webwork of causal explanation that runs all the way from quantum physics to the brain sciences and evolutionary biology . . . . The explanatory network now touches the edge of culture itself" [15, p.137]. However, extending Wilson's explanatory network to the Humanities, and to History in particular, remains a difficult challenge, for few historians seem willing to move outside the 5,000-year framework that has framed the discipline for so long. Even within sub-disciplines such as "World History," the vast bulk of contemporary scholarship focuses on the period since 1500 CE.[10]

Are there good intellectual reasons for the continued isolation of disciplines such as History? Or is the separation largely a matter of institutional and intellectual inertia, of ancient habits of thought and scholarship? My own belief, after 20 years of experience of trying to construct a university program embracing the entire historical continuum, is that the chronometric revolution has removed some of the most important barriers between history and the sciences. There now exist no serious intellectual or scientific or philosophical barriers to a broad unification of historical scholarship.[11] The barriers that remain are institutional and conventional. They are nevertheless significant as they are embedded in institutional structures such as modern scholarly journals and associations, and in

---

[10] In a recent conference on Research Agendas in World History, only four of 36 presenters were researching eras before 1500 CE [16, pp. 3, 20].

[11] On this course and the story it tells, see David Christian [17, 18].

patterns of recruitment and training which, like the conventional PhD dissertation, assume traditional definitions of the meaning of good scholarship. Overcoming these barriers will require a fundamental rethinking of what history means within the single historical continuum.

However, historians also have much to gain by trying to integrate their discipline within the single historical continuum. Above all, they can begin to see their own research within a larger context. Historians are accustomed to the principle that understanding something as complex as human societies means understanding their origins and roots. How can we understand modern China without understanding the role of Mao, or the decline of the Qing dynasty, or even the foundational role of the Han dynasty? Can we understand the role of the major religions without understanding their origins and histories? Yet exactly the same principle applies to human society as a whole. How can we understand the complex societies that generated the first written records without understanding the simpler societies from which they evolved? What was the source of the technological and artistic creativity that generated them? Such questions lead us quickly back to questions about the origins of our species and the nature of our distinctiveness as a species. In other words, the single historical continuum provides a way of integrating historical scholarship within the larger explanatory networks of modern science as a whole. By doing so, it promises to deepen our understanding of historical processes by tracing human societies to their Paleolithic and pre-Paleolithic roots. Before the chronometric revolution such questions could not be pursued seriously. Now they can.

In the rest of this chapter, I will explore some of the questions historians will face as they engage more seriously with the single historical continuum. I will focus on three main problems. First, is there a single explanatory or thematic network that embraces all the historical disciplines? Can there be any coherence to accounts of the past that traverse so many diverse disciplines? Second, will the traditional History discipline dissolve within the single historical continuum? Or will its identity perhaps become clearer within this larger framework? Third, how will integration within a single historical continuum affect the research methods and paradigms of historians? How will it affect the questions historians ask, the evidence they use, and the way they think about history in general?

Complexity as a Unifying Theme for an Expanded View of History

~14~

Many important themes unite the different disciplines of the single historical continuum, beginning with questions about the nature of change and of time itself. One of the most powerful of these themes may turn out to be that of complexity. During 14 billion years, the level of complexity of the most complex entities in the Universe seems to have risen. Where once there existed little more than energy, dark matter, and hydrogen and helium atoms, distributed more or less randomly through an expanding space, there have since appeared galaxies and stars, almost 100 new chemical elements, planets, living organisms and human beings. As Richard Dawkins puts it:

> There is a hierarchy, ranging from fundamental particles below the atomic level up through molecules and crystals to the macroscopic chunks which our unaided sense organs are built to appreciate. Living matter introduces a whole new set of rungs to the ladder of complexity: macromolecules folding themselves into their tertiary forms, intracellular membranes and organelles, cells, tissues, organs, organisms, populations, communities and ecosystems. . . . At every level the units interact with each other following laws appropriate to that level, laws which are not conveniently reducible to laws at lower levels [19, pp.112-113].

Is it possible that this large story may have something to teach historians about the evolution of complexity within human societies?

Eric Chaisson has suggested that it might be possible to quantify increases in complexity by measuring the "free energy rate densities" of different complex entities, the amounts of free energy flowing through a given mass in a given amount of time.[12] Whether or not this idea is correct, the general idea of increasing complexity can help us to think of galaxies, stars, planets, living organisms, and modern human societies as different expressions of similar underlying processes of change. That idea, in turn, suggests an entire research agenda about the similarities and differences between different levels of complexity, and the processes that generated them. Is it true that increasing complexity in human history has also been associated with increasing energy flows? (The answer, as we will see, is *yes*.) If so, why? And how and why were those energy flows generated?

~15~

What Makes Human History Distinctive?

The idea of increasing complexity also suggests a helpful way of distinguishing between the different entities studied within the single historical continuum. Different levels of complexity appear to yield new "emergent properties," properties that can not be deduced from understanding lower levels in the hierarchy. This means we can usefully ask: what are the emergent properties studied at each level, from subatomic physics, to the molecular level of chemistry, to the level of galaxies, stars and planets, and on to the level of complexity represented by living organisms. How do these levels differ? How are more complex entities built up from less complex entities? Such questions are familiar within the natural sciences, but the idea of a single historical continuum encourages us to extend them to human history as well.

Within such a framework, it is natural to ask whether there may be emergent properties that distinguish human history from the histories of all other organisms, including our close relatives, the great apes? Does human history represent a new level of complexity? If so, can we perhaps define History more precisely than Collingwood did, with his insistence that human history is distinguished primarily by the unpredictable,

---

[12] Eric Chaisson [20, pp.132-135] expresses the free energy rate density in units of energy per time per mass.

subjective decisions of individual actors? I believe we can. The suggestions that follow are tentative, though I believe they are compatible with a significant body of recent work on the evolution and early history of our species.

The best evidence that human history represents a new level of complexity can be found in the accelerating human control over biospheric resources. Human energy use has increased by about two hundred times in just the last thousand years, and even per-capita energy use (the amount used on average by each individual) has increased by almost 10 times.[13] According to some estimates, our species may now be controlling, consuming, or destroying between 25 and 40 percent of all the carbon fixed by plants and other photosynthesizing organisms on land.[14] No single species has ever enjoyed the degree of biospheric control that our species collectively enjoys today.[15] Vaclav Smil writes: "The diffusion and complexification of human societies have led to a large array of environmental changes that have transformed this planet during the past 5 ka, and particularly during the past 100 years, more rapidly than any other biogenic process in the planet's history" [22, p.240]. That these revolutionary changes are accompanied by a rapid increase in rates of extinction of other species, and by signs of global climate changes should not seem surprising.

What is less obvious is that these changes are not confined to the modern era of human history, or even to the 5,000

~16~

---

[13] Christian [18, p.141], using estimates from I.G. Simmons [21 p.27].

[14] Vaclav Smil [22, p.240]. Strictly, what is being measured is global terrestrial Net Primary Productivity, the amount of carbon fixed by photosynthesizing organisms on land minus the amount they return to the atmosphere through respiration [22, p.182].

[15] Groups of species, such as the social insects, have indeed had significant environmental impacts, but not as single species. They acquired their ecological power in genetic rather than cultural time, and it is this acceleration in the pace of change in the human era that needs to be explained. But even when compared with whole groups of species, the human impact is striking. For example, Vaclav Smil estimates that collectively all modern species of termites may account for about 25 percent of all global terrestrial Net Primary Productivity, which is close to the lower estimates for contemporary human impacts [22, p.222].

years of traditional historical scholarship. Their roots lie deep
in the Paleolithic era. For most of the 200,000 or so years since
modern humans first evolved, our species's extraordinary
ecological virtuosity has shown up most clearly in migrations
to new environments requiring new forms of adaptation [22,
p.231]. Spotty evidence for increasing human artistic and
technological creativity appears within Africa from perhaps
as early as 250,000 years ago and then becomes impossible
to ignore from 50,000 years ago. That is when our ancestors
became the first large mammals to enter the Australian continent, after what must have been a technologically demanding
sea crossing. The settling of ice-age Siberia from perhaps
30,000 years ago required even greater technological skills as
our ancestors adapted to cold climates by improving their control of fire, their ability to hunt large animals such as the mam-
moth, and their tailoring and building skills. By 10,000 years
ago, humans had settled all continents except for Antarctica.
The number of humans rose from a few hundred thousand
to 5 or 6 million by 10,000 years ago.[16] By then, our species
was already having a significant impact on the biosphere. The
widespread practice of firing the land altered biota over large
areas (the evidence is particularly clear from Australia); while
improved hunting methods may help explain the disappearance of many large animal species in regions of recent colonization (Australia, Siberia, and the Americas) during the last
50,000 years.[17] The emergence of agriculture in different parts
of the world from about 10,000 years ago sharply increased
human control over resources and allowed for the emergence
of dense, compact, and increasingly complex communities.
The pace of technological change accelerated. Another significant gear shift in human numbers, social complexity, and

---

[16] See, for example, the estimates in Massimo [23, p.31]. There is now powerful genetic evidence of a sharp drop in human numbers to perhaps as few as
10,000 individuals about 70,000 years ago, caused, perhaps by sharp climatic
deterioration or even by a huge volcanic eruption in Indonesia, creating a
"volcanic" winter. See Chris Scarre [24, p.140].

[17] For accounts of how these processes worked in Australia, see Tim Flannery
[25].

ecological impacts has occurred with the emergence of modern industrial societies. To give just one spectacular example, John McNeill estimates that by the end of the twentieth century human activities (above all mining and various forms of human-caused erosion) were moving about 42 billion tons of rock and soil every year. This is more than wind (1 billion tons), glaciers (4.3), mountain-building processes (14), and oceanic volcanoes (30) and is exceeded only by the impact of moving water (53 billion tons) [26, p.30].

~18~   It may help to think of three interlinked vectors at work, with many others working in the background. The three main vectors of human history are increasing control over biospheric resources leading to increasing populations leading to increasing social complexity, in a powerful feedback cycle. The contrast with our closest relatives, the great apes, is striking. For apes, we have no evidence of significant migrations in the same period, or of significant increases in ape populations or social complexity, or of measurable increases in ape control of biospheric resources. The astonishing ecological virtuosity of our species really is something new.

How can we explain these distinctive emergent properties of human history? Though there is broad agreement on the main mechanism that drives change in the biological realm — natural selection — there is no such consensus about the drivers of change in the human realm. There is, as yet, no "Kuhnian" paradigm for human history. Indeed, most historians resist the idea of seeking such a paradigm, and remain content to offer ad hoc explanations of particular changes. But it may be possible to do better than that, for currently several lines of argument within different disciplines seem to be converging on a single answer. I will summarize that answer as I understand it, using the idea of "collective learning" [18].[18]

The challenge is to explain our species's unique ecological prowess. All living organisms are the products of evolutionary

---

[18] See Michael Tomasello [27], for a similar argument, though it places less emphasis on the importance of language; Tomasello's "cumulative cultural evolution" is close to what I call "collective learning."

changes that allow them to procure the energy and resources they need to live and reproduce. We say they are "adapted" to a particular environment. Darwin's great achievement was to explain, in general terms, how adaptation works through natural selection. But not all adaptation results from natural selection. Species with brains can learn new ways of adapting to their environments within a single lifetime. Individual learning is a second, and much faster, adaptive mechanism than natural selection. However, its long-term impact is limited because most learning species can pass on only insignif icant amounts of what they learn to other members of their species. Even species such as birds or primates that can share some information (such as bird songs), do not share enough for that knowledge to accumulate in a sustained way. We know this because sustained accumulation of ecological knowledge ought to show up in the archaeological record, as it does, uniquely, in the case of our own species. In practice, limitations on their ability to exchange learned information ensure that, in all species but our own, each individual has to start the learning process more or less from scratch.

We are different because we can share information with precision and in great volume through the gift of symbolic lan guage. Strictly, of course, the difference is quantitative, but it is the sort of quantitative difference that makes a qualitative difference. Humans can exchange so much information so pre cisely that, even allowing for much waste, ecologically signif icant information can accumulate within the memory of each community, within what anthropologists call its "culture." We can get some feeling for how collective learning may have worked within early human communities from accounts of modern foraging societies. Richard Lee describes the chatter around a !Kung San camp in the 1960s:

> *The buzz of conversation is a constant background to the camp's activities: there is an endless flow of talk about gath ering, hunting, the weather, food distribution, gift giving, and scandal. No !Kung is ever at a loss for words, and often two or three people will hold forth at once in a single conversation,*

giving the listeners a choice of channels to tune in on [28, p.359].

At the evening camps, those who had been out hunting or gathering shared information: " . . . the men relate in detail the latest news of the rainfall, the ripening of fruit and of food plants, and the movements of game. Visitors arriving from other camps add to the discussion what they have observed along the way. In this manner, the members of the camp are kept fully informed about what their environment currently has to offer" [28, p.346]. As a result, the Bushmen accumulated an immense amount of useful knowledge about their environment. "This knowledge," comments Lee, "is, in effect, a form of control over nature: it has been developed over many generations in response to every conceivable variation in climatic conditions" [28, p.361]. Over many generations, such exchanges stored useful information within large and constantly growing tribal encyclopedias of learnt knowledge. This third adaptive mechanism, which I call "collective learning," is unique to our species, and uniquely powerful. It explains why human history moves not at the pace of genetic change but at the much faster pace of cultural change.

The results are transformative, allowing rapid, cumulative, and accelerating adaptation. That is what makes our species so different. As individuals contribute what they have learned to the common stock of knowledge, that stock grows, allowing later generations to exploit their environments more effectively and sometimes to enter new environments, which adds to the stock of information available to later generations, and so on.[19] This positive-feedback mechanism explains the accelerating pace of change in human history which has set us apart from all other animal species. Collective learning is what distinguishes human history from the histories of all other species.

These are large and tentative hypotheses about human history. I raise them not in the hope of convincing readers

---

[19] As Clive Gamble notes, the "tribal encyclopedias" of Paleolithic communities contained the information that enabled them, when necessary, to migrate into new environments [29, p.120].

immediately of their correctness, but rather to suggest the types of research agenda suggested naturally by seeing human history as part of a single historical continuum.

Implications of the Single Historical Continuum for Scholarship in Human History

Closer collaboration with scholars in other historically oriented disciplines will surely encourage historians to see what they can borrow from the methods, the insights, and the paradigms of other disciplines. But it will also encourage historians to explore the past on multiple scales, and doing that may introduce new types of questions into historical scholarship.

~21~

Written documents, mostly generated by the powerful or by their scribes and officials, biased historical scholarship towards the temporal and spatial scales most familiar to human actors and placed those actors at the center of the stories historians told. This may help explain why human agency plays such a central role in most historical explanation, as well as in Collingwood's definition of the discipline. A focus on human agency highlights the unpredictability of human decisions and human whims, just as a focus on subatomic particles highlights the contingent nature of quantum processes.[20] However, once they start exploring the larger temporal scales of the single historical continuum, historians will find it both possible and necessary to explore very different types of explanations. The great French historian, Fernand Braudel, may have been anticipating just such a shift in perspective when he wrote: " . . . the way to study history is to view it as a long duration, as what I have called the *longue durée*. It is not the only way, but it is one which by itself can pose all the great problems of social structures,

---

[20] Even many archaeologists seem more comfortable with the "quantum" perspective typical of historians. In a recent survey, Colin Renfrew writes that for most archaeologists, "The world . . . is constructed through individual actions by individual people. It is a rich palimpsest, testifying to human creativity, and perhaps little more is to be expected than the collection and collation of regional narratives" [30, p.74].

past and present. It is the only language binding history to the present, creating one indivisible whole" [31].

Historians such as Braudel have explored changes occurring at scales of decades or centuries or even, in some cases, millennia. At these scales, which are familiar to demographic and economic historians, human agency loses some of its explanatory salience, and crucial changes such as large population movements or waves of economic growth seem to occur behind the back of individual human actors. But even at these scales, human agency can sabotage the most elegant explanatory models. How can one discuss the demography of modern China without discussing the politics of the "one-child policy," or how can one discuss large economic trends of the twentieth century without mentioning Keynes or Stalin? Or, to pick an even more powerful illustration, how can one discuss world history in the thirteenth century without taking seriously the personality and the political skills of Chinggis Khan? Even at these large scales, agency often trumps structure.[21]

One reason why historians remain so attached to the notion of human agency may be that you need to shift to even larger scales before individual agency loses its salience as an explanatory factor. Indeed, you need to shift to scales that most historians would regard as outside their competence and beyond the scope of historical scholarship as traditionally understood. However, within the context of a single historical continuum, it is now possible to study change at these scales, and to do so with rigor. We now have enough well-dated archaeological and paleontological evidence to make reasonable empirical generalizations about the long-term trajectory of human history since the appearance of our species, some 200,000 years ago. At this scale, the scale of human history as a whole, the large patterns stand out, just as, in the world of particle physics, we can say confidently when half of a lump of uranium-238 will decay though

---

21 Peter Turchin's [32] sophisticated attempt to tease out general principles of empire building in *War and Peace and War: The Life Cycles of Imperial Nations*, illustrates some of these difficulties; the best recent biography of Chinggis Khan is Michal Biran [33].

we can never predict when an individual atom will decay.[22] At the very large scales, even in human history, structure begins to trump agency. We see processes so large that they seem to take place without any awareness of individual actors. These processes include the Paleolithic migrations of our species, the long trend of increasing human numbers, the accelerating increase in human control over energy and resources, and the striking increases in social complexity since the agricultural revolution.

We also face questions that we cannot solve by studying the ideas and intentions of individual actors. Why, after living as foragers for perhaps 200,000 years, did human communities in parts of the world that had no contact with each other (such as Mesopotamia and Mesoamerica) take up agriculture within just a few thousand years of each other?[23] The puzzles get stranger with the spread of agriculture. Wherever agriculture appeared, it generated similar changes on a similar timetable. In both Afro-Eurasia and the Americas, agriculture supported numerous small sedentary communities which expanded in range and size until some spawned towns and cities. As societies expanded, they became more complex. There appeared a division of labor, and social hierarchies organized by lineage, wealth, ethnicity, and gender. Eventually, states emerged: power structures in which elites exacted tributes from farmers, artisans, and traders, ruling through powerful religious and civilian bureaucracies and large armies. To manage the resources they collected, elites developed accounting systems from which the earliest writing systems evolved. (Even the Inca *quipu*, a way of recording information on knotted strings, was probably an embryonic writing system.) Everywhere, elites built monumental structures,

~23~

---

[22] The answer is in about 4.5 billion years, or roughly the age of Earth, which means that about half of the uranium-238 present in the early Earth has since decayed.

[23] The best recent survey of the origins of agriculture is Peter Bellwood [34]; note that even in Australia, widespread changes in recent millennia hint at the sort of intensification that preceded the appearance of agriculture in other regions of the world. The notion of intensification was pioneered in the work of Harry Lourandos. For a survey of the debate and the evidence, see John Mulvaney and Johan Kamminga [35, chs. 14 and 15].

....

... ONLY WHEN WE MOVE WELL BEYOND THE 5,000-YEAR

TIMESCALE OF TRADITIONAL HISTORICAL SCHOLARSHIP CAN

WE BEGIN TO SEE THE LARGE PATTERNS IN HUMAN HISTORY,

PATTERNS SO LARGE THAT WE CANNOT EXPLAIN THEM WITH

THE NOTION OF INDIVIDUAL AGENCY.

....

usually in the same basic form: that of a pyramid. The transition from early agriculture to cities and states took 5,000–6,000 years in Mesopotamia, Egypt, and parts of China; in the Americas it may have taken longer, but the broad similarities in sequence and timing are remarkable nonetheless, particularly given the near-certainty that there was no significant contact between these regions.

As Colin Renfrew points out, these odd parallels "must imply some commonality both in practicality and in potential, as both are products of the human condition."[24] At this scale, we are dealing with patterns of change so large that they appear to be emergent properties of human history as a whole. These patterns include the vectors I have already referred to. These, in turn, were driven by our species's extraordinary capacity for sustained ecological innovation leading to increased control of biospheric resources. As I have suggested, that, in turn, may be a consequence of a new emergent property that distinguishes our species from all others: our capacity to keep adapting in new ways through the novel adaptive mechanism of collective learning.

In short, only when we move well beyond the 5,000-year timescale of traditional historical scholarship can we begin to see the large patterns in human history, patterns so large that

---

[24] Colin Renfrew [30, p.71] points out that Robert Adams, who did pioneering work on the parallels between Mesopotamia and pre-Columban America, argued that both societies were clearly "variants of a single processual pattern."

we cannot explain them with the notion of individual agency. Instead, we need to look for the sort of general principles familiar within other parts of the single historical continuum: principles such as that of collective learning. These principles, in turn, raise profound questions about the way we handle historical questions at smaller scales, such as questions about the rise to dominance of particular regions of the world in different historical epochs. Why, if collective learning is so critical, should it apparently work more effectively in some eras and regions than others? Can such models help us place phenomena such as the "rise of the West" within a larger explanatory framework?

~25~

Once again, I stress that the point is not to demonstrate the correctness of the particular arguments I have offered, but to suggest the kinds of problems that become apparent at larger scales, and the explanatory possibilities that may emerge once historians start to explore the place of human history within the single historical continuum.

Conclusion: Are We on the Verge of a Grand Unification of Historical Sciences?

So far I have talked about constructing a Grand Unified Story (a GUS?) embracing all parts of the single historical continuum. Is it possible to think even more ambitiously? Might it be possible, through collaborative work between all the disciplines that make up the single historical continuum, to tease out general principles of change that explain how change works across the entire continuum? Might it be possible to unify our understanding of change in the human and the biological realms just as the discovery of an "electro-weak" force unified understanding of the electromagnetic and weak forces in the early 1980s? Is it possible that, lurking behind the emerging GUS there is the historical equivalent of a GUT, a Grand Unified Theory of History? ⚡

References

[1]   Clark, Grahame. *Space, Time and Man: A Prehistorian's View*. Cambridge: Cambridge University Press, 1992.

[2]   Christian, David. "Historia, complejidad y revolución cronométrica" ["History, Complexity and the Chronometric Revolution"]. *Revista de Occidente* 323 (2008): 27-57

[3]   Smail, Dan. "In the Grip of Sacred History." *American Historical Review* 110(5) (2005): 1337-1361.

[4]   Mahathera, Nyanatilok. *Buddhist Dictionary: Manual of Buddhist Terms and Doctrines*, 3rd ed. Colombo [Sri Lanka]: Frewin, 1972.

[5]   Renfrew, Colin, and Paul Bahn. *Archaeology: Methods and Practice*. London: Thames and Hudson, 1991.

[6]   Toulmin, Stephen, and June Goodfield. *The Discovery of Time*. Chicago and London: University of Chicago Press, 1965.

[7]   Novick, Peter. *That Noble Dream: The "Objectivity Question" and the American Historical Profession*, Cambridge: CUP, 1988.

[8]   Mehta, Ved. *Fly and the Fly-Bottle: Encounters with British Intellectuals*. Boston: Little, Brown and Co, 1962.

[9]   Collingwood, R. G. *The Idea of History*, Rev. Ed., ed. Jan van der Dussen. Oxford: OUP, 1993.

[10] Iggers, Georg. *Historiography in the Twentieth Century*. Middletown. Conn.: Wesleyan University Press, 1997.

[11] Appleby, Joyce, Lynn Hunt, and Margaret Jacob. *Telling the Truth about History*. New York: Norton, 1994.

[12] McNeill, William H. "History and the Scientific Worldview." *History and Theory* 37(1) (1998): 1-13.

[13] Roberts, Neil. *The Holocene: An Environmental History*, 2nd ed. Oxford: Blackwell, 1998.

[14] Renfrew, Colin, and Paul Bahn. *Archaeology: Theories, Methods and Practice*, 1991.

[15] Wilson, E.O. *Consilience: The Unity of Knowledge*. London: Abacus, 1998.

[16] Christian, David, Marilyn Lake, and Potukuchi Swarnalatha. "Mapping World History: Report on the World History Research Agenda Symposium." In *Global Practice in World History: Advances Worldwide*, Ed. Patrick Manning. Princeton, NJ: Markus Wiener, 2008.

[17] Christian, David. "The Case for 'Big History.'" *The Journal of World History*. 2(2) (1991): 223-238.

[18]   Christian, David. *Maps of Time: An Introduction to Big History*. Berkeley CA: University of California Press, 2004.

[19]   Dawkins, Richard. *The Extended Phenotype: the Long Reach of the Gene*. Oxford: OUP, 1982, 1999.

[20]   Chaisson, Eric. *Cosmic Evolution: The Rise of Complexity in Nature*. Cambridge, MA: Harvard University Press, 2001.

[21]   Simmons, I.G. *Changing the Face of the Earth: Culture, Environment, History*, 2nd ed. Oxford: Blackwell, 1996.

[22]   Smil, Vaclav. *The Earth's Biosphere: Evolution, Dynamics, and Change*. Cambridge, MA: MIT, 2002.

[23]   Livi-Bacci, Massimo. *A Concise History of World Population*, trans. Carl Ipsen. Oxford: Blackwell, 1992.

[24]   Scarre, Chris, ed. *The Human Past: World Prehistory and the Development of Human Societies*. New York: Thames & Hudson, 2009.

[25]   Flannery, Tim. *The Future Eaters: An Ecological History of the Australasian Lands and People*. Australia: Reed Books, 1995.

[26]   McNeill, John. *Something New Under the Sun*. New York & London: W.W. Norton & Co., 2000.

[27]   Tomasello, Michael. *The Cultural Origins of Human Cognition*. Cambridge, MA: Harvard University Press, 1999.

[28]   Lee, Richard. "The !Kung Bushmen of Botswana." In *Hunters and Gatherers Today: a Socioeconomic Study of Eleven such Cultures in the Twentieth Century*, Ed. M.G. Bicchieri, pp.327-368. New York: Holt, Rinehart and Winston, 1972.

[29]   Gamble, Clive. *Timewalkers: The Prehistory of Global Colonization*. Penguin, 1995.

[30]   Renfrew, Colin. *Prehistory: Making of the Human Mind*. London, Weidenfeld & Nicolson, 2007.

[31]   Braudel, Fernand. *On History*. Chicago: University of Chicago Press, 1980, p. viii, from the 1969 Preface to a collection of Braudel's historiographical essays.

[32]   Turchin, Peter. *War and Peace and War: The Life Cycles of Imperial Nations*. New York: Pi Press, 2006.

[33]   Biran, Michal. *Chinggis Khan*. Oxford: One World, 2007.

[34]   Bellwood, Peter. *First Farmers: The Origins of Agricultural Societies*. Oxford: Blackwell, 2005.

[35]   Mulvaney, John, and Johan Kamminga. *Prehistory of Australia*. Sydney: Allen and Unwin, 1999.

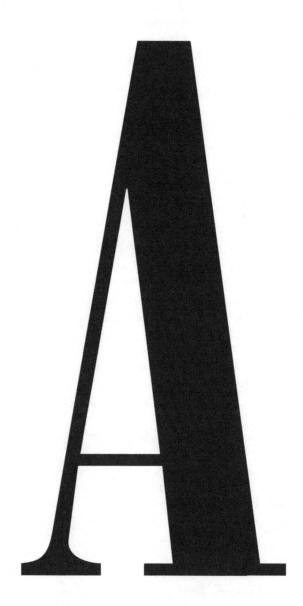

6

A PALEONTOLOGICAL LOOK AT HISTORY

Douglas H. Erwin, National Museum of Natural History

THE FOSSIL RECORD of animal life is far more incomplete and patchy than even the most obscure historical records. Consequently, some of the approaches developed by paleobiologists over the past couple of decades to assess the reliability of the fossil record, investigate patterns, and infer underlying processes may be useful in analyzing historical data as well. Here I discuss two examples where paleontologists have investigated historical questions, in one case, the evolution of cornets, in the second, estimating the survival rate of Medieval manuscripts. Depending on the scope of Big History, there are a number of areas where history and paleontology overlap, particularly in the investigation of early human history. More rigorous analysis of the biases of the historical record may be of some use in determining which historical patterns are sufficiently reliable for further exploration.

Introduction

Paleontology, astronomy, geology, and archaeology and aspects of evolutionary biology are historical sciences. They differ fundamentally in their approach and methods from largely ahistorical disciplines such as physics, chemistry, physiology, and much of molecular biology [5, 21, 25]. Physicists often assert that because they are not predictive, historical sciences are no more science than history. Such assertions commit at least two errors.

The first is to ignore the vastly greater number of potential variables in historical disciplines than in physics, with an attendant increase in the complexity of interactions between them (physics is predictive because its subject matter is relatively simple). Complex dynamics make a mockery of prediction, as evidenced by the lack of reliable climate and earthquake forecasts (see discussion by Krakauer, ch. 6, this volume). But not even the most arrogant physicist (perhaps a redundant class) would doubt that the study of climate and earthquakes is scientific.

The second logical error is that of uniformitarianism (also known as *actualism*). Physicists *assume* (the proof is more difficult) that their underlying laws are constant through time and space. They are not perplexed by the possibility that the speed of light or the nature of the neutrino was different 2.5 billion years ago or on the other side of the Universe. In historical disciplines the uniformitarian assumption is far less reliable and often demonstrably false. Indeed a promising question to explore in many historical sciences is how historical processes change through time. True, the historical sciences have less recourse to direct experiment, and their evidence may often be fragmentary or missing. Yet the historical sciences have developed a range of statistical and quantitative techniques to assess the reliability of historical data, quantify patterns of change, and develop models of the underlying processes and the more limited use of narrative.

Physicists have a role here, bringing a powerful set of quantitative tools and approaches, particularly in the development of first-order, process-based models. Statistical techniques are hardly unknown in history and have been widely adopted throughout the social sciences. What may be useful in the conversation between historians and scientists is an exploration of some of the approaches developed by paleobiologists over the past couple of decades to assess the reliability of the fossil record and investigate historical patterns and the inference of underlying processes. Here I also discuss two examples where paleontologists have used such approaches to investigate historical questions: in one case, the evolution of cornets, in the second, estimating the survival rate of Medieval manuscripts. Depending on the scope of Big History, there are a number of areas where history and paleontology overlap, particularly in the investigation of early human history, and the conceptual framework discussed here may be of some use as the field expands. Finally, I will explore some of the implications of non-uniformitarian issues in understanding historical disciplines.

The Missing Record

Many of the works of classic antiquity are known only from comments in other classical manuscripts: of the more than 80 plays of Aeschylus, only seven remain; seven of the 120 plays of Sophocles; and some 18 of 90 by Euripides. There are works of Pliny and other authors of which there are no known copies. Cisne applied a Markov model of birth and death processes to the probability of survival of manuscripts on arithmetical and calendrical calculations from Late Antiquity and the Middle Ages (Cisne [4]; see comment by Gilman and Glaze [15]). In such a model a manuscript has a probability of being copied (analogous to giving birth in a model of population demography) and being destroyed (analogous to death). Since manuscripts are copied by hand, their intrinsic growth rate should be exponential. Cisne shows that the resulting model of the birth and death dynamics of manuscripts is identical to the Verhulst-Pearl logistic equation for population growth, familiar to generations of ecologists. Using data from the number of copies of four of the Venerable Bede's technical works, Cisne shows that their age distribution closely follows age distributions expected for populations with logistic growth. Based on this model, Cisne comes to the somewhat surprising conclusion that many, if not most, scientific texts in existence in the early Middle Ages are likely to have survived to today. He suggests that the reason for the demise of copies of Aristotle's missing works, and others from Antiquity, is preservational (an issue also familiar to paleontologists): manuscripts on parchment were more likely to survive than older ones on papyrus. This is a sharp departure from the more general assumption that the disappearance of manuscripts from Antiquity is simply a function of time. The

~41~

assumptions in Cisne's models have been criticized [6, 15], but to dismiss the effort would be too harsh; his work might better have been seen as an opening effort—in the development of more robust models and assumptions—to document patterns of cultural transmission.

Cisne came to the issue of the survival rate of manuscripts from a paleontologist's concern with the quality of the fossil record. To a first approximation, the record of the history of life is entirely missing. The fossil record reflects the fortuitous preservation and recovery of durably skeletonized, common, and often geographically widespread species, usually from the marine realm rather than on land. (To a geologist, terrestrial deposits are generally being eroded and deposited in the oceans, so it is nice when dinosaurs and other land-based organisms are preserved, but it is not the way to bet.) The fossil record may record one to two percent of all the marine animal species that have lived during the 575 million years since the origin of animals, and an even smaller percentage of the plants and animals that have lived on land. Paleontologists have some sources of information of the history of life, including tracks and trails preserved in sediments (trace fossils) and molecular fossils (biomarkers), but the bulk of our knowledge of the history of life is dependent upon the preserved body fossils of now extinct organisms. Moreover, some depositional settings are better at preserving organic remains than others: limestones and shales are, for example, generally better than sandstones. This produces considerable spatial and temporal variability in the quality of the fossil record.

For historians and archaeologists, as for paleontologists, the quality of the record declines the further one goes into the past. For paleontologists, this decay in the fidelity of the fossil

FOR HISTORIANS AND ARCHAEOLOGISTS, AS FOR PALEONTOLOGISTS, THE QUALITY OF THE RECORD DECLINES THE FURTHER ONE GOES INTO THE PAST.

record means that there are fewer deposits of greater age; it is more difficult to correlate between rocks of similar age as their age increases (a necessary precondition of determining a global pattern); the uncertainties on the age of fossils at a particular locality increase with age; and the quality of preservation generally declines. One consequence of this is that the sorts of questions that we can address necessarily change for older deposits. My colleagues working on the past few million years of time are able to ask, and answer, questions about ecological relationships. Working in rocks 270 or 510 million years old, I can only dream of having similar resolution.

~43~

Practitioners of Big History face similar problems, and some of the solutions devised by paleontologists may prove useful. Consider, for example, the issue of the domestication of agriculture. It is exceedingly unlikely that archaeologists have actually recovered the earliest sites where plants or animals were domesticated, although they have greatly narrowed the geographic region in most of the centers of domestication [3, 42]. Techniques that paleontologists have developed for placing statistical confidence intervals on the first and last appearances of fossil clades based on the frequency of recoveries [24, 30] may prove similarly useful in assessing historical problems.

A critical question for paleontologists is to reconstruct the pattern and eventually the underlying processes of the history of life. With this knowledge in hand, paleontologists can then investigate the significance of changes in the environment, the importance of evolutionary innovations, and what other factors control diversity. The literature in this area is too rich and diverse to address here, so I will confine myself to using a long-standing debate over the record of global marine diversity through the past 600 million years as an example of the issue.

There are many components of diversity, including the variety of form, the range of developmental styles, and the generation of different ecological groupings [10]. Many of these have no ready metrics, so paleontologists have tended to focus on the number of *taxa* (taxonomic units such as species, genera, or families) over this time. Some paleontologists argued that global diversity had been expanding nearly exponentially since the end-Permian mass extinction 252 million years ago [38, 40], while others suggested that diversity reached a maximum early in the history of animals, perhaps 450 million years ago, and subsequent changes have largely been changing relative frequency, rather than absolute diversity [28, 29]. In the later model, lack of sediments and other preservational problems have produced a pattern very different from the "real" one. Resolving the difference between these two end members remains the object of considerable effort, and even if no resolution is yet available, the problems are better understood [36, 37].

Unfortunately, the vagaries of preservation mean that counting fossil species is too subject to error. Instead, paleontologists have agglomerated species into more inclusive units in the Linnean taxonomic hierarchy, generally *genera* or families (groups of related genera). Sepkoski generated an exhaustive compilation of the first and last occurrences of marine families through the past 600 million years [31-34] and eventually expanded this to marine genera [35]. Although the patterns revealed by Sepkoski's analysis achieved iconic status, there are a number of potential biases that cloud the results. The first and last occurrences of a taxon are unlikely to represent the actual origin or extinction of the lineage. Statistical tools have been developed to adjust range durations to account for this problem, but doing so requires knowledge of not just the first and last occurrences, but the frequency of occurrences of a taxon near the range endpoints [7, 24, 30]. In the absence of such data, global compilations have not been adjusted for this problem. In these analyses, Sepkoski was concerned that the more complete sampling of living biotas might artificially extend the ranges of some taxa across intervals where they are unrecorded from the fossil record. In other words, a genus of fossil crab might be known only up to the late Miocene, 5 million years ago, but is also known from living representatives. Thus the range of the genus extends to today. To adjust for this "Pull of the Recent" Sepkoski removed all recent taxa and analyzed only the fossil occurrences.

Variations in sampling and collecting intensity produce a related set of problems. Intervals of geologic time with abundant, well-preserved, and easily accessible fossiliferous rock in Europe and North America tend to be far better sampled by paleontologists than intervals with more poorly preserved fossils or greater difficulties in access. Fortunately these variations in sampling intensity between regions can be corrected through the use of rarefaction techniques. Rarefaction is a statistical technique to compare samples of different sizes to determine the number of taxa if the same number of specimens had been sampled between the two time intervals [27].

~45~

In Sepkoski's original study, he lacked information on how often taxa had been found between their first and last occurrences. For his purposes, such information was not critical, but as better datasets were developed (often by his own students), the issue of how to count diversity became more critical. Does one count all the taxa found in an interval? What about taxa found before and after an interval, but not within a specific interval? Should one count only taxa that are found in adjacent intervals ("boundary crossers") but not those found only within a single interval? Such "singletons" may reflect poor taxonomy or other problems These and other problems have led to the generation of a wide range of diversity metrics, and applied to large data sets, they will produce very different patterns of diversity [12, 13]. Recently a group of paleontologists has produced a new picture of marine diversity for the past 600 million years, based on a compilation of diversity from specific localities, rather than just first and last occurrences [1, 2]. This group also used a variety of new statistical methods, including rarefaction and different counting metrics. Their results are considerably different from Sepkoski's in showing a much smaller increase in marine diversity toward the recent, and a very different pattern of crises and expansions. For example, the apparent exponential increase in diversity over the past 100 million years disappeared, as have some mass-extinction events and a rapid increase in diversity beginning about 480 million years ago. In short, this new diversity plot emphasizes very different events than those many paleontologists have spent the past two decades studying. Unfortunately there are problems with this new analysis as well, so paleontologists and evolutionary biologists are even more in the dark about the patterns in the history of life than before.

Here my goal is not to advocate the adoption of specific methods, but rather to show how such a seemingly simple issue as the global diversity over the past 600 million years raises some difficult issues when examined more thoroughly. Since understanding process requires a basic agreement on pattern, this dispute threatens to paralyze parts of the paleontological research agenda. In the absence of a better understanding of diversity patterns, it is difficult to determine, for example, how climate has influenced diversity [11], or even when major increases have occurred in biodiversity and what environmental circumstances or new adaptations may have facilitated them. Some of these statistical techniques from paleobiology, ecology, and evolutionary biology might have relevance for the description of specific historical patterns in Big History, and specifically for establishing which "patterns" are sufficiently robust to warrant further study.

Reconstructing Evolutionary Trees

The only figure in Charles Darwin's *The Origin of Species* is an evolutionary tree, used to illustrate the concept of descent with modification. Darwin's evolutionary perspective was grafted onto a pre-existing system of systematics developed by Carl Linnaeus, the means of classifying and organizing the relationships between species, genera, and more inclusive evolutionary groups. Overall morphologic similarity was often the primary evidence for inferring a relationship between two entities and provided the basis for classification. Since the 1980s, however, systematists have realized that overall similarity is a poor guide to evolutionary relationships, as it fails to distinguish similarity due to descent from a common origin from convergence on a common form for other reasons. New methods of reconstructing these phylogenetic relationships were developed, relying on the statistical analysis of large datasets of specific character states. Such techniques have recently been profitably used to explore technological evolution and to provide much-needed rigor to historical linguistics [18, 26]. They have also been applied to aspects of cultural evolution [23], although it is not always clear whether the horizontal transmission of cultural information violates the assumptions of vertical transmission embedded within phylogenetic methods.

Although cornets are now similar in form and tone to a small trumpet, they are historically descended from a coiled horn and thus independently derived from trumpets. One question in the evolution of musical instruments is how this transition came about [8]. Temkin and Eldredge applied phylogenetic methods to elucidate this evolutionary transition, coding a matrix from historical collections of cornets. The character matrix was based not on overall similarity of the shape of the cornets, but on specific, discrete characters. The pattern of shared, derived characters defined the patterns of evolutionary descent, and also illuminated horizontal transmission of ideas and technologies between different makers of cornets [39]. But since the historical evolution of cornets is so well documented, Temkin and Eldredge were able to identify areas where the phylogenetic methods failed as well. Such applications of phylogenetic methods are often informative because both biological and cultural evolution share certain properties of descent with modification. The application of such biological approaches to cultural evolution is criticized because of the extensive horizontal transmission that occurs in cultural evolution and learning. Yet microbes also happily transfer useful genetic information among quite disparate lineages [16, 43]. The application of comparative phylogenetic methods to the evolution of cultural diversity has been explored [22].

~47~

Contingency and Pattern in the History of Life

Properly characterizing the patterns in the history of life is critical for evaluating one of the most divisive issues among paleontologists: the likelihood of regularities governing the history of life. This is an area that cuts to the core of Big History as well, and to the issue of whether one can, in principle, develop a science of history. The late Stephen Jay Gould of Harvard was one of the foremost proponents of the "contingency matters" school of evolutionary history. Beginning with his book *Wonderful Life* [17] Steve argued that the course of life, and the waxing and waning of different *clades* (major groups of organisms that share a common line origin, for example mammals) does not reflect adaptive superiority, as pure Darwinian evolutionist might argue, but has often been driven by chance or contingent events. Steve based much of his argument on the fossils of the Burgess Shale, an extraordinary 505-million year-old Middle Cambrian deposit of soft-bodied and lightly skeletonized marine animals. The Burgess Shale reveals animals otherwise unrecorded from the fossil record, including armored *onycophorans* (think of a short earthworm with legs and spines), and my personal favorite, *Opabinia regalis*, a cousin of arthropods with five eyes (each on its own eye stalk) and a single long proboscis ending in a claw positioned like an elephant's trunk. Steve famously argued that if one could "run the tape of life again" annelids (earthworms and their allies) might be less common than priapulids, or arthropods might not be one of the most dominant phyla; perhaps the descendants of *Opabinia* might be among us still.

Sea urchins provide one of my own favorite examples of contingency. Some 270 million years ago, there were about seven different genera of sea urchins, but only one or two species survived the great end-Permian mass extinction 252 million years ago, when about 95 percent of all marine species became extinct [9]. The primary survivor (*Miocidaris keyserlyi*) belonged to a genus with a particular morphology that is shared by all the descendants of this now very diverse and abundant group. One can of course come up with a story, perhaps even a plausible one, about why *Miocidaris* survived the Permian calamity. But any such story is inherently untestable. It is just as likely that its survival was due to luck and nothing more. But if luck it was, the approximately 800 living species of echinoids reflect a far greater array of morphologies and life habits than seemed possible before the end-Permian mass extinction. So this contingent event had a tremendous impact on the history of this group, and arguably on the structure of modern marine ecosystems. Steve Gould argued that often the events leading to the disappearance of a group could not have been predicted, nor could the effect they had on diversity (number of taxa) and abundance (number of individual organisms). If this argument is generally correct, then it seems to limit the possibility of identifying general patterns in the history of life.

The alternative argument is that whatever the importance of contingency in individual cases, such as the effect of the 10-kilometer diameter bolide that struck the earth nearly 66 million years ago, the general trends in the history of life persist despite the occasional random events. One line of evidence in support of this view is the ubiquity of convergence. Consider, for example, studies of Jurassic and Cretaceous fossil mammals that evolved during the "Age of Dinosaurs" and long before the modern, placental mammals. Paleontologists have identified a Jurassic beaver (*Castrocauda*), a fossorial (digging) insectivore (*Fruitafossor*) analogous to an armadillo or an aardvark, and even a Jurassic "bat" (*Valticotherium*) [20]. A more recent example is of saber-toothed cats, more generically known as hypercarnivores because of their extreme specialization. Americans are familiar with saber-tooth cats from the La Brea tar pits in Los Angeles, but such cats evolved at least five separate times during the Plio-Pleistocene (the past few million years) as a result of the abundance of large prey species. And one of the five species was not a true cat at all, but a marsupial, only distantly related to true cats. A final example comes from work on the radiation of a single group of spiders in Hawaii [14] and lizards in the Caribbean [19]. Both the spiders and lizards have diversified into different color morphs on different islands. For the Hawaiian spiders, it is possible that all of the green spiders, for example, could have been descendants of a single green spider that dispersed to different islands from the island where it first arose. But when researchers developed a highly resolved phylogeny (evolutionary tree) they found that in each case independent radiations occurred on each island, so that the various green spider species were only distantly related to each other. In other words, the same color morphs appeared independently on different islands. Caribbean lizards displayed a similar pattern. In each case, evolution generated a very similar morphology because of the similarities in ecological opportunities and evolutionary responses. Similar spiders appeared on different islands because similarities in the structure of the environment and the ecological communities produced an ecological opportunity (or niche) on a variety of different islands within the Hawaiian archipelago.

~50~

The ubiquity of convergence and parallelism in evolution, even, in the case of Jurassic and modern beavers separated by some 170 million years, demonstrates several points about evolution: (1) There is a structure to ecosystems that produces similar opportunities in similar environments; (2) sufficient evolutionary variation is available within some lineages to take advantage of these opportunities essentially (to a geologist!) simultaneously; and (3) over longer durations, these opportunities can persist, or at least recur over tens of millions of years. This line of reasoning suggests that while contingent events may interrupt long-term trends, and even remove once-favored groups, enough structure remains so that the patterns will become re-established (see also Vermeij [41]).

The history of life is unlikely to be explicable either as a product of pure contingency or as purely a result of pervasive trends, but as a more complicated mélange of the two. The challenge for those seeking general laws is, I think, twofold: First to determine those particular aspects of the history of life where generalities are likely to hold; and secondly, to establish the boundaries of such generalities. Many generalities may be universal through the history of life, as appears to be the case with certain scaling relationships. Others may apply only over a limited range of clades or environments, for specific intervals of time, until the rules change through biotic crisis or some other cause.

This dichotomy misses a deeper issue, one that reflects the anomalous role of history in evolutionary thought. In *The*

....

THE HISTORY OF LIFE IS UNLIKELY TO BE EXPLICABLE
EITHER AS A PRODUCT OF PURE CONTINGENCY, OR AS
PURELY A RESULT OF PERVASIVE TRENDS, BUT AS A MORE
COMPLICATED MÉLANGE OF THE TWO.

....

Origin of Species Charles Darwin articulated the concepts of evo-   ~51~
lution, descent with modification, and natural selection (adding
sexual selection in a latter book). Since the 1940s the leading
intellectual perspective on evolution (known as the Modern
Synthesis or the Evolutionary Synthesis) has been framed
around the field of population genetics. Population genetics
has developed an enormously powerful set of mathematical
and analytical tools for understanding the role of changes in
the frequencies of genes over time through selection, drift, and
mutation. This work has established evolutionary biology as
a far more robust discipline than was the case earlier, but the
Modern Synthesis is a curiously ahistorical view of a historical
discipline. Beyond the fact that it provides little insight into how
form evolves (something we know now a great deal about from
comparative studies of molecular developmental biology), the
Modern Synthesis is silent (and indeed probably antagonistic)
to issues such as whether the nature of variation upon which
selection can act has systematically changed over time, whether
the relative significance of selection, mutation, and genetic drift
(the principle drivers of evolution) has changed over time,
or how the changing structure of ecological relationships has
altered evolutionary opportunities through time.

The changes in historical processes are more obvious: the
economic foundation of societies has changed from hunter-gath-
erers to agriculturalists, with the development of states, through
a variety of economic systems over the past millennium: from
feudalism and mercantilism to various flavors of capitalism.
Political systems have undergone similar transformations during

this interval, particularly with the rise of the nation-state. There may be "laws" of history that transcend these changes, and there is little doubt that contingent factors have played a significant role in historical events. But there is a clear pattern of change in the rules by which societies are organized. Here, I think is an area where historical sciences have a great deal to learn from history, and conversely, where the conversation between history and the historical sciences may be most fruitful. The success of any dialog between these two disparate areas must begin with the rigorous establishment of the patterns for which we are seeking to understand the underlying process (as discussed in the early part of this chapter). I think the next pressing question is to understand the different classes of historical processes likely to be primarily influenced by contingency, by pervasive laws, or by rules which themselves evolve over time. 𝄞

~52~

References

[1] Alroy, J., M. Aberhan, D. J. Bottjer, M. Foote, F. T. Fursich, P. J. Harries, A. J. Hendy, S. M. Holland, L. C. Ivany, W. Kiessling, M. A. Kosnik, C. R. Marshall, A. J. McGowan, A. I. Miller, T. D. Olszewski, M. E. Patzkowsky, S. E. Peters, L. Villier, P. J. Wagner, N. Bonuso, P. S. Borkow, B. Brenneis, M. E. Clapham, L. M. Fall, C. A. Ferguson, V. L. Hanson, A. Z. Krug, K. M. Layou, E. H. Leckey, S. Nurnberg, C. M. Powers, J. A. Sessa, C. Simpson, A. Tomasovych, and C. C. Visaggi. "Phanerozoic Trends in the Global Diversity of Marine Invertebrates." *Science* 321(5885) (2008): 97-100.

[2] Alroy, J., C. R. Marshall, R. K. Bambach, K. Bezusko, M. Foote, F. T. Fursich, T. A. Hansen, S. M. Holland, L. C. Ivany, D. Jablonski, D. K. Jacobs, D. C. Jones, M. A. Kosnik, S. Lidgard, S. Low, A. I. Miller, P. M. Novack-Gottshall, T. D. Olszewski, M. E. Patzkowsky, D. M. Raup, K. Roy, J. J. Sepkoski, Jr., M. G. Sommers, P. J. Wagner, and A. Webber. "Effects of Sampling Standardization on Estimates of Phanerozoic Marine Diversification." *PNAS* 96 (2001): 6261-6266.

[3] Brown, T. A., M. K. Jones, W. Powell, and R. G. Allaby. "The Complex Origins of Domesticated Crops in the Fertile Crescent." *Trends in Ecology and Evolution* 24 (2008): 103-109.

[4]   Cisne, J. L. "How science survived: Medieval manuscripts'
        "demography" and classic texts' extinction." *Science* 307
        (2005):1305-1307.

[5]   Cleland, C. E. "Methodological and epistemic differences
        between historical science and experimental science". *Philosophy
        of Science* 69 (2002):474-496.

[6]   Declercq, G. 2005 Comment on "How science survived:
        Medieval manuscripts' "demography" and classic texts' extinc-
        tion". Science 310:1618b

[7]   Dingus, L., and P. M. Sadler. "The Effects of Stratigraphic
        Completeness on Extimates of Evolutionary Rates." *Syst. Zool*
        31 (1982): 400-412.

[8]   Eldredge, N. "A brief history of piston-valved cornets."
        Historical Brass Society *Journal*. 14 (2002): 337-390.

[9]   Erwin, D. H. *Extinction: How Life Nearly Died* 250 *Million Years
        Ago*. Princeton, NJ: Princeton University Press, 2006.

[10]   Erwin, D. H. "Extinction as the Loss of Evolutionary History."
        Proceedings of the National Academy of Sciences, USA (2008).

[11]   Erwin, D. H. "Climate as a Driver of Evolutionary Change."
        Current Biology 19 (2009): R575-R583.

[12]   Foote, M. "Origination and Extinction Components of
        Taxonomic Diversity: General Problems." *Paleobiology*, Supp.
        to Issue 4(27) (2000): 74-102.

[13]   Foote, M. "Origination and Extinction through the Phanerozoic:
        A New Approach." *Journal of Geology* 111 (2003): 125-148.

[14]   Gillespie, R. "Community Assembly through Adaptive Radiaion
        in Hawaiian Spiders." *Science* 303 (2004): 356-359.

[15]   Gilman, S. L. and Glaze, F. E. "How Science Survived—
        Medieval manuscripts as fossils". Science 307 (2005):1208-1209.

[16]   Gogarten, J. P., W. F. Doolittle, and J. G. Lawrence.
        "Prokaryotic Evolution in Light of Gene Transfer." *Mol Biol Evol*
        19(12) (2002): 2226-2238.

[17]   Gould, S. J. *Wonderful Life*. New York: Norton, 1989.

[18]   Gray, R. D., and Q. D. Atkinson. "Language-Tree Divergence
        Times Support the Anatolian Theory of Indo-European
        Origin." *Nature* 426(6965) (2003): 435-439.

[19]   Losos, J. B., T. R. Jackman, A. Larson, K. de Queiroz, and
        L. Rodriguez-Schettino. "Contingency and Determinism in
        Replicated Adaptive Radiations of Island Lizards." *Science* 279
        (1998): 21115-2118.

~53~

[20] Luo, Z. X. "Transformation and Diversification in Early Mammal Evolution." *Nature* 450 (2007): 1011-1019.

[21] Lyman, R. L., and M. J. O'Brien. "Nomothetic science and ideographic history in Twentieth-Century Americanist anthropology". *Journal of the History of the Behavioral Sciences* 40(2004): 77-96.

[22] Mace, R., C. Holden, and S. Shennan. *The Evolution of Cultural Diversity*. London: University College, London Press, 2005.

[23] Mace, R., and C. J. Holden. "A Phylogenetic Approach to Cultural Evolution." *Trends in Ecology and Evolution* 20 (2005): 116-121.

[24] Marshall, C. R. "Confidence Intervals on Stratigraphic Ranges." *Paleobiology* 16 (1990): 1-10.

[25] O'Hara, R. J. "Homage to Clio, or, Toward an historical philosophy for evolutionary biology." *Systematic Zoology* 37(1988):142-155.

[26] Pagel, M., Q. D. Atkinson, and A. Meade. "Frequency of Word-Use Predicts Rates of Lexical Evolution throughout Indo-European History." *Nature* 449 (2007): 717-720.

[27] Raup, D. M. "Taxonomic Diversity Estimation Using Rarefaction." *Paleobiology* 1 (1975): 333-342.

[28] Raup, D. M. "Species Diversity in the Phanerozoic." *Paleobiology* 2 (1976a): 279-288.

[29] Raup, D. M. "Species diversity in the Phanerozoic: an interpretation." *Paleobiology* 2 (1976b): 289-297.

[30] Sadler, P. M. "Quantitative Biostratigraphy—Achieving Finer Resolution in Global Correlation." *Annual Review of Earth and Planetary Science* 32 (2004): 187-213.

[31] Sepkoski, J. J., Jr. "A Kinetic Model of Phanerozoic Taxonomic Diversity II. Early Paleozoic Families and Multiple Equilibria." *Paleobiology* 5 (1979): 222-251.

[32] Sepkoski, J. J., Jr. "A Factor Analytic Description of the Phanerozoic Marine Fossil Record." *Paleobiology* 7 (1981): 36-53.

[33] Sepkoski, J. J., Jr. "A Compendium of Fossil Marine Families." *Milwaukee Public Museum Contributions in Biology and Geology* 51 (1982): 125.

[34] Sepkoski, J. J., Jr. "A Kinetic Model of Phanerozoic Taxonomic Diversity. III. Post-Paleozoic Families and Mass Extinction." *Paleobiology* 10 (1984): 246-267.

[35] Sepkoski, J. J., Jr. "Biodiversity: Past, Present, and Future." *Journal of Paleontology* 71 (1997): 533-539.

[36] Smith, A. B. "Large-Scale Heterogeneity of the Fossil Record: Implications for Phanerozoic Biodiversity Studies." *Philisophical Transactions of the Royal Society, London. Ser. B* 356 (2001): 351-367.

[37] Smith, A. B. "Marine Diversity through the Phanerozoic: Problems and Prospects." *Journal of the Geological Soc., London* 164 (2007): 731-745.

[38] Stanley, S. M. "An Analysis of the History of Marine Animal Diversity." Paleobiology 33(4s) (2007): 1-55.

[39] Temkin, I., and Eldredge, N. "Phylogenetics and material cultural evolution". *Current Anthropology* 48 (2007): 146.153.

[40] Valentine, J. W. "How Many Marine Invertebrate Fossil Species? A New Approximation." *Journal of Paleonotology* 44 (1970): 410-415.

[41] Vermeij, G. J. "Historical Contingency and the Purported Uniqueness of Evolutionary Innovations." *PNAS* 103 (2006): 1804-1809.

[42] Zeder, M. A., E. Emshwiller, B. D. Smith, and D. G. Bradley. "Documenting Domestication: The Intersection of Genetics and Archaeology." *Trends in Genetics* 22 (2006): 139-155.

[43] Zhaxybayeva, O., and J. P. Gogarten. "Cladogenesis, Coalescence and the Evolution of the Three Domains of Life." *Trends in Genetics* 20 (2004): 182-187.

WAR, PEACE, & EVERYTHING:
THOUGHTS ON TOLSTOY

John Lewis Gaddis, Yale University

WHAT CLAUSEWITZ AND TOLSTOY were trying to do was to derive from the experiences of history the laws governing it. Although they failed, these 19th-century thinkers, each operating from a different perspective, anticipated what we've come to call chaos and complexity theory.

There is a curious moment in Tolstoy's account of the Battle of Borodino—page 774 in the new Richard Pevear and Larissa Volokhonsky translation of *War and Peace*—when two of the central characters of the novel, Pierre Bezukhov and Prince Andrei Bolkonsky, are interrupted by the sound of hoofbeats, look up, and see Carl von Clausewitz and another officer riding by. One of the horsemen is saying to the other: "War must be extended in space. I cannot put too high a price on this view." The other agrees: "The aim is to weaken the enemy, so one cannot pay attention to the loss of private persons." This disgusts Andrei, whose family estate lies within the space through which this particular war is to be extended. "[A]ll there is in a German head," he complains bitterly to Pierre, "is reasoning, which isn't worth a tinker's damn. . . . They gave him [Napoleon] the whole of Europe and came to teach us. Fine teachers!" [6, p.117-19; 10, p.774].

Pierre and Prince Andrei were at Borodino only in Tolstoy's imagination, but Clausewitz really was there: when Napoleon invaded Russia in 1812, Clausewitz resigned his commission in the Prussian Army, joined the Russians, and participated in the great battle [7]. The meticulous Tolstoy would have known this, and could well have read Clausewitz's great work *On War*, published posthumously in 1832, before writing *War and Peace* in the 1860s. If he did, Tolstoy's portrayal suggests that, like many other readers of Clausewitz, he misunderstood the point of the book. For not only are there similarities in the way that Clausewitz and Tolstoy depicted war, they also appear to have shared a sense of the relationship between theory and reality. And that relationship, in turn, relates to everything else.

Begin with war. Here is a famous passage from Clausewitz, which leaves no doubt that he knows what he's writing about:

Let us accompany a novice to the battlefield. As we approach, the rumble of guns grows louder and alternates with the whir of cannonballs, which begin to attract his attention. Shots begin to strike close around us. We hurry up the slope where the commanding general is stationed with his large staff. Here cannonballs and bursting shells are frequent, and life begins to seem more serious than the young man had imagined. Suddenly someone you know is wounded; then a shell falls among the staff. You notice that some of the officers act a little oddly; you yourself are not as steady and collected as you were: even the bravest can become slightly distracted. Now we enter the battle raging before us, still almost like a spectacle, and join the nearest division commander. Shot is falling like hail, and the thunder of our own guns adds to the din. Forward to the brigadier, a solder of acknowledged bravery, but he is careful to take cover behind a rise, a house, or a clump of trees. A noise is heard that is a certain indication of increasing danger—the rattling of grapeshot on roofs and on the ground. Cannonballs tear past, whizzing in all directions, and musketballs begin to whistle around us. A little further we reach the firing line, where the infantry endures the hammering for hours with incredible steadfastness. The air is filled with hissing bullets that sound like a sharp crack if they pass close to one's head. For a final shock, the sight of men being killed and mutilated moves our pounding hearts to awe and pity.

The novice cannot pass through these layers of increasing intensity of danger without sensing that here ideas are governed by other factors, that the light of reason is refracted in a manner quite different from that which is normal in academic speculation [11, p. 113].

Now here is Tolstoy on Borodino:

> *From the battlefield the adjutants he had sent and his marshals' orderlies constantly came galloping to Napoleon with reports on the course of events; but all these reports were false: both because in the heat of battle it is impossible to tell what is going on at a given moment, and because many of the adjutants did not reach the actual place of battle, but told what they had heard from others; and also because, while an adjutant was riding the mile or so that separated him from Napoleon, the circumstances changed, and the news he was bringing became incorrect. . . . On the weight of such unavoidably false reports, Napoleon gave his instructions, which either had been carried out before he ever gave them or were not and could not be carried out.*

> *The marshals and the generals who were closer to the battlefield, but who, like Napoleon, did not take part in the battle itself, but only occasionally rode into the fire, gave their own instructions and orders about where to shoot and from where, and where the cavalry were to ride and the infantry to run, without asking Napoleon. But even their instructions were carried out as rarely and to as small a degree as Napoleon's instructions. For the most part, what came out was the opposite of what they had ordered. Soldiers who were told to advance would come under canister shot and run back; soldiers who were told to stay where they were, suddenly seeing the Russians appear unexpectedly before them, sometimes ran back and sometimes rushed forward, and the cavalry galloped without orders in pursuit of the fleeing Russians. . . . As soon as these men left that space through which the cannonballs and bullets flew, their commanders, who stood in the rear, formed them up, established discipline, and, under the effect of that discipline, again led them into the zone of fire, in which (under the effect of the fear of death) they again lost*

*discipline and rushed about according to the chance mood of
the crowd* [10, pp.799-801].

You might wonder, from reading these passages, how
battles could ever accomplish anything. And yet Borodino —
despite the fact that there was no clear winner — accomplished
a lot.

The battle weakened the French and the Russians about
equally; but the Russians had a vast country into which to retreat,
abandoning Moscow as they did so. The French were far from
their country, and advanced even farther when Napoleon could
not resist taking the city, hoping that this would shock Tsar
Alexander I into making peace. When it did not, Napoleon had
no idea of what to do next: he was like a dog who had chased a
car and actually caught it — then what? Meanwhile winter was
coming, a fact of which the Emperor's lowliest private could
have reminded him.

Clausewitz called this the "culminating point" of the French
invasion, by which he meant that the French defeated themselves
by exhausting themselves. The "center of gravity" had shifted
against them, and now, with only a minimal military effort, the
Russians were able to chase them out of the country. Tolstoy's
portrayal of old, fat, seemingly slow-moving General Kutuzov
makes this Clausewitzian point better even than Clausewitz
did. As a result, Napoleon lost his army and within a year and
a half, his throne. The Russian tsar toured Paris triumphantly,
was received in London respectfully, and even dined at Oxford
in the Radcliffe Camera while the dons, perched on ladders,
gawked at him through the windows.

And at the end of another great war in another century,
an American expert on Russia who was a careful student of
Tolstoy also happened to read Clausewitz for the first time,
connecting him with Borodino and its aftermath. He was
George F. Kennan, and he did this in the summer of 1946
while preparing to teach at the new National War College
in Washington. It was from Clausewitz's example of how
advances can exhaust themselves and centers of gravity can
shift that Kennan devised his strategy of "containing" the

Soviet Union during the Cold War without exhausting the United States. Four decades later, with containment having been achieved and the Cold War ending, Mikhail Gorbachev, the last leader of the USSR, paid tribute to the elderly Kennan as "the friend of another country and . . . a loyal and devoted citizen of his own" [9, p.351].[1] So who says battles don't accomplish anything?

As these examples suggest, wars are full of surprises. They provide the most brutal of all interfaces between what is expected and what is achieved; and because there have been so many wars over so long a period of time, reflections on war have provided some of our most durable commentaries on the distance that lies between theory and practice. From Homer, Sun-Tzu and Thucydides through B. H. Liddell-Hart, Bernard Brodie, and Henry Kissinger—and certainly for the great war novelists like Patrick O'Brian, Pat Barker, and Joseph Heller—the gap between orders given and actions taken has been a constant concern. Nowhere more so, though, than with Clausewitz and Tolstoy, both of whom wrestled as seriously as anyone ever has with this problem, and neither of whom resolved it to their satisfaction, or for decades afterwards for even their most conscientious readers.

Clausewitz died in 1831 before finishing *On War*, leaving us with a massive, unwieldy, and often contradictory text, the meaning of which has been debated ever since. To undertake a close reading of Clausewitz, I tell my students, is to risk schizophrenia: you will come out of it unsure of what he said, but also with grave doubts about who you are. Tolstoy did finish *War and Peace* in 1868, but felt obliged to accompany it with this puzzling disclaimer: "It is not a novel, still less an epic poem, still less a historical chronicle. *War and Peace* is what the author wanted and was able to express, in the form in which it is expressed" [10, p.1217]. Isaiah Berlin is not the only critic to have detected in Tolstoy "a tormenting inner conflict"—just what I warn my students about in Clausewitz— "between the universal and all-important but delusive experience

---

[1] I've seen Kennan's National War College reading notes in connection with my biography of him.

of free will," on the one hand, and on the other "the reality of inexorable historical determinism" [3, p.458].

What both Clausewitz and Tolstoy were trying to do, I think, was to derive from the experiences of history the laws governing it. In this, they both failed. Clausewitz concluded that "no prescriptive formulation universal enough to deserve the name of law can be applied to the constant change and diversity of the phenomena of war" [11, p.152]. Tolstoy was more emphatic:

> *If even one man out of millions in a thousand-year period of time has had the possibility of acting freely, that is, as he pleased, then it is obvious that one free act of this man, contrary to the laws, destroys the possibility of the existence of any laws whatever for the whole of mankind* [10, p.1200].

In this failure, they had a distinguished successor. Henry Adams, more than either Clausewitz or Tolstoy, grew up in a scientific age: a distinguished historian, he set himself the task of reconciling the infinite variables that populate the past with some "great generalization" that would not only explain it all but would also predict the future. History would become a kind of linear mathematics, establishing clear connections between causes and effects, and presumably between intentions and consequences.

But then, thanks to his friend Henri Poincaré, Adams encountered nonlinear mathematics. "[I]f our means of investigation should become more and more penetrating," Poincaré pointed out, "we should discover the simple under the complex; then the complex under the simple; then anew the simple under the complex; and so on without ever being able to foresee the last term." Adams was appalled: "A mathematical paradise of endless displacement promised eternal bliss to the mathematician, but turned the historian green with horror." For if the simple and the complex interacted with one another, then "[al]ways and everywhere the Complex had been true and the Contradiction had been certain. . . . Chaos was a primary fact even in Paris — especially in Paris — as it was in the Book of Genesis; but every thinking being in Paris or out of it had exhausted thought in the effort to prove Unity, Continuity, Purpose, Order, Law, Truth, the Universe" [2, pp.454-56; 5, pp.72-74].

That, then, is what Clausewitz, Tolstoy, and Adams had in common: they "exhausted thought" in the effort to reconcile the general with the specific. To put it in Berlin's terms, they set out to become hedgehogs: to find out how one very big thing worked. For Clausewitz it was war, for Tolstoy it was history, for Henry Adams it was (in a phrase another Adams made famous), "life, the universe, and everything" [1]. All three, however, were too honest with themselves—and with us—to escape being foxes: they could not resist taking an interest in all kinds of little things. They were, as a result of this tension, tortured souls.

~63~

Fewer souls torture themselves with that sort of thing these days, perhaps because there are more serious things to worry about, but perhaps also because the sciences of the twentieth century—at least the physical and natural sciences—have made us comfortable with the idea that randomness and regularity co-exist. There are, to be sure, a few social science holdouts, but exhaustion is taking its toll among them, as it did with Clausewitz, Tolstoy, and Adams. Reconsiderations are setting in [5, pp.52-70].

What's interesting, though, is the extent to which these three nineteenth-century thinkers, each operating from a different perspective, anticipated what we've come to call chaos and complexity theory. Alan Beyerchen and N. Katherine Hayles have documented this for Clausewitz and Adams, respectively [4, pp.59-90; 8, pp.61-90]. I'm not aware, though, that anyone has tried to link Tolstoy's theory of history—which weaves its way in and out of *War and Peace* and then gets 45 pages of its own at the end—with these more recent developments in the history of ideas. The new Pevear-Volokhonsky translation provides a good opportunity to explore that connection, and so in what follows I want offer a few suggestions for where such an inquiry might lead us.

The principal issue Tolstoy raises is what causes events — great and small — to happen. Divine will, whether emanating from one god or many, answered this question for the ancients, he noted, and no doubt would still have for the majority of the world's peoples at the time he was writing. Modern history, however, had rejected that explanation in principle but sustained something like it in practice, for did it not assume a pre-determined progression through a series of otherwise disconnected events? Here's how historians, in Tolstoy's view, accounted for the events of 1789-1815 (the passage is long, but uncharacteristically funny):

> *Louis XIV was a very proud and presumptuous man; he had such-and-such mistresses and such-and-such ministers, and he ruled France badly. Louis's heirs were also weak men and also ruled France badly. They, too, had such-and-such favorites and such-and-such mistresses. Besides, certain men were writing books at the time. At the end of the eighteenth century, some two dozen men got together in Paris and started talking about all men being equal and free. That led people all over France to start slaughtering and drowning each other. These people killed the king and many others. At the same time there was in France a man of genius — Napoleon. He defeated everybody everywhere — that is, he killed a lot of people — because he was a great genius. And he went off for some reason to kill Africans, and he killed them so well, and was so cunning and clever, that, on coming back to France, he ordered everybody to obey him. And everybody obeyed him. Having become emperor, he again went to kill people in Italy, Austria, and Prussia. And there he killed a lot. In Russia there was the emperor Alexander, who decided to restore order in Europe and therefore made war with Napoleon. But in the year seven, he suddenly made friends with him, then in the year eleven quarreled again, and again they started killing a lot of people. And Napoleon brought six hundred thousand men to Russia and captured Moscow; then he suddenly ran away from Moscow, and then the emperor Alexander . . . united Europe to take up arms against the disturber of its*

peace. All Napoleon's allies suddenly became his enemies; and this armed force marched against Napoleon, who had gathered new forces. The allies defeated Napoleon, entered Paris, made Napoleon abdicate, and exiled him to the island of Elba, not depriving him of the dignity of emperor and showing him every respect, though five years earlier and one year later everybody considered him a bandit and an outlaw. And so began the reign of Louis XVIII, whom until then both the French and the allies had only laughed at. . . . Then skillful statesmen and diplomats . . . talked in Vienna, and with these talks made people happy or unhappy. Suddenly the diplomats and monarchs nearly quarreled; they were already prepared to order their troops to kill each other again; but at that moment Napoleon arrived in France with a battalion, and the French, who hated him, all submitted to him at once. But the allied monarchs were angered by that and again went to war with the French. And the genius Napoleon was defeated and taken to the island of St. Helena, having suddenly been recognized as a bandit. And there the exile, separated from those dear to his heart and from his beloved France, died a slow death on the rock and bequeathed his great deeds to posterity. But in Europe there was reaction, and the sovereigns all started mistreating their own people again.

This is not what today's political scientists would call a "parsimonious" explanation of the European interRNAtional system in those years, and that of course was Tolstoy's point: that the proliferation of variables—any one of which could easily have taken a different path—explains nothing. "[M]odern history," he complained, "is like a deaf man, answering questions that no one has asked him" [10, p.1181].

So if not God, and if not "modern history," what else? Was there any way to find patterns in the past that explained its course, and perhaps could predict the future? "To find the component forces equal to a composite or a resultant," Tolstoy insisted, "it is necessary that the sum of the components equal the composite." But what if the "components" are the individual decisions made by millions of people as each of them lives through thousands of experiences? What if the "composite," as a consequence, is beyond calculation? Just because two dozen Frenchmen started talking about freedom does not begin to explain why millions of Frenchmen made a revolution. Just because Napoleon ordered an invasion of Russia does not explain why hundreds of thousands of troops—some French and some not—carried out his orders. Just because great battles ensued does not explain why one side won the war: indeed it's not even clear from Tolstoy's accounts of what happens in battles— which closely parallels Clausewitz's—how they could have had any result at all apart from confusion, panic, devastation, injury, and sudden death.

Clausewitz, at least, had an answer to this last question. It lay in what he called military "genius"—a combination of skills that allows a leader to embark on a campaign with a clear objective, to hold on to it in the face of all that will go wrong because it can go wrong ("friction" or, as a later generation would have it, "Murphy's Law"), to size up the situations that result from this at a single glance ("coup d'oeil" or, as a later generation would have it, a "blink"), to scrap existing plans on the spot and improvise new ones, to inspire courage while enforcing discipline, and in the end to win the greatest possible victory at the least possible cost, preferably by so shaking the adversary's self-confidence that he chooses not to fight in the first place—while at all times keeping military operations subordinate to the interests of the state on whose behalf they are being conducted.

These qualities could only arise, Clausewitz believed, from a mastery of theory—but he used that term in a particular way. It meant a distillation of past lessons for future leaders, but it did not mean trying to tell them what to do in circumstances no one could foresee:

Theory exists so that one need not start afresh each time sorting out the material and plowing though it, but will find it ready to hand and in good order. It is meant to educate the mind of the future commander, or, more accurately, to guide him in his self-education, not to accompany him to the battlefield; just as a wise teacher guides and stimulates a young man's intellectual development, but is careful not to lead him by the hand for the rest of his life [11, p.141].

We teach Clausewitz at Yale by comparing theory to coaching. No coach would seek to prescribe every movement in every game. No player would deny, though, that coaching produces the skills that win games. That's the sense in which Clausewitz claims a connection between theory and military "genius," and that in turn is how he thinks the conduct of battles—despite the confusion inherent in them—can be made to win wars.

~67~

Is there anything comparable in Tolstoy? He disparages, throughout *War and Peace*, the role of "great men"—unlike Clausewitz, he has no obvious conception of "genius." He is at times contemptuous of theory: those who seek to apply Darwin's ideas to human behavior, he writes at one point:

> . . . are like plasterers assigned to plaster one side of a church wall, who, taking advantage of the foreman's absence, in a fit of zeal smear their plaster all over the windows, the icons, the scaffolding, and the as yet unreinforced walls, and rejoice at how, from their plastering point of view, everything comes out flat and smooth [10, p.1203].

Tolstoy is the least plasterer-like of novelists: there is nothing flat or smooth about *War and Peace*. And yet Tolstoy chose that improbable vehicle to carry his own theory of history: what other novelist has attempted anything like this, or has taken the task more seriously? So what was going on here?

One hint, I think, resides in what everyone acknowledges to be the most distinctive characteristic of *War and Peace*: the great shifts of scale that take place within it. Tolstoy places himself, and us, within the mind of Natasha at her first great ball, and within Pierre's as he gets himself into and survives a duel, within those of Prince Bolkonsky and Count Rostov, arguably the most difficult and indulgent fathers in modern literature. Yet Tolstoy zooms out from this intimacy to show us great armies sweeping across Europe, and then back in to

....

....

focus on the emperors and officers who commanded them, and then still further in to give us as vivid a sense as anyone ever has of what it must have been like, from the ordinary soldier's point of view, to have lived, marched, and fought in such armies. Then he zooms out again after Borodino to show us Moscow in flames, and then in again to depict refugees from the burning city, among whom is the grievously wounded Prince Andrei, who dies in the arms of Natasha, with whom he had fallen in love, three years and several hundred pages earlier, at her first great ball. Google Earth, for all its own zooming in and zooming out, has nothing on Tolstoy.

He saw great significance, I believe, in this shifting of scale, not just for what it contributes to his narrative: it seems to be critical to Tolstoy's understanding of how history works. He's telling us that however we go about the writing of history — whether from the top down or the bottom up — history itself is happening simultaneously across an infinite number of levels. No historian has captured this phenomenon of simultaneity across scale as successfully as Tolstoy the novelist has done; and given the constraints under which historians operate — that they're not supposed to go beyond their sources — probably no historian ever will. For most of what happens in history leaves no sources behind to begin with. So who's to say who's better equipped to recapture "what actually happened" — the historian or the novelist?

None of this, though, was of much consolation to Tolstoy, because he wanted to do more than just portray the past: he wanted to lay the basis for a science of history. The problem that confounded him was a very old one, dating at least as far back as Adam and Eve: how do you reconcile free will with determinism? It's understandable that Tolstoy saw a single free act as destroying all possibility of laws in history, for he would have been taught as a small boy that from just such an act arose Original Sin. One little mistake, and that's it. But read on, as hardly anyone does, in his final difficult pages of *War and Peace*:

> *[T]he new methods of thinking which history should adapt for itself are being worked out simultaneously with the self-destruction towards which, ever subdividing and subdividing the causes of phenomena, the old history is moving.*
>
> *All of mankind's sciences have followed this path. Having arrived at the infinitely small, mathematics, the most exact of sciences, abandons the process of subdividing and starts on a new process of summing up the unknown infinitesimals. Renouncing the concept of cause, mathematics seeks laws, that is, properties common to all unknown infinitely small elements.*
>
> *Other sciences, though in a different form, have followed this same path of thinking. When Newton formulated the law of gravity, he did not say that the Sun or the Earth has the property of attraction; he said that all bodies, from the largest to the smallest, have this property of attracting each other. . . . History stands on the same path. And if history has for its subject of study the movements of peoples and of mankind, and not the descriptions of episodes from people's lives, it should set aside the notion of causes and seek for the laws common to all the equal and inseparably bound together infinitely small elements of freedom* [10, pp.1212-1213].

I'm not at all sure that I understand this, and I doubt that I'm alone: it's as if Tolstoy meant for us to wrestle with his meaning, even as he himself was wrestling with larger issues.

But here's what I think he may have meant: (a) that everything is connected to everything else, hence there is an inescapable interdependency of variables—forget about distinguishing the independent ones from the dependent ones; (b) that because of this interconnectedness, there will always be things that cannot be known—breaking things down into components will not make them more comprehensible because there will always be still smaller components; (c) that because there are limits to knowledge, people will always retain some illusion of free will, however infinitesimal it might be; and (d) that while laws may indeed govern these infinitesimals, they make no difference because we cannot feel their effects, therefore our illusion of freedom is, for us, freedom itself.

Any way you look at it, this was a tortuous argument. It tortured Tolstoy so much so that he eventually went back to the belief in God he had once derided as characteristic of primitive peoples: he even tried in his old age, not very successfully, to become primitive himself.[2] I cannot help wondering, though, whether all this would have happened if Tolstoy had lived a century later, had been granted a fellowship at the Santa Fe Institute, and had thus acquainted himself with the co-existence of randomness (for which, read: "freedom") and regularity (for which, read: "laws") that the sciences of complexity now more or less take for granted.

Tolstoy in Santa Fe is admittedly a stretch. But I do think that he, like Clausewitz and Adams, sensed the nature of complexity before they had the words to express it or the means to visualize it. They were in that sense, however unhappily, Founding Fathers. ✇

---

[2] Both Berlin [3] and Gallie [6] make this connection between *War and Peace* and Tolstoy's later life.

References

[1]   Adams, Douglas. *The Hitchhiker's Guide to the Galaxy*. New York: Harmony Books, 1980.

[2]   Adams, Henry. *The Education of Henry Adams: An Autobiography*. Boston: Houghton Mifflin, 1918.

[3]   Berlin, Isaiah. "The Hedgehog and the Fox." In *The Proper Study of Mankind: An Anthology of Essays*, edited by Henry Hardy and Roger Hausheer. New York: Farrar, Straus and Giroux, 1997.

[4]   Beyerchen, Alan. "Clausewitz, Nonlinearity, and the Unpredictability of War." *International Security* 17(3) (Winter 1992/93): 59-90.

[5]   Gaddis, John Lewis. *The Landscape of History: How Historians Map the Past*. New York: Oxford University Press, 2002.

[6]   Gallie, W. B. *Philosophers of Peace and War: Kant, Clausewitz, Marx, Engels and Tolstoy*. New York: Cambridge University Press, 1978.

[7]   Gat, Azar. *A History of Military Thought: From the Enlightenment to the Cold War*. New York: Oxford University Press, 2001.

[8]   Hayles, N. Katherine. *Chaos Bound: Orderly Disorder in Contemporary Literature and Science*. Ithaca: Cornell University Press, 1990.

[9]   Kennan, George F. *Sketches From a Life*. New York: Pantheon, 1989.

[10]   Tolstoy, Leo. *War and Peace*, translated by Richard Pevear and Larissa Volokhonsky. New York: Knopf, 2007.

[11]   von Clausewitz, Carl. *On War*, edited and translated by Michael Howard and Peter Paret. Princeton, NJ: Princeton University Press, 1976.

R

10

REGULARITIES IN HUMAN AFFAIRS

Murray Gell-Mann, Santa Fe Institute

WHEN WE REVIEW THE COURSE of human history
or the results of anthropological research, we see a
delicate interplay of regularity and randomness. This
article discusses several regularities in human affairs,
including approximate mathematical laws, such as
the logistic equation, and semi-empirical regularities,
such as a power law or a Guttman scale. The search
for regularities in human history is becoming a trifle
more respectable than it was formerly. That could well
portend some significant improvement in our ability to
discuss the human future.

Research at the Santa Fe Institute is inherently transdisciplinary. We have found that among the best scientists and
scholars, there are many who long for collaboration with other
brilliant researchers trained in fields distant from their own. At
universities, such collaborations are difficult to arrange, and in
fact they encounter barriers nearly everywhere, not only in the
form of university departments, curricula, and degree requirements, but also through institutions such as professional societies and journals. However, the enthusiasm of the researchers
who are eager to collaborate helps to overcome those barriers
as well as others perhaps even more important, stemming from
differences in terminologies, methods, and ways of thinking.

When we founded SFI, I did a good deal of the telephoning
to invite some distinguished scientists to our early meetings, scientists we had heard might be interested in transdisciplinary
work. Many of them were trained in fields very different from
the one in which I was known, and they had barely heard of

me or perhaps didn't know my name at all. I was certain that the reply would be something like the following: "What you are doing sounds interesting, but I'm quite busy with my research and teaching, the books that I'm writing, and my consulting work. Please don't call me. I'll call you." Instead, the answers tended to be more like this: "I've been waiting for this opportunity all my life. May I come sooner?"

The work at SFI is nearly all theoretical and much of it is based on computer modeling. The relevant observational research is carried on elsewhere, but of course careful attention is paid to the facts revealed by observation.

There are significant mathematical parallels between phenomena in very different sciences. It is natural, if barriers are removed, for theoreticians of varied backgrounds to form transdisciplinary teams, quite spontaneously or sometimes in response to some request for proposals, to exploit those similarities.

A great deal of our research is connected, in one way or another, with issues of simplicity and complexity, regularities and randomness, and complex adaptive systems, including biological evolution and various aspects of social evolution. Nearly everything one encounters exhibits regularities along with random or incidental features. All around us we find the interplay of law and chance. Closely related to regularities and randomness is the distinction between the simple and the complex.

What is complexity? It would take many different concepts, many different quantities to capture all of our notions of what is meant by complexity or its opposite, simplicity. But there is one quantity that corresponds best to what we mean in everyday conversation and in most scientific discourse by complexity, and that is what I call *effective complexity*. In non-technical language, we can say that the effective complexity of an entity is the length of a very concise description of its *regularities*, as distinct from features treated as random or incidental. Complexity does not mean randomness.

A complex novel has many characters, scenes, subplots, and so forth. The US tax code is complex; every provision is a regularity. This chart in a 1998 ad for Hennessy cognac is somewhat sexist but illustrates quite well the concept of effective complexity (Figure 1).

Neckties can be used to illustrate simplicity and complexity, but we would be likely to concentrate on the patterns rather than on the soup stains, wine stains, and so on. However, a dry cleaner would perhaps pay more attention to the stains. What matters is the coarse-graining, the distinction between features that are treated as important and those treated as unimportant.

The distinction between the regular and the random is often context-dependent. Music and static on the radio would seem to exemplify that distinction perfectly, but then we may reflect that the science of radio astronomy arose out of the study of static on the radio. In science, we search for regularities. As Isaac Newton wrote, "It is the business of natural philosophy to find them out."

What gives rise to complexity? The fundamental laws of physics are simple, as far as we can tell, but they are probabilistic, not fully deterministic. The history of the Universe is co-determined by those laws and by an unimaginably long sequence of chance events (or "accidents") governed by probabilities.

The alternative possible histories of the Universe form a branching tree with probabilities at the branchings. (Remember *The Garden of Forking Paths*, by Borges.) Some of the accidents produce, in conjunction with the fundamental laws, a great deal of regularity over regions of space and time. Those are the "frozen accidents." For example, the little fluctuation that produced our galaxy may be a minor event on a cosmic scale, but it is quite important for anything in our galaxy, such as the inhabitants of this planet. Likewise the chance events that produced the earth and gave rise to geology are frozen accidents.

Only elementary particle physics and cosmology are truly fundamental and universal in scope. All the other sciences depend to a greater or lesser extent on historical accident, as well as on the fundamental laws. Even chemistry, which we tend to regard as derivable in principle from physics, is dependent to some extent on historical accident. After all, the validity of chemistry requires temperatures and pressures that permit atoms and molecules to exist. In the center of the Sun, there is little or no chemistry, because it is too hot for the particles in atoms and molecules to stay together. There is nuclear physics in the center of the Sun, but in the very early Universe it was too hot even for nuclear physics.

~76~

Just as geology depends on historical accidents, including the ones that produced the planet Earth and others that occurred in the course of its early development, so biology on Earth depends

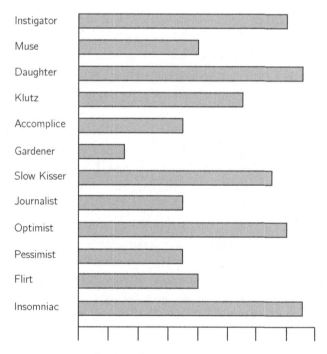

Figure 1. *Appropriately Complex Hennessy.*

on numerous accidents having to do with the ancestral life form and with biological evolution over four billion years or so.

Also, there are fairly regular "laws" associated with social and behavioral sciences, and there must be some for human history. We should not be put off by discovering that they are approximate and exhibit occasional exceptions.

Since the fundamental laws of physics are simple, almost all complexity originates in the regularities that are consequences of frozen accidents. When the accumulation of such consequences outstrips the processes that erase them, then we observe the familiar phenomenon that more and more complex entities come into being as time goes on. That by no means requires that individual things increase in complexity. For example, organisms die and civilizations die, as well, with a decrease in complexity.

~77~

Think of all the accidents that have gone to make up the people assembled here. Many of those are just individual local events with important consequences mainly for us, while others are associated with the whole of the solar system, our galaxy, and so forth.

When we review the course of human history or look at the results of anthropological research, including data from linguistics and archaeology, we see a delicate interplay of regularity and randomness. Whether we are considering the alternative possible histories of the Universe from the fundamental physical and cosmological point of view or contemplating alternative possible courses of human history on the planet Earth from the much coarser-grained perspective appropriate to that case, we are faced with a branching tree with probabilities at the branches. At both scales we can think in terms of frozen accidents contributing to a whole range of regularities that are not inherent in the fundamental laws alone.

There are historians of human affairs who are tolerant of speculation about contingent or "What If?" history and they are growing in number. Some articles about particular counterfactual speculations are to be found in the collections *What If? I* and *What If? II* and in a collection edited by Niall Ferguson. The authors have picked out a number of apparently random events that may, as frozen accidents, have divided the branching history after them into well-defined domains. But historians have long disputed to what extent these wounds in the fabric of history remain indefinitely as scars and to what extent they are eventually healed by grand historical forces.

This is related to the argument between the *great person, great idea* view of history and the *great historical force* view. We can look at the European Union today and ask to what extent its development was essentially inevitable and to what extent it resulted from the genius and foresight of Jean Monnet and his founding of the Action Committee for the United States of Europe.

The following quotations are from Mark Sullivan's book *Our Times, the United States 1900—1925, I: The Turn of the Century.*

> **Thomas Carlyle:** "All things that we see standing accomplished in the world are properly the outer material result, the practical realization and embodiment, of Thoughts that dwelt in the Great Men sent into the world."

> **Walt Whitman:** "Produce great persons; the rest follows."

But on the other side we have

> **George Bernard Shaw:** "[the world is]. . . finally governed by forces expressing themselves in religions and laws which make epochs, rather than by vulgarly ambitious individuals who make rows."

> **Louis Napoléon, 1841:** "Marchez a la tête des idées de votre siècle, ces idées vous suivent et vous soutiennent. Marchez a leur suite, elles vous entraînent. Marchez contre elles, elles vous renversent."

> **William Jennings Bryan, letter to Mark Sullivan, 1925:** "You are entirely correct in describing public men as the creatures of their age. I have often used the same explanation in regard to myself. I lived in the very center of the country out of which the

reforms grew, and was quite naturally drawn to the people's side."

If we look at those published collections of counterfactual speculations, we soon encounter the story of Buffalo Bill's Wild West Show touring Europe in 1889. The star was, of course, the noted female marksman, Annie Oakley. She would challenge the men in the audience, asking for a male volunteer to smoke a cigar and let her shoot the ash off the end. Normally there were no male volunteers and her husband, himself a noted marksman, would step forward, start to smoke a cigar, and have the ash shot off by his wife. When the show reached Berlin, however, there was a male volunteer, the Kaiser, Wilhelm der Zweite. He had come to the throne just the previous year, after the premature death of his father, Friedrich, the son-in-law of Queen Victoria. The Kaiser came forward, pulled out an expensive Havana cigar, clipped off the end, removed the band, and lit it. As the ash grew at the end of the cigar, he waited for Annie to shoot. She was worried. She had been drinking quite a lot the night before. Her husband was one thing, the Kaiser was another. After a while, she took aim and fired, and we know what happened. The Kaiser was unharmed.

But he went on to fire Bismarck, to cancel the Reinsurance Treaty with Russia, to engage in a naval arms competition with Great Britain, and to contribute in other ways to the tragedy of the First World War. What if Annie had killed him? Would the World War have taken a different course? Would it have occurred at all? A number of the scholars and researchers assembled here have pondered this kind of question at length.

In a talk I gave some years ago to the IIASA in Laxenburg, near Vienna, Austria, I mentioned the role of chance in the branching alternative histories. I alluded to such incidents and how they appear to affect history profoundly, as do assassinations, the results of famous battles, the lives of great persons, and so on. Fortunately, I mentioned too the countervailing arguments about the grand forces. I say fortunately because a gentleman named Cesare Marchetti, trained, like me, as a physicist, got up to argue strongly against the tyranny of the individual chance events. If I had not mentioned the alternative point of view favorably, I'm sure he would have launched a verbal attack. As it was, we got on famously.

He was, however, not thinking so much about the kind of historical forces that I had in mind. Marchetti was thinking, rather, of certain mathematical regularities, approximate mathematical laws that seem to go on holding without reference to specific events or individual people. He provided me with many examples that he had collected, some of which I plan to share with you. But let me start with another one, provided by the distinguished Russian journalist, Sergei Petrovich Kapitsa, also a physicist by training and the son of the famous physicist Pyotr Kapitsa.

He took a very crude look at the time variation in human world population, using the differential equation

$$(1) \qquad \frac{\partial N}{\partial t} = \frac{N^2}{b}$$

not a totally implausible formula when we remember that it takes two people to make one new person. The solution is $(T-t) = b/N$ or

$$(2) \qquad N = \frac{b}{T-t}$$

where T is an arbitrary constant, a critical time.

In this approximation, N becomes infinite when the time t equals the critical value T. Obviously, the equation loses its validity as t approaches that value, but for a long time before that, the equation agrees fairly well with people's estimates of world population. Say we look at the fifteen hundred years leading up to 1925, when the population was around two billion. The critical value T turns out to be around 2025, and the populations then come out to one billion in 1825, ½ billion in 1625, ¼ billion in 1225, and ⅛ billion in 425. These numbers are not so far from educated guesses that have been made about the actual values of N at those times.

Since the population will evidently not be infinite in 2025, the equation must be modified by adding a term that becomes important at large N and avoids the singularity. However, that modification should begin to change the solution appreciably only during the last quarter of the twentieth century, when the observed departure from the simple singular solution provides the first *direct* indication of the leveling-off of the world population that is now taking place. In fact, the point of inflection, the time when the rate of increase reached its maximum and started to decline, was in the late twentieth century.

For the sake of completeness, we should remark that the simple equation requires another modification — at small N — in order to agree with plausible estimates of N for times many thousands of years ago. Eq. (2) gives populations that are thought to be a bit too large for those early times. But that modification does not have appreciable effects during the last couple of millennia and, like the modification at late times, we can ignore it in this discussion.

Between 425 and 1975, say, the simple equation (2) is thus not that bad, provided we smooth out fluctuations like those associated with the Black Death. The result is that a hypothetical student of world population working, say, seven hundred years ago, having access to world population figures since the year 400 or so, and fitting the trivial formula above to those figures, could have identified correctly the approximate time (around 2000) when N versus t would start to level off, without having any information about future technology or future contraceptive devices or future trends in the education of women. Of course, we know of no such student around 1300 and no way for such a person to obtain at that time the requisite population data, but it is still true that the estimate we are discussing was there to be found, without going into the root causes of demographic change.

A familiar example of a mathematical regularity in today's world is Moore's Law, the observation by Gordon Moore, a cofounder of Intel, that the information capacity per unit area of computer chips is increasing exponentially, in fact doubling every 18 months. That has been going on since the 1980s. Of course, it cannot continue forever, and it is usually supposed that the curve will start to level off in a decade or two, perhaps when the size involved has decreased to atomic dimensions.

Neither of the simple laws we have discussed is fully explained, in my opinion. Nor is another one, emphasized by Cesare Marchetti. Consider France, a typical Western European country, and look, over the last two hundred years, at the average distance covered in a day of travel using a vehicle, taking into account the mix of transport modes. (Not traveling in a vehicle scores zero for that day.) That distance has been increasing in roughly exponential fashion over the last two centuries, if we smooth out the fluctuations. The rate of increase is around 3.8 percent per year. But here we are dealing first with travel on horseback or by horse-drawn coach; then railway travel is added to the mix, followed by automobiles, propeller-driven airplanes, and jet planes. (We should probably omit the supersonic jet, which was never an important part of the mix and has now been discontinued.) Somehow all these developments have accommodated themselves approximately to a rising exponential. Using nineteenth-century data and the idea of an exponential, one could have estimated crudely the average daily distance of vehicular travel at present without knowing the nature of the vehicles involved.

What do we make of such regularities that seem to proceed without regard to mechanism? If people in the past could have used them for making crude predictions about today's world, can't we find similar ones today that facilitate some approximate insights into the future? We shall return to that question.

A noted economist is quoted as saying, " When something can't go on forever, it doesn't." When exponentials level off, as they must eventually do, they usually turn into logistic curves, obeying the equation

$$(3) \qquad \frac{\partial y}{\partial t} = ay \left(1 - \frac{y}{Y} \right)$$

instead of

$$(4) \qquad \frac{\partial y}{\partial t} = ay$$

which yields the pure exponential.

Here Y is the asymptotic value of y, which y approaches as t goes to infinity. We can define F to be the fraction of Y that y has attained at a given value of the time t. Then the differential equation for F is

$$(5) \qquad \frac{\partial F}{\partial t} = aF(1-F)$$

and the solution is

$$(6) \qquad a(t-m) = \ln \frac{F}{1-F}$$

~83~

The fraction F increases steadily with time, going from 0 at minus infinity to 1 at plus infinity, while $\ln[F/(1-F)]$ increases linearly with time.

Here m is the value of the time at which F is ½, so that $F/(1-F)$ is 1 and $\ln[F/(1-F)]$ is zero.

We see that the solution of the logistic equation is characterized by only three parameters, the relative rate of increase a, the midpoint m in time of the process, and the absolute scale Y, which we have eliminated above, leaving only a and m. The diagnostic feature is the linearity in time of the quantity $\ln[F/(1-F)]$. The original quantity y follows an S-shaped curve with the absolute height determined by Y (the asymptotic value), the midpoint in time given by m, and the relative rate of increase at early times (when we are close to a pure exponential) given by a.

Logistic enthusiasts like Marchetti go wild applying Eq. (4) above to all manner of processes for which historical data are available. We can start with the cumulative deaths in almost any plague, such as the Great Plague of London in 1665. The equation fits very well indeed. One can use it also for the cumulative casualties in nearly any war, as long as fluctuations are smoothed out. The important point is that the logistic curve marches steadily on, without much regard for famous battles and skillful generals. Again certain features of the broad outlines of history are not very sensitive to the detailed accidents along the way.

Peter Turchin has shown me logistic curves that fit very well the phenomenon of mass religious conversion, say to some brand of Islam or Christianity.

Marchetti is particularly pleased with the results of applying Eq. (6) to the work of individual artists or scientists. He looks at the cumulative production of various famous people (using, on the whole, just quantitative measures without judging quality) and finds linearity of $\ln[F/(1-F)]$. He can estimate the midpoint time m (when the logarithm is zero) and see where in the process death (or some other cause of a halt in production) takes place. He finds the surprising result that Mozart's death at the age of 35 actually took place when F had already come close to saturation. But most of the results are quite straightforward and simply support the idea that careers of great artists and scientists follow logistic trajectories that don't depend much on historical accident.

Sometimes a great person has two distinct careers, one getting under way as the other is saturating. Marchetti then finds two logistic curves.

He likes to speak of "clockwork geniuses." But we must always keep in mind that it is only certain very general features of history that exhibit these particular remarkable regularities. It is not the actual musical achievement of Mozart that is captured by Cesare, but only its distribution over time, and even then only in its quantitative aspects. Of course, more such regularities may turn up, but they will still not address the whole picture, only a few characteristics of it. There may well be additional regularities, however, that are connected with the deep aspects of human history, say, with the rise and fall of civilizations, which Arnold Toynbee and others have tried to describe.

At the Santa Fe Institute, we are often concerned with attempts to construct simple models or simulations for complex real phenomena, say, in the life sciences or in the social and behavioral sciences. We hope to treat some phenomena of human history in the same fashion. Now how do we judge whether a model is successful? Normally a scientist would test a theory by comparing its predictions with the results of

observation. But here we are dealing with theoretical models —
whether computer-based or analytical — that are so simplified
that it would be astonishing, even disconcerting, to find detailed
agreement with reality. What can we do then? Most of us are
convinced that the best course of action is to look at "middle
level theory" — to find semi-empirical regularities in the real
world that might be reproduced in the model and try to find
reasons why they might exhibit a kind of continuity all the way
from the real world down to the highly simplified model. If
so, then one can seek an explanation for the regularities in the
model — perhaps not such a difficult task — and have some hope
of extending that explanation to the complex reality.

~85~

That notion fits in very well with what we are doing here
when we call attention to regularities in human history and the
social sciences, particularly ones that could have been used in
the past to predict certain gross features of history fairly well
without going into detailed mechanisms. But we must make
every effort to understand why these regularities persist the
way they do.

In the social and behavioral sciences, as well as the life
sciences, one often finds power laws holding over wide ranges
of certain variables. Sometimes one quantity varies like a
power of another. For example, the average metabolic rate of a
mammalian species varies like the three-quarters power of the
average body weight. Often we have power laws of distribution,
where the frequency with which a certain quantity attains a
particular value varies like a power of that value. A famous
example is Vilfredo Pareto's observation that incomes obey a
power law of distribution over a considerable range.

His law illustrates how regularities can affect proposals
for public policy. Suppose someone wants to reduce the gap
between rich and poor. If Pareto's power law is really a robust
regularity, then it may not be so wise to try to fight the power
law itself by means of public policy. Rather one might try to
reduce the exponent, thus flattening the curve.

We also see how important it is to make a judgment about
whether a supposed regularity really is one and is robust. For

example, it was claimed for a long time that the fraction of GDP assignable to wages (or "the share of the national income accruing to labor") was always in the range 60 to 70 percent. In a well-known paper the noted economist Bob Solow tried to debunk this regularity by questioning whether there is anything surprisingly small about that amount of variation. According to another economist, Sam Bowles, a more serious objection is that after the collapse of communism in Eastern and Central Europe, the wage share in a number of ex-Communist countries was actually notably different, showing that the regularity was at least not universal.

Of course the best way to avoid being fooled by spurious regularities is to understand the reasons behind the empirical relationships in question. Then the applications both to forecasting and to the realm of public policy will be much more secure.

Let us review the place of the regularities we have been discussing in thinking about the human future. It is fascinating, and important for forecasting and for application to public policy, that such regularities go marching on without much regard to changes in the underlying mechanisms, and clearly we need to understand how these things can happen and to identify which regularities are really robust. But they do not usually capture the most important features of the human condition or of the policy landscape, and they fail to solve the problem of neglect of human passions (or human volition in general) in so many otherwise very scholarly treatises on the future.

An additional concern is that so many studies divide up the world situation into economic, social, political, ideological, informational, environmental, demographic, military, and diplomatic issues and hope, through essays on all these separate aspects by suitable experts, to be able to put together a picture of the world. But this is a case where the whole is different from the sum of its parts. We have neglected the crucial supplementary discipline of taking a crude look at the whole. The situation is highly nonlinear and very complex, and the interactions among these domains are very strong. In an analogous situation in physics, we might say that perhaps there are collective variables in terms of which the description might be simplified, but those would have to be variables that cut across the conventional boundaries of the subjects and they would have to be discovered, not arbitrarily imposed at the beginning.

We mentioned power laws as a type of middle-level theory. Let me go on to discuss another one, called "Guttman scaling" or "implicational scaling." The sociologist Louis Guttman introduced it during the early years of the Second World War, when it was important to measure American attitudes toward Great Britain. Were Americans friendly enough, on the whole, to support massive aid to the beleaguered British? Did they have faith in the British armed forces? Guttman devised a questionnaire composed of many questions. Say each one required a "yes" or "no" answer, with "yes" indicating a friendlier attitude than "no." What he discovered was that it was possible to arrange the questions in a particular order so that the answers came out, roughly speaking, all "yes" up to some point, and then all "no." Say there were 50 questions. Out of the 2^{50} (more than a quadrillion) possible response patterns, most of the actual ones clustered around just 51 different patterns, ranging from all "yes" to all "no" and characterized by one parameter: the place where the "yes" responses ended and the "no" responses began. That was a most remarkable and completely non-trivial result. If the questions were of the following kind, the result would not be surprising: Can you jump over a two-foot hurdle? Can you jump over a two-and-a-half foot hurdle? Can you jump over a three-foot hurdle? Of course you can arrange those questions so that the answers are "yes" up to a point and then "no." But the questions were not like that at all.

In 1961 the linguist David DeCamp found a linguistic example of Guttman scaling in connection with Jamaican Creole. Most of the vocabulary of Jamaican Creole is drawn from English, which is also the official language of Jamaica, even though most people there speak Jamaican Creole among themselves at home. (In some other Caribbean countries, the official language is different from the "lexifying" language that supplies most of the vocabulary of the local Creole; for example, on St. Lucia the Creole is French-based although the official language is English.) In Jamaica, we encounter the phenomenon of progressive decreolization. As people become more urbanized and more highly educated, their Creole is affected more and more by standard English. The resulting distribution of linguistic behavior is sometimes called the *decreolization continuum*. DeCamp took six linguistic traits, two of pronunciation and four of vocabulary, and looked at how they were affected by decreolization. Out of $2^6 = 64$ possible responses, most were concentrated on only 7, forming a Guttman scale (Figure 2).

Now we can go on to discuss Guttman scaling and related matters in anthropology, particularly as they turn up in cross-cultural surveys. The late George Peter ("Pete") Murdock of the Yale Department of Anthropology left behind, as one valuable part of his remarkable scientific legacy, the Human Relations Area Files, carefully coded summaries of anthropological data about hundreds of cultures around the world, indexed so as to

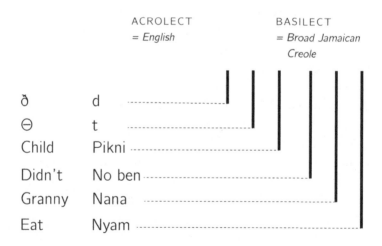

Figure 2. *Six traits in Jamaican speech (DeCamp 1961). Out of 2^5 possibilities, he found only these 7. "Implicational scale or ladder."*

facilitate cross-cultural comparisons. His professional heirs, those now running the Files and others who collaborated with Murdock but have since moved elsewhere, have fallen out over a number of things, particularly an issue of data analysis, the so-called problem of Galton.

The distinguished statistician Sir Francis Galton was present when the anthropologist E. B. Tylor presented, in 1889, his classic paper on cross-cultural comparisons. Galton pointed out the distortions that result from failure of cultures to be independent of one another. Common descent or cultural diffusion can create such correlations. As a result one mustn't treat all the cultures in a cross-cultural sample as independent cases. Sometimes, two of them may have separated from each other only recently. For instance, the aKamba and aGikuyu in Kenya were one people only a few hundred years ago. Likewise the baLuba and baLunda of the Democratic Republic of Congo became distinct only a few centuries ago. One cannot count them as independent cultures to the same extent as, say, the baLuba and the Blackfeet of North America. Also, two peoples in the same region with very different languages and no evidence of recent common descent may have similar customs as a result of borrowing, just because they are neighbors.

Nowadays there are known mathematical methods for coping with this kind of situation, using a correlation matrix to describe the failure of the cultures to be independent of one another. It is especially Douglas R. White and his collaborators who insist that attention be paid to this matter. Another solution is to select only cultures that are clearly quite far apart, thus sacrificing a large body of data. White et al. have turned out a reduced cross-cultural sample in which the autocorrelation difficulties are largely absent.

Here, in Figure 3, is a very clean example of Guttman scaling applied to a cross-cultural study in anthropology. This, along with a good deal of the work presented here later on, is in papers by Robert L. Carneiro. For nine tribes of South American Indians there are eight questions with "yes" or "no" replies. Does the tribe have this trait or not? In the first diagram, the traits are not in any particular order, and neither are the tribes. In the second diagram, the traits and the tribes are ordered so as to exhibit the Guttman scaling phenomenon, which in this case is perfect.

The example goes far beyond perfect scaling: the array is nearly square, no two societies have exactly the same number of plus signs, and each one differs from its neighbor in the diagram by just one trait. A scaling situation could violate any of these conditions and still be perfect. In the artificial example in Figure 4, we see a hypothetical perfect scaling situation without any of those simplifications.

~90~

	Kuikuru	Anserma	Jivaro	Tupinamba	Inca	Sherente	Chibeha	Yahgan	Cumana
Social Stratification	–	X	–	–	X	–	X	–	X
Pottery	X	X	X	X	X	–	X	–	X
Fermented Beverages	–	X	X	X	X	–	X	–	X
Political State	–	–	–	–	X	–	X	–	–
Agriculture	X	X	X	X	X	X	X	–	X
Stone Architecture	–	–	–	–	X	–	–	–	–
Smelting of Metal Ores	–	X	–	–	X	–	X	–	–
Loom Weaving	–	X	X	–	X	–	X	–	X

	Yahgan	Sherente	Kuikuru	Tupinamba	Jivaro	Cumana	Anserma	Chibeha	Inca
Stone Architecture	–	–	–	–	–	–	–	–	X
Political State	–	–	–	–	–	–	–	X	X
Smelting of Metal Ores	–	–	–	–	–	–	X	X	X
Social Stratification	–	–	–	–	–	X	X	X	X
Loom Weaving	–	–	–	–	X	X	X	X	X
Fermented Beverages	–	–	–	X	X	X	X	X	X
Pottery	–	–	X	X	X	X	X	X	X
Agriculture	–	X	X	X	X	X	X	X	X

Figure 3.

In Figure 5 we have another real example, with many more traits and a large number of cultures. It is not perfect (there is some scatter in the results), but the regularity is evident. How close the scaling comes to perfection is measured by a "coefficient of reproducibility" that has values between zero and one. It is one minus the number of "errors" divided by the product of the number of traits and the number of tribes. An "error" is a place where the position of an x violates Guttman scaling. When the "coefficient" is greater than 0.9, it is thought that we have a pretty good scaling situation.

The deviations from perfect agreement are themselves significant and analyzable. On this diagram they occur mainly near the diagonal, indicating that reversals of order are largely restricted to items that are very close to each other on the list. When items are far apart, there are few reversals. Thus the exceptions represent merely a little local sloppiness in the order of traits, not a substantial failure of the whole pattern.

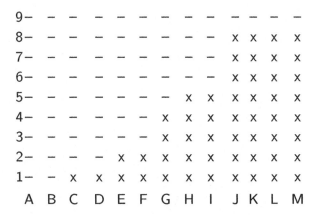

Figure 4.

		King [all; 36]	Leader's Assistants [35]	Succession [34]	Supra-Community [33]	Political Leadership [32]	Inauguration [33]	Leader as Specialist [26]	Retainers for Leader [25]	Supra-Provencil Org. [24]	Leader Grants Audience [24]	Admin. Hierarchy [22]	Deference to Leader [21]	Home of Leader [20]	Leader Names Officials [20]	Ruler Bestows Riches [20]	Deceased Ruler Honored[16]	Ruler Buried [16]	Monarchy [15]	Appointed Governors [14]	Ruler & Bodyguard [14]	Court [14]	Royal Estates [14]	Territorial Admin. [13]	State [13]	Capital City or Town [13]	Admin. Centers [10]	State Inspectors [9]	King with Harem [7]	Ambassadors [7]	Empire [6]	Municipal Officers [6]	State Ministers [5]	Professional Civil Service [4]
Menomini	[5]	x	x	x	x	x																												
Tupinamba	[5]	x	x	x	x		x																											
Nama Hottentot	[5]	x	x	x	x		x																											
Kayan	[5]	x	x	x		x		x																										
Cheyenne	[6]	x	x	x	x	x	x																											
Omaha	[6]	x	x	x	x	x	x																											
Maori	[6]	x		x	x	x		x				x																						
Iroquois	[7]	x	x	x	x	x	x			x																								
Acoma	[7]	x	x	x		x	x	x						x																				
Batak	[8]	x	x	x		x	x	x	x		x																							
Flathead	[8]	x	x	x	x	x	x	x	x																									
Creek	[9]	x	x	x	x	x	x		x		x	x																						
Tuareg	[10]	x	x	x	x	x	x	x	x					x																				
Mano	[10]	x	x		x		x		x		x	x			x	x																		
Rwala	[10]	x	x		x		x	x	x		x		x	x		x																		
Tanala	[12]	x	x	x	x	x	x	x		x	x	x	x	x																				
Thonga	[12]	x	x	x	x	x	x	x		x	x	x				x			x															
Futuna	[14]	x	x	x	x	x	x	x	x		x	x	x		x		x	x																
Fiji	[15]	x	x	x	x	x	x	x	x	x	x	x	x	x	x	x																		
Marquesans	[16]	x	x	x	x	x	x	x	x	x	x		x	x	x	x	x	x																
Tahiti	[19]	x	x	x	x	x	x	x	x	x	x	x	x	x	x	x	x	x	x			x												
Suku	[19]	x	x	x	x	x	x	x	x	x	x	x	x	x				x	x	x	x		x	x										
Bemba	[20]	x	x	x	x	x	x	x	x	x	x	x	x		x	x	x		x			x	x	x		x								
Bavenda	[21]	x	x	x	x	x	x	x	x	x	x	x	x	x	x	x	x	x		x	x	x	x											
Vikings	[21]	x	x	x	x	x	x	x	x	x	x	x		x		x	x	x	x		x	x	x		x	x								
Hawaii	[25]	x	x	x	x	x	x	x	x	x	x	x	x	x	x	x	x		x	x	x	x	x	x	x	x	x							
Leon	[26]	x	x	x	x	x	x	x	x	x	x	x	x	x	x	x		x	x	x	x	x	x	x	x	x	x			x				
Baganda	[27]	x	x	x	x	x	x	x	x	x	x	x	x	x	x	x	x	x	x	x	x	x	x	x	x	x	x	x						
Ashanti	[27]	x	x	x	x	x	x	x	x	x	x	x	x	x	x	x	x	x	x	x	x	x		x	x	x		x	x	x				
Dahomey	[29]	x	x	x	x	x	x	x	x	x	x	x	x	x	x	x	x	x	x	x	x	x	x	x	x	x	x	x	x				x	
Roman Empire	[30]	x	x	x	x	x	x	x	x	x	x	x	x	x	x	x	x	x	x	x	x	x	x	x	x	x	x	x		x	x	x		
Assyria	[31]	x	x	x	x	x	x	x	x	x	x	x	x	x	x	x		x	x	x	x	x	x	x	x	x	x	x	x	x	x	x	x	
Inca	[31]	x	x	x	x	x	x	x	x	x	x	x	x	x	x	x	x	x	x	x	x	x	x	x	x	x	x	x	x		x	x		x
Aztec	[33]	x	x	x	x	x	x	x	x	x	x	x	x	x	x	x	x	x	x	x	x	x	x	x	x	x	x	x	x	x	x	x	x	x
Egypt (*New Kingdom*)	[33]	x	x	x	x	x	x	x	x	x	x	x	x	x	x	x	x	x	x	x	x	x	x	x	x	x	x	x	x	x	x	x	x	x
China (*Han*)	[33]	x	x	x	x	x	x	x	x	x	x	x	x	x	x	x	x	x	x	x	x	x	x	x	x	x	x	x	x	x	x	x	x	x

Figure 5.

Carneiro also looks at neighboring traits on the scalogram and asks how *often* a given pair gets interchanged. Probably one can say that if they are rarely interchanged, then the "distance" between them is greater than if they are often interchanged (very little "distance" between them.) Thus the list of traits on the scalogram can be regarded as a sort of staircase with risers of variable heights, some small and some much greater.

Now what are we to make of these remarkable successes of Guttman scaling in dealing with cultural traits? They could be attributed to a pattern of development in time, an "evolutionary sequence." In the late nineteenth century and the first half of the twentieth century, ideas about such sequences were popular, as in the work of Tylor, Lewis Morgan, and Elman Service. Think of the sequence band, chiefdom, etc.

But there was a great deal of opposition to such notions, too, most of it on an *a prioristic* basis rather than a scientific one. Franz Boas taught that there were hardly any regularities to be found, each culture being unique, and that evolutionary sequences were certainly not a fruitful area for study. Marxists felt they had a monopoly on evolutionary sequences (slaveholding societies, feudal societies, capitalist societies, then happy socialist societies). Anti-Marxists were sometimes displeased with evolutionary sequences because the Marxists had one. And so on. It is shocking how impressive regularities, well supported by data, were simply discarded by famous anthropologists on ideological grounds.

There is at least one good reason for sympathizing with the scholars who rejected (or still reject) the ideas we have been discussing. Those ideas might be misused by racists to justify their bigotry. We must all fight against such abuses.

One can try to check whether an evolutionary pattern is involved (in other words, a time sequence), by looking at a case studied by Carneiro where at least some of the innovations can be dated. Here, in Figure 6, is an attempt to do that using data on 34 selected traits from Anglo-Saxon England.

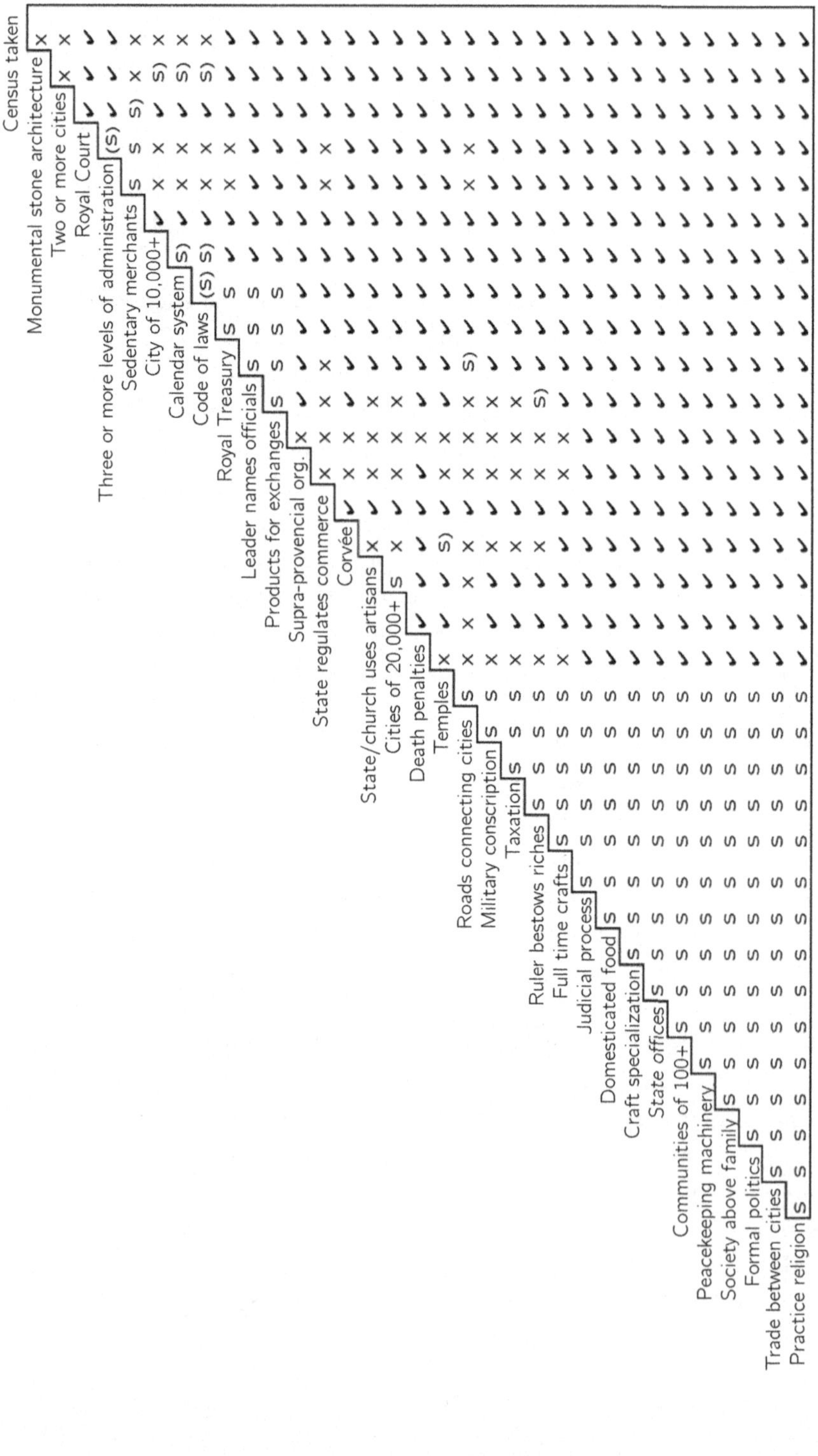

Figure. 6. *Diagram showing the order of 34 selected traits in Anglo-Saxon England.*

The temporal order is compared with the order expected from the "scalogram" showing Guttman scaling for the traits in question in Anglo-Saxon England. Check-marks indicate that there is agreement, while crosses indicate disagreement. The S entries mean that some information is lacking. The result has some scatter, but it does definitely point in the direction of confirmation of the evolutionary interpretation of Guttman scaling for this case.

Social complexity as used by archaeologists and other anthropologists can be regarded as an application of effective complexity to things like the diversity of social roles. Here there is a certain trend toward higher social complexity as we go through the sequence of traits. To the extent that the sequence of traits corresponds to a temporal sequence, a trend toward higher social complexity (as time goes on) is indicated. The scalograms can be compared with estimates by various authors of levels of social complexity or other, related scales attributed to societies. We have A. L. Kroeber's personally estimated "levels of cultural intensity" and Raoul Naroll's index of social development. Robert Carneiro takes a list of 354 societal traits and notes how many of them a given society possesses, thus obtaining an "index of cultural accumulation." All of these indices agree to a remarkable extent.

The rates at which various cultures take the steps, while conforming to the pattern, can differ a great deal from culture to culture, thus accounting for the wide variation across the world in the number of steps taken by a given time. There are also numerous details, not captured in the analysis, that give rise to cultural individuality. Appreciating the regularities does not mean that we totally ignore the features that are unconstrained by them. Regularities do not exclude individuality.

Here and there we see flaws in Guttman scaling that are very instructive. Certain traits are "skipped" in particular cultures. One reason can be that environmental factors render that trait less desirable or less necessary or less easily acquired for the particular culture concerned. For instance, pottery and

....

APPRECIATING THE REGULARITIES DOES NOT MEAN THAT WE

TOTALLY IGNORE THE FEATURES THAT ARE UNCONSTRAINED

BY THEM. REGULARITIES DO NOT EXCLUDE INDIVIDUALITY.

....

loom weaving are absent for some rather advanced Polynesian societies, but the necessary clays and fibers were hard for them to obtain.

An important point to mention is that in the course of history, cultural complexity can occasionally regress as well as advance. We are not always dealing with pure accumulation. For example, a migrating people passing through a difficult environment may lose a number of traits that have little value there. This devolution process may be quite significant for certain cultures. On reaching a richer environment, the social complexity may start to increase again. Now if and when some traits on the list are lost, how are those traits situated on the scalogram? Are they peeled off the end, in reverse order, so to speak? And if so, are they re-acquired in the usual order when the environment permits? If those questions are answered in the affirmative, then the evidence would continue to support the scalogram. If in the negative, then loss and re-acquisition of traits would disturb the scalogram, at least to some extent.

In any case, the predominance of accumulation over loss is extremely striking. That is what makes the index of cultural accumulation so useful as a measure of cultural complexity.

What is most fascinating in each case is the sequence. Why do the traits occur in the order in which they actually appear? Why do the death penalty and the calendar occur in a particular order, for example?

We should mention an important generalization of Guttman scaling, a weaker condition emphasized by Douglas White, in which certain traits are only partially ordered rather than well ordered, in other words forming a tree instead of a line and leading to an "entailogram" instead of a "scalogram." Again, it is remarkable that certain traits entail others when there is no obvious connection between them.

Evolutionary patterns revealed by the anthropological and historical research to which we have been referring may not be very helpful in speculations about aspects of the human future, since external influences on traditional societies are likely to outweigh in the future the internal influences in forecasting important developments. We may ask, however, "are there other regular aspects to cultural development, ones more relevant to modern conditions?"

For example, we could consider processes connected with acculturation or, more generally, cultural mixing consequent on migration. Those are issues of very great contemporary and future significance. Does the history of culture contact following migration exhibit regularities that have been overlooked or underemphasized? Can material about earlier periods illuminate what is happening or starting to happen in the modern world?

The evidence for implicational scaling of many traits is impressive. The theoretical interpretation in terms of an evolutionary sequence is very attractive, even though the direct evidence so far adduced for that interpretation still leaves something to be desired. Also, a standard time sequence is not the only possible explanation of implicational scaling. For example, the linguistic case we discussed seems to have social class rather than time as the relevant variable. (Still, there is a tendency for people to rise in social class, so time may actually play its accustomed role.) Despite possible criticisms, the

....

AN IMPORTANT POINT TO MENTION IS THAT IN THE COURSE

OF HISTORY, CULTURAL COMPLEXITY CAN OCCASIONALLY

REGRESS AS WELL AS ADVANCE. WE ARE NOT ALWAYS

DEALING WITH PURE ACCUMULATION.

....

PERHAPS THE MOST IMPORTANT LESSON WE CAN LEARN FROM THIS SAD STORY IS THAT TODAY HISTORIANS AND SOCIAL SCIENTISTS MAY BE OVERLOOKING CORRESPONDING REGULARITIES WITH IMPLICATIONS FOR FORECASTING AND FOR PUBLIC POLICY. IF THE REMARKABLE EVOLUTIONARY SEQUENCES COULD BE SO EASILY DISMISSED, WHY NOT OTHER INSIGHTS OF EQUAL IMPORTANCE AND GREATER REL- EVANCE FOR THE LONG-RANGE FUTURE?

case for the evolutionary sequence is a strong one, and the widespread rejection, for many years, mostly on ideological grounds, of this "main sequence" of trait accumulation and of the whole idea of an evolutionary model of social development is unsettling.

Perhaps the most important lesson we can learn from this sad story is that today historians and social scientists may be overlooking corresponding regularities with implications for forecasting and for public policy. If the remarkable evolutionary sequences could be so easily dismissed, why not other insights of equal importance and greater relevance for the long-range future? What ideological prejudice is operating today in history and in the social sciences to suppress work on regularities that combine with random influences to produce history?

One should certainly mention Arnold Toynbee's ambitious attempt to describe and compare the rise and fall of more than 20 civilizations. Of course some aspects of his work lend themselves to caricature, such as his apparent belief that all of history can be viewed as leading up to the foundation of the Anglican Church. And in such a far-ranging work, he undoubtedly made a number of mistakes that horrified experts on the various cultures he considered. But as a first attempt was it really so bad that one should not build on it?

On a less grandiose note, we have some recent books on the rise and fall of great powers, such as one by Paul Kennedy. There are also attempts to create a somewhat mathematical theory of historical dynamics, as in the books by Peter Turchin and in the journal *Cliodynamics*.

Perhaps the search for regularities in human history is becoming a trifle more respectable than it was formerly. That could well portend some significant improvement in our ability to discuss the human future. ❧

~99~

M

METAHISTORY'S DANGEROUS DREAM

Geoffrey Galt Harpham, National Humanities Center

"BIG HISTORY" AND "METAHISTORY" are grounded
in an ancient lamentation over the segmentation of
human existence, the alienation from an original sense
of oneness. In this chapter I am doing my disciplinary
duty by providing a deflating historical counterweight
to the desire to overcome those last remaining obstacles on the path to a complete account. For me at least,
the difficulties in reaching a complete account in a
common language remain; nor am I persuaded that
the difficulties are merely technical. The difficulties
are deeply engrained not just in modern disciplinary
thought but in cognition as such. Indeed, the very goal
of a complete account in a common language seems to
me to be based on a false view of disciplinary distinctions as well as a false understanding of what we ought
to wish for, our real interests.

At the end of his extremely stimulating paper, "The Quest for
Patterns in Metahistory," [1] David Krakauer invokes the shim-
mering possibility of a "complete account" of historical events
that would embrace all frequencies on the "epistemic spectrum." A 2005 meeting sponsored by the Santa Fe Institute had
revealed, as he put it, "the will towards a common language"; it
must, he and others felt, be possible to break out of "the tombs
of disciplinary scholarship" and come up with a way of speaking
that embraces both individuals and types, events and patterns,
concrete particulars and universal laws. Sadly, that meeting
ended with the recognition that certain "significant technical
difficulties" continued to impede progress on this front, and so
other meetings were planned in the hope that these could be

overcome. The Waikiki Beach setting of the March 2008 SFI conference certainly encouraged a spirit of reconciliation, and the papers were deeply impressive. But for me at least, the difficulties in reaching a complete account in a common language remain; nor am I persuaded that the difficulties are merely technical. In fact, I will argue, the difficulties are deeply engrained not just in modern disciplinary thought but in cognition as such. Indeed, the very goal of a complete account in a common language seems to me to be based on a false view of disciplinary distinctions, as well as a false understanding of what we ought to wish for, our real interests.

In making this case, I speak from within the disciplinary tomb of the humanities, which are oriented towards the past. This orientation produces, or is produced by, a characteristic mindset, an anti-utopian skepticism. It is historically anomalous that so many humanists today identify themselves as politically left, because for most of the history of humanistic study, the scientists were the radical innovators and modernizers, while the humanists encouraged a spirit of reverential attention to the great names of the tradition; this was in fact the basis for the low value placed on the humanities by C.P. Snow in 1959. Today, of course, the situation is complicated—if not reversed—by the fact that the scientists are all on government funding while the humanists, who have little hope of such support, have become comfortable describing themselves and their work as politically radical. This reorientation may, however, be merely superficial, because humanists still churn out examples from history of how wars, revolutions, utopian projects, and good intentions of all kinds worked out badly; they still throw up cautionary red flags, and introduce a reflective doubt into structures of unquestioned conviction or unexamined enthusiasm. The humanistic disposition has its limits, but the scientific optimism that collective effort will bring us to an ultimate truth is also limited, in its way. When Max Planck, voicing this optimism, identifies the goal of theoretical physics as "nothing less than the unity and completeness of the system . . . not only with respect to all particulars of the system, but also with respect to physicists of all places, all times, all peoples, all cultures . . . not merely for the inhabitants of this earth, but also for the inhabitants of other planets," I have to wonder what planet he's living on [2]. In any event, I will in this chapter be doing my disciplinary duty by providing a deflating historical counterweight to Krakauer's characteristically scientific desire to overcome those last remaining obstacles on the path to a complete account.

"Big History" and "metahistory" are exciting new terms, but they do not describe an altogether new practice, much less a new ambition, for they are grounded in an ancient lamentation over the segmentation of human existence, the alienation from an original sense of oneness. The complaint about the arbitrary and deadening character of academic disciplines is a modern version of a complaint that has in the past taken mythic, religious, and political forms. Over the course of the last century, when disciplines have assumed their current forms, such complaints have been heard frequently. But before that time, they were not heard at all because there was a discipline that combined science, history, and literary studies. Having assumed its modern form at the end of the eighteenth century, the discipline of philology was seeking to construct a complete account that combined human history and human nature, one that began in an empirical study of observable linguistic data and ended in nothing less than an understanding of the origins, and thus the natural and normative forms, of human existence. Considered by its advocates to be the science of sciences, philology was also the most prestigious form of what would come to be called the humanities: it was the fertile seed out of which the modern division of disciplines would grow.

To get a sense of how the philological project was imagined, we can turn to the great French scholar Ernest Renan's 1849 treatise, *The Future of Science*, which, coming on the heels of the great events of the previous year, confidently stated that science had brought humankind to the brink of a new era of emancipation and reason. Renan was completely persuaded that science was heading in the right direction, guided by what he (and not only he) considered the preeminent science of the day, philology. The "modern spirit," he wrote, "that is, rationalism, criticism, liberalism, was founded on the same day as philology. *The founders of the modern spirit are the philologists*" [3, p.138]. In the empirical and scientific study of ancient languages, Renan thought he had found the key to both the past and the future.

If such a statement seems preposterous to us, that is only because our sense of the possible has been channeled by the disciplines to which philology gave birth half a century after Renan wrote. Philology *circa* 1849 claimed for itself a vast terrain. The discipline began with the attempt to create a clean and error-free text (of Homer), and then to study the language of that and other texts, noting anomalous case terminations, marking first usages, and establishing the geographical diffusion of languages. But its real ambitions were not so limited, and they were quickly revealed. Philology was always *in search of* something, and then something more. At first, the object was to locate, in the corrupted extant texts of the *Iliad* and the *Odyssey*, traces of the pure, authentic voice of the bard. But in order to determine which utterances might be Homer's, one had to have a view of who Homer might have been, which meant one had to know about the culture he inhabited, which meant one had to know, for comparative purposes, other contemporary cultures, and the origins of all those cultures. Ultimately, philologists found—and I am abbreviating a fascinating collective tale— that you need an account of human origins, and the best way to obtain that account was through the formal and historical study of language.

Such a project drew on everything that could be known about the human past. One of the early German philologists, P. A. Boeckh, saw philology as a master-discipline encompassing a total knowledge of antiquity, including history, geography, law, religion, mythology, art, epigraphy, and social history— "the knowledge of the known." No subsequent philologist made quite such expansive claims, but philology under any nineteenth-century description was, by today's standards, an exceptionally capacious discipline. In the first instance, its commitment to a systematic examination of the textual object qualified it as a science. Throughout the nineteenth century, it was routinely compared to anatomy, botany, anthropology, archeology, and particularly to geology, inasmuch as its objects could, like stones, be seen as preserved forms of the past. But with its historical orientation and its focus on poetry and "artistic" language, philology also had strong claims to be considered what we would today regard as a humanistic discipline. And it was a philosophy. The founder of "modern" philology, F. A. Wolf, said that his real project, beyond the analysis of Homeric language, was to create *"the philosophy of the history of human nature in Greece"* [2, p.233]. Philosophy, history, classics, poetry, and biology—it was, in short, all in all.

~105~

So if we are looking for an actual historical example of the common language and complete account David Krakauer projects as the goal of metahistory, philology qualifies. It is the most capacious discipline ever to have the name of a discipline, and it enlisted the energies of many of the most accomplished scholars of the nineteenth century.

How did it fare?

At first, spectacularly well. One of the tasks that occupied the early philologists was the attempt to find the common ancestor of Latin, Greek, and Sanskrit. This effort began with the classification of languages into "families" and then reverse-engineering those families in order to arrive at their history. Within a few decades, scholars had accomplished a monumental task, the recovery of "Proto-Indo-European," a language that, according to philologists, stood to a great many existing natural languages as Adam stood to the human race today. And with the discovery of Proto-Indo-European, scholars thought, they could infer the thought-forms prevailing at the origin of civilization itself; they could re-enter Paradise and study the human mind in its uncorrupted form. The early philologists were, of course, Christians or, like Renan, reluctant post-Christians, and it is not difficult to see in the mighty effort of reconstructing the original human language an attempt to provide through science a compensation for what science—geology, and the Higher Criticism of the Bible—had stolen, the Biblical account of human history that had for so many centuries comforted human beings by linking the secular present to a sacred origin.

But the attempt to recapture, if only in a scholarly sense, this sacred origin produced its own distinctive kind of corruption. The study of language was always also a study of the people who spoke and wrote that language; indeed, one studied a language only in order to learn about its users, who were always, therefore, in the frame—if not always in focus. As the project of classification advanced, linguistic distinctions began to harden into ethnographic distinctions. The term "Indo-Germanic languages," which Franz Bopp had proposed in 1833, was understood by many to be a scientific way of defining a "racial" group, a highly useful concept that gave point and heft to linguistic analyses by suggesting that the differences between languages were really differences between kinds of people. Comparing languages, philologists could imagine the cultural mindsets that had created them and the people who spoke them. This was such an absorbing task that, over time, linguists found it difficult to sustain a methodological distinction between language and its speakers, and many failed to see the point of the effort. Thus the idea of race was taken up by philologists, who saw in it a way of concretizing—making more scientific— their account of linguistic characteristics by describing them in terms of observable cultural attributes.

The slide from language use to language users seems innocent enough, but the impression of innocence fades rapidly when we consider the particulars. Some of the decisive formulations of the mother tongue, or *Ursprache*, were given by Max Müller, a German-born scholar who settled in London in the 1840s to work in the archives of the East India Company. Müller proposed the name "Indo-European" as the common ancestor of Greek, Latin, and Sanskrit; and in his *Lectures on the Science of Language* (1861-63) [4], he made a fateful leap by suggesting that this ancient tongue was spoken by what he called the "Aryans," an ancient tribal group that had been the object of intense and often wild speculation and mythologizing in German thinking since the late eighteenth century. He located the Aryan homeland somewhat north and east of the supposed site of the Garden of Eden, either in the Caucasus Mountains between the Caspian and Black Seas or, more likely, in the Pamir Mountains of Central Asia (now Tajikistan); others, excited by the thought of an early Aryan civilization from which (European) civilization itself had descended, put the Aryans in Persia, Anatolia, the Himalayas, southern Germany, southern Sweden, the Boreal Pole, and even North Africa [5-8]. Largely through Müller's influence, language became widely accepted as the primary body of evidence, and philology the master-discipline, for theorizing in a quasi-normative way about human origins in general and races in particular.

~107~

Others less liberal and cosmopolitan than Müller drew strength from his stature as a scholar, and turned his arguments in their own direction. One of these was Comte de Gobineau who, in his *Essay on the Inequality of Races* [9], had deployed linguistic evidence to argue for Aryan superiority and the need for preserving racial purity, especially from Semitic influences. According to Gobineau, language indicated the character of a race, and race was the most powerful explanation for human difference in general, particularly the difference between healthy and degenerate civilizations. Gobineau gave voice to a consensus view when he said that Aryans were not simply an ancient race, but the most masterly and "creative" of races; and he spoke to a smaller but still sizable and committed group when he argued that the corruption or contamination of Aryan stock by Semitic or other races, wherever it occurred, constituted a species disaster.

Müller's views were completely different. He believed fervently in the unity of the human race and held that philology was premised on that unity. He argued, in fact, that the Aryan (Indo-European), Semitic, and "Turanian" linguistic families all derived from some even earlier source, a Central Asian language spoken at the dawn of human existence that could only be speculated about. And, in his later statements at least, he insisted on the perniciousness of racial theory and its utter irrelevance to linguistic scholarship. He was appalled at the way in which linguistics was conscripted to make such arguments, singling out for special opprobrium the United States, where "comparative philologists have been encouraged to prove the impossibility of a common origin of languages and races, in order to justify, by scientific arguments, the unhallowed theory of slavery. Never," he said, "do I remember to have seen science more degraded than on the title-page of an American publication in which, among the profiles of the different races of man, the profile of the ape was made to look

more human than that of the Negro" [4, vol.1(12)]. He may have encountered another American publication, a popular book called *Types of Mankind* (1857) written by Josiah Nott (who, among his other accomplishments, translated Gobineau's *Essay*) and George Gliddon [10]. They concede that the Negro falls inside the boundaries of the human race, to be sure, but at the lowest margin of humanity, just above the line separating humans from primates. If he had seen this book, Müller would have been immensely irritated by their complaint about the way in which philologists were always seeking to prove a common human origin, an absurd hypothesis, Nott and Gliddon thought, which was utterly falsified by the fact that, whatever language Negroes speak, they still retain "that peculiar, unmistakably-*Negro*, intonation, which no culture can eradicate" [10, p.282].

Over Müller's objections, linguistic scholarship continued to be used to buttress racialist theorizing. Nor were all theorists of race racists. Renan himself was one of the most liberal and learned minds of his age, a professor of Hebrew and a scholar of Semitic languages. Like Müller, Renan sought a complete account in a common language that would combine the rigor of empirical science with the historical dimension of the humanities. He sought, in other words, to articulate the universal laws of society. But as with Müller, Renan's earnest scholarship lent itself to its own vulgar inversion, a common anti-Semitism.

Renan was unlike Müller in one important respect: while Müller believed in human unity and the inevitability of Christian dominion, Renan believed that there were two groups at the dawn of time, Aryans and Semites. There were differences between them, of course, and Renan sought to enumerate these in a dispassionate and scholarly way. Semitic peoples in the ancient world, he said, made an indispensable but largely negative contribution. The historical record suggests that they were incapable of science, philosophy, civilization, personal courage, and tolerance; they were selfish, rigid, and righteous; their culture displayed a "want of fertility both of imagination and language," a "startling simplicity of ideas," a stubborn incompleteness [11, pp.13, 39]. All this could be seen in their culture and especially in their religion, but the hard evidence for, and real mechanism of, these racial characteristics, was language. In Renan's view, language, once established in a community, becomes a form into which thought is poured like "a mould, a corset so to speak, more binding than even religion, legislation, manners, and customs" [11, p.30]. A close study of the Bible and other texts would reveal the inner essence of Semitic culture. Such a study would focus on "roots," defined as the irreducible kernel of meaning. In the Aryan languages, Renan said, nearly all roots "contained an embryo divinity," but the roots of Semitic languages were "dry, inorganic, and quite incapable of giving birth to a mythology" [11, p.40]. Limited by their language, the ancient Semites could not think abstractly; and their conjugation of verbs displayed a dismaying primitivism.

~109~

Renan had devoted his life to studying the Semitic peoples and their languages, and in many respects, he had advanced and liberal views on the subject of race. But his scholarly and deeply informed understanding of this concept was as wobbly as the popular view it sought to correct. Renan believed that an admirable language denoted an admirable race, and an inferior language denoted an ignoble race, one eligible for subjugation. At the peak of his career, he wrote that there was "nothing shocking about the conquest of a nation of inferior race by a superior race"; Christian Europeans were emphatically the latter, "a race of masters and soldiers" [12]. Müller and Renan both equivocated on the question of race, but Renan's pendulum swung farther than Müller's in the direction of Gobineau.

This story does not get better. Scholars, especially in Germany, continued to promote the linkage between language and race, and after the Great War, the entire discipline of philology in Germany, including some of the most distinguished scholars in the country, became a hotbed of monarchist nostalgia and anti-Semitic reaction. Decades of concentrated effort by the most learned and exacting scholars had "discovered" in Semitic languages a host of limitations and deficiencies that explained in scientific terms the particular role of Jews in history and accounted, as well, for the Jews' current position of isolation and inferiority. With these accomplishments behind them, scholars during the Third Reich felt they were on a firm foundation when they espoused what has been called "mother-tongue fascism," which must be considered the ultimate profanation of what was, in Müller's work, a mere suggestion made in the context of an argument about the unity of the human race [13].

The history of philology in the nineteenth century was dominated not by people like Gobineau but by people like Müller, Renan, Friedrich Schlegel, the Grimm brothers, the Humboldt brothers, Theodor Mommsen, and Boeckh, all big-brained, large-souled, and deeply learned men who thought they were using scientific methods to extend the range of human connectedness, provide a secular and rational account of human origins, articulate ways of understanding and valuing cultural differences, and hold up for general approval those fascinating instances in which an original purity had been preserved. Scholars in the late nineteenth century had no way of knowing what forms the theory of Aryan supremacy would take after it left their hands. But the real point is that ideas of Jewish inferiority and Aryan superiority were developed by scholars, who regarded them as hard-won scientific knowledge about language. The work of numerous admirable sages lent itself in ways both obvious and subtle to the purposes of others less scrupulous and learned than they, and it was these others who influenced more directly the course of events.

If the goal had been to establish a discipline, a specific way of knowing based on a methodology, an object, and a clear set of objectives, it must be said that philology's reach exceeded its grasp. After a century and a half, philology had been affiliated or identified with an astonishing variety of causes, including those mentioned — modernity, liberalism, science, colonialism, and race theory — and others I have not mentioned, including nationalism and Darwinism.[1] It had been enlisted in support of theories of the unity and disunity of the human race; it had lent credence to theories of a master race, the superiority of Christianity, and the natural dominance of the weaker by the stronger; it had given to race theory a scientific credibility it never could have won on its own, as long as "scientific racism" was based on such dubious indicators as cranial measurements [15, 16]. Many of the intellectual and sub-intellectual currents of the time circulated through it; others had brushed up against it, often leaning on it for support, or lending theirs. It had accomplished a great deal, but not all of its accomplishments were genuine; indeed, many were rejected on both methodological and moral grounds. And it had failed to establish itself as a modern discipline.

~111~

Both literary studies and linguistics broke away from philology early in the twentieth century, leaving in the manner of angry young people everywhere, with vows never to return. Philology was seen to have betrayed its own scientific status by permitting its empirical dimension to be determined by ideological forces in the general social surround. With these two disciplines representing major components of its overall project, having established themselves independently, philology was never able to flourish in the climate of the modern research university, and after the second World War, departments of philology all but disappeared in the United States, with remaining philologists being absorbed by other departments, particularly Classics.

Still, history has not been entirely unkind to philology. With the institutional rejection of philology now complete, at least in

---

[1] For a fuller account of the extraordinary career of philology, including an account of the calls for a "return" to philology that have been heard ever since the discipline all but disappeared, see Geoffrey Galt Harpham [14].

the American academy, philology has become something of an object of nostalgic reverie, its virtues seeming to some to be more compelling than its vices. One factor in the partial rehabilitation of philology is undoubtedly the fact that the holistic aspirations of philology echo the perennial desire of academic discourse, arbitrarily carved up into disciplines, for a master discourse that covers what Krakauer calls the "full *historical spectrum*" [1, p. 38]. This echo is particularly loud and clear in those disciplines that trace their genealogy back to philology, where a number of calls for a redemptive or rejuvenating return to philology have been heard in recent years. But in a sense, all modern disciplines strain to transcend themselves, to break out of their artificial limits. The return to philology is one form of this desire, and metahistory is another. A third has been voiced in the relatively new discipline of evolutionary literary studies, whose leading proponent, Joseph Carroll, describes his aspirations candidly as the unification of science and literature:

> *Who knows? Perhaps in ten or twenty years, looking back, cultural historians will be denying that the humanities and the evolutionary social sciences were ever in any way at odds with one another. The integration of historical scholarship with a knowledge of human universals will have become standard equipment in literary study. Humanistic expertise in manipulating cultural figurations will have flowed into a smooth and harmonious stream with Darwinian findings on the elemental features of human nature. Humanistic sensitivity to the fine shades of tone and style in literary works will have blended seamlessly with a rigorous empirical analysis of cognitive mechanisms, and a facility in writing elegantly nuanced prose will mingle happily with the severe logic of a quantitative methodology.* [17]

With this prophetic vision of lions lying down with lambs, the apocalyptic yearnings of academic discourse are laid bare.

Reviewing my argument so far, I see that in order to suggest the dangers inherent in Krakauer's call (which he may well have regarded as an entirely unproblematic proposal) for a complete account expressed in a common language, I have invoked the holocaust, racism, anti-Semitism, imperial conquest, and, in a final flourish, the apocalypse. But I do this in a friendly attempt to isolate what I consider the dangerous but inessential part of his argument, and to peel it off from the part I find essential to his larger case, and completely unexceptionable. For the most part, Krakauer displays an admirable sensitivity not just to disciplinary differences, but to differences of style and scale within disciplines. Spengler, he notes, chose one way of doing history, Oakeshott another, ~113~ and scientists have made similar choices. Within any discipline, one can find practitioners who, having chosen the point on the epistemic spectrum that suits them, conduct their work in a given way. These intra-disciplinary differences are played out at a higher level in inter-disciplinary distinctions. With respect to these distinctions, Krakauer concedes, "there seems to be a level at which history and natural science is [sic] probably untranslatable" [1, p. 39].

I agree. Where I part company with Krakauer is on the question of how to feel about this untranslatability, which he regards as a largely regrettable circumstance that we should try to overcome as best we can, and I regard as almost entirely positive, something that must be preserved (lest we replicate the holocaust or hasten the apocalypse).

We have become accustomed to demonizing disciplinarity as if it kept us from realizing our full human cognitive destiny, something we could achieve if we were not burdened with academic departments — or if we had a giant brain like Newton's. But beneath those arbitrary disciplinary divisions by which modern knowledge is organized is the deeper and non-arbitrary fact of disciplinarity or division itself, which, I would submit, has both epistemological and even moral justifications. We should not underestimate the value in having a large number of sectoral discourses that aspire to adequacy only within their frames. Such knowledge sectors, which directly announce their own inability to generate a complete account of any event, object, or process, invite their own completion or

....

BUT BENEATH THOSE ARBITRARY DISCIPLINARY DIVISIONS BY WHICH MODERN KNOWLEDGE IS ORGANIZED IS THE DEEPER AND NON-ARBITRARY FACT OF DISCIPLINARITY OR DIVISION ITSELF, WHICH, I WOULD SUBMIT, HAS BOTH EPISTEMOLOGICAL AND EVEN MORAL JUSTIFICATIONS. WE SHOULD NOT UNDERESTIMATE THE VALUE IN HAVING A LARGE NUMBER OF SECTORAL DISCOURSES THAT ASPIRE TO ADEQUACY ONLY WITHIN THEIR FRAMES.

....

~114~

complementation by other discourses that are similarly limited, if not limited in the same way. The gaps between the disciplines are not mere empty spaces to be crossed by exceptionally brainy and imaginative people, but are the very spaces of freedom. They should be preserved and cherished, for so long as they remain open, like oceans or forests or interstellar space, thought of a different kind, from a different perspective, on a different wave-length, is still possible. It is our failure to find a common language that paradoxically preserves our cognitive freedom; similar failures ensure our political and moral autonomy as well, by preserving distinctions between, for example, the public and the private, the local and the national, the governed and the governors. It is the inadequacy of our explanations that stands between us and the closure of futurity. The spaces between disciplines are, perhaps, the best parts of the disciplines, and the strongest justification for disciplinarity itself. ✣

References

[1] Krakauer, D. C. "The Quest for Patterns in Metahistory." *Santa Fe Institute Bulletin* (winter 2007), 32-39.

[2] Planck, M. *Ach Vorlesungen über theoretische Physik: Gehalten an der Columbia University in the City of New York im Frühjahr* 1909, p.6. Leipzig: Hirzel, 1910; translated in *Objectivity*, by Lorraine Daston and Peter Galison, 254. New York: Zone Books, 2007.

[3] Renan, Ernst. *The Future of Science* (Boston, 1891), 131; emphasis in the original. Originally published as *L'Avenir de la science: Pensées de* 1848.

[4] Müller, M. *Lectures on the Science of Language*, 2 vols. (1864; London, 1994).

[5] Arvidsson, S. *Aryan Idols: The Indo-European Mythology as Science and Ideology*. Chicago, 2006.

[6] Poliakov, L. *The Aryan Myth: A History of Racist and Nationalistic Ideas In Europe*. 1974; New York, 1996.

[7] Trautman, Thomas R., ed. *The Aryan Debate*. Delhi, 2005.

[8] Kennedy, Kenneth A. R. *God-Apes and Fossil Men: Paleoanthropology of South Asia*, 80-85. Ann Arbor, 2000.

[9] de Gobineau, Joseph Arthur Comte. *The Inequality of Human Races* (1853-55). New York, 1999.

[10] Nott, Josiah Clark, and George R. Gliddon, *Types of Mankind; or, Ethnological Researches, Based upon the Ancient Monuments, Paintings, Sculptures, and Crania of Races, Based on the inedited papers of Samuel George Morton*, 8th ed. (1854; Philadelphia, 1857), p. 459.

[11] Renan, Ernest. *Till the Time of King David*, vol. 1 *History of the People of Israel* (Boston, 1892), 39, 13.

[12] Renan, Ernest. *Questions contemporaines*, vol. 1 of *Oeuvres complètes de Ernest Renan*, ed. Henriette Psichari (Paris, 1868), 390. My translation.

[13] Hutton, Christopher M. *Linguistics and the Third Reich: Mother-Tongue Fascism, Race, and the Science of Language*. London, 1988.

[14] Harpham, Geoffrey Galt. "Roots, Races, and the Return to Philology," Chapter 2 in *The Humanities and the Dream of America* (Chicago, 2011).

[15] Hannaford, Ivan. *Race: The History of an Idea in the West*. Baltimore, 1996.

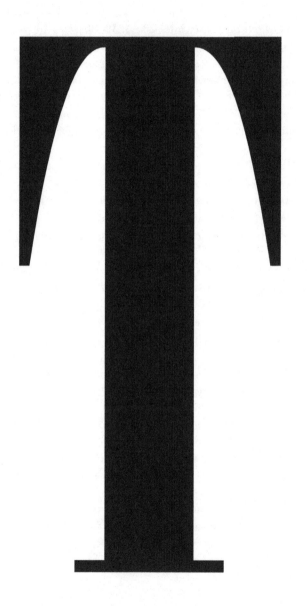

ॐ

THE STAR GAZER & THE FLESH EATER:
ELEMENTS OF A THEORY
OF METAHISTORY

David C. Krakauer, Santa Fe Institute

*I have not as yet been able to discover the reason for these prop-
erties of gravity from phenomena, and I do not feign hypotheses. For whatever is not deduced from the phenomena must be
called a hypothesis; and hypotheses, whether metaphysical or
physical, or based on occult qualities, or mechanical, have no
place in experimental philosophy. In this philosophy particular propositions are inferred from the phenomena, and after-
ward rendered general by induction.*

—Isaac Newton, *Philosophiae Naturalis
Principia Mathematica*, 1687

*The Canaanites who fled from Joshua, retired in great num-
bers into Egypt, and there conquered Timaus, Thamus, or
Thammuz King of the lower Egypt, and reigned there under
their Kings Salatis, Bon, Apachnas, Apophis, Janias, Assis,
etc. until the days of Eli and Samuel. They fed on flesh, and
sacrificed men after the manner of the Phoenicians, and were
called Shepherds by the Egyptians, who lived only on the fruits
of the earth, and abominated flesh-eaters. The upper parts
of Egypt were in those days under many Kings, Reigning at
Coptos, Thebes, This, Elephantis, and other Places, which by
conquering one another grew by degrees into one Kingdom, over
which Misphragmuthosis Reigned in the days of Eli.*

—Isaac Newton, *The Chronology of
Ancient Kingdoms Amended*, 1728

Historical Modes: Particular Events and General Trends

When considering these two quotes from Newton's early and late scholarship [23, 24], we can discern a significant shift of interest and of approach or method. In the *Principia*, Newton sought to reconcile the regular motion through space and time of all massive bodies, regardless of size, position or composition. The tone is one of parsimonious reasoning coupled to a mild contempt for storytelling or "hypotheses." In the *Chronology*, Newton provides a list of names and places which he sought to tether to an objective astronomical calendar. There is no effort to discern regulatory, only a temporal sequence. These two perspectives can be seen to constitute two poles of historical inquiry, one mechanistic and regular, and the other, incidental and particular. This tension lies at the core of most, if not all, historical inquiries. In this chapter I shall outline a few of the implications of these polarizing tendencies of history through the lens of evolutionary biology and complexity science, and search for a means of overcoming them through an appropriate transdisciplinary language. The example of Newton serves to establish that these two approaches to dynamics can reside within the same research mind and program, and secondarily, serves to preemptively refute a few of the more tendentious dichotomies that arise in discussions between the "star-gazing" scientist and "flesh-eating" humanist.[1]

I take the position that historical explanation (as opposed to historical recreation or reconstruction in the form of systematic description and other forms of historical scene-setting and portraiture) seeks to account for some pattern of behavior in what we might call *the arbitrary present*. The arbitrary present (AP), in contrast to the chronological present (CP) —the temporal now. The arbitrary present is any date over the course of history for which we seek an explanation in terms of a series of antecedent events. The AP could just as well be 1492, 1687, 1914, or 2050. This idea was articulated, somewhat furtively, by

---

[1] We typically think of Thales (the "father of science," according to Bertrand Russell), who fell into a pit and died while contemplating the firmament, and the humanist, who has no appetite for nature beyond human nature.

Braudel when he suggested that "is it not the secret aim and underlying motive of history to seek to explain the present?" [2]. Perhaps this is the primary aim of history, and that reconstruction of the past is a step towards this goal, and not the natural terminus of historical inquiry. I will have much to say about "events" in the course of this argument. The claim is that when historians move towards the analysis of well-curated, quantitative data sets in the near future, this concept will again become central, as it will be necessary to organize observations in a time series, and events will represent preferred and principled levels of granularity for these observations.

~119~

Newton's work reveals at least two tendencies, or modes of historical explanation (these are in contrast to non-historical means of accounting for the AP which I shall discuss shortly). One historical mode is to enumerate, in as much detail as there are facts available, the causal sequence of events culminating in the desired variables describing the AP. Hence if we are interested in the colonial history of Mexico, to take one classic example [25]:

> *While at Cempoalla Cortes received a message from Escalante, his commander at Villa Rica, informing him there were four strange ships hovering off the coast, and that they took no notice of his repeated signals. This intelligence greatly alarmed the general, who feared they might be a squadron sent by the governor of Cuba to interfere with his movements. In much haste, he set out at the head of a few horsemen, and, ordering a party of light infantry to follow, posted back to Villa Rica. The rest of the army he left in charge of Alvarado and of Gonzalo de Sandoval, a young officer, who had begun to give evidence of the uncommon qualities which have secured him so distinguished a rank among the conquerors of Mexico.*
>
> —William H. Prescott,
> *History of the Conquest of Mexico*

The AP in this case is Cortes in Villa Rica and the circumstance of his army at Cempoalla. The putative, local explanatory events required to account for this state of affairs consist in the implications of the four Cuban ships, and the trust Cortes placed in his officers. This passage, which I think is fairly typical of historical explanation, also illustrates the great challenge of identifying plausible, causal events. The four ships stand in for the scale of military intervention, and their effects are felt subsequently at the scale of individuals sensitive to geopolitical gaming. Prescott's passage provides an *explanation* only insofar as we share or trust his classification of the event sequence and the authority of his informal psychological insights contributing to the history.

~120~

If this all seems a little dated, exactly the same structure and logic of argument is made by contemporary historians:

> *As before, events in Europe influenced the direction of events in New Spain. In May 1814, Ferdinand VII was restored to the throne and quickly reasserted his power. First, he eliminated Cortes (a parliamentary body was created to establish a constitution in the absence of monarchical rule when the French occupied Spain), and in Mexico, he named General Calleja the new viceroy. Calleja aggressively campaigned against insurgent sympathizers. Moreover, with stability reestablished in Spain, the Crown sent more troops to Mexico.*
>
> —Burton Kirkwood, *The History of Mexico* [18]

Once again, the argument invokes key events operating at multiple different scales, and appeals to individual psychological needs, such as the desire for power. And there is nothing at all wrong with this; it illustrates the complexity of historical argument.

We might think about a history in terms of fitting a curve to time series data (time on the x-axis and observations on the y-axis through which we draw a curve). So, for example, if we choose an informative, quantitative variable in the present (size of population or army, birth rate, GDP, exchange rate, etc), then we could simply describe each event as it unfolds in time through a chronology. This is a sequence that is interesting in itself (Figure 1).

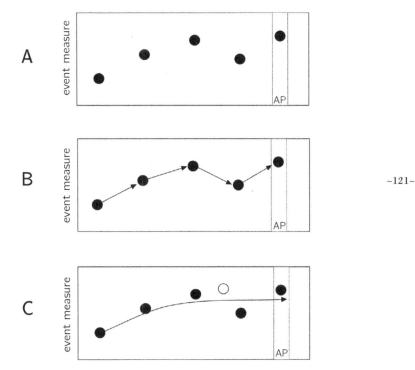

Figure 1. *Descriptive, narrative, and scientific models of historical sequences. In all three panels, salient events and their corresponding dates are illustrated with circles. The arbitrary present is represented by the final circle. (A) In a purely descriptive history, or chronology, events are reliably placed in temporal order according to a suitable calendar or clock. (B) In a narrative history, events are connected by a credible, causal mechanism (illustrated as an arrow connecting contiguous events). The mechanism represents a mapping from a previous event to a future event, and typically invokes processes for which there exists some informal consensus (psychological or economic theory, for example). (C) A scientific history seeks to fit a dynamical system to the sequence, and is typically approximate, capturing patterns in the data but failing to reproduce the particular character or value of an event. The value of the scientific history is that it can accommodate new observations (open circle) without having to provide an additional causal link and is less sensitive to noise in the sequence. The new observation (open circle) in panel C suggests that*

the causal link in B connecting the third and fourth event is spurious, as these events are contiguous by virtue of under-sampling of the historical time series, and not causally successive. In physical theory, the dynamics are often sufficiently simple that the dynamical system is as good as the narrative fit — low residual variation. In biology, the social sciences, and human history, this is almost never the case, and a good theory is often very weak when it comes to accounting for particular events. Thus, the standard according to which we judge scientific history should be statistical, rather than mechanical, principles.

We can go one step further and "fit" a model through every point in the data set ending in the present. Statistically speaking, this is the best possible description of the current data. This is the essence of narrative history. Thus each chronological "event," or observation at a preferred scale of description, for which we have data is described and provides the causal condition for subsequent events. However, if the data set is incomplete, this mode suffers from two critical weaknesses: (1) errors in the reconstruction of the sequence, and (2) over-fitting of the data. Errors in the causal sequence posit relationships among non-contiguous, temporally unrelated, events. Over-fitting the data risks inventing causal transformations for largely independent events and obscures possible trends. Since our observations are incomplete, in both cases there is the risk that further observations (observations not used to reconstruct the observed sequence — observations out of sample) will fall a large distance from the narrative arc that best describes the data we currently possess. Hence, we have failed to account for the historical processes by adhering too closely to imperfect data.

The alternative historical mode, not typically associated with historians but with dynamical phenomena in the natural sciences, is to derive a compressed representation for regular sequences in the time series based on a mechanical model of putative variables. This was the achievement of Newton in the *Principia*, where, among other things, he dealt with the problem of the path of a body subjected to a centrally directed force that varies as the inverse square of the distance.

In terms of data, this approach involves describing a small subset of the observations and predicting a larger fraction of the data, rather than fitting the data, with as few parameters as is possible or recommended, subject to some parameter cost.[2] Hence, the motions of the planets can be described in terms of their initial positions and momenta, and the gravitational constant, rather than describing their orbits in detail. This law-like approach to history, which seeks to minimize the role of contingencies and narrative explanation, is a rather weak fit to history as currently practiced, but it provides a useful reference point towards which a scientific history might move. Furthermore, this approach is a very natural complement to narrative and should in no way be thought of as mutually exclusive with it.

~123~

Positivism or Phenomenology

Not all "scientific" descriptions of data—parsimonious and predictive—make use of mechanically informed models [21]. When a fit is performed without prior knowledge of mechanism, the model represents a phenomenological, and typically statistical, fit. This is generally of less value than the mechanical fit. Thus, we might fit circles or ellipses to the motions of the planets without invoking gravity, as both Tycho Brahe and Kepler did with considerable success before Newton provided a principled explanation for elliptical orbits [9]. An obvious limitation of the purely statistical model is that it does not suggest unifying mechanisms. Hence, each orbit has its own independent description. The purely statistical models thus suffer from over-fitting of the data.

In practice, the degree of mechanical justification for a theory tends to fall on a continuum, including both free parameters for uncertain variables, and compressed formal relationships for the regular features. Even Newton was accused of a reliance on phenomenological regularity (gravity), which accounts for his somewhat defensive epithet, *Hypotheses non*

---

[2] There is always a tradeoff between the robustness of the fit and the number of parameters.

....

WE MIGHT FIT CIRCLES OR ELLIPSES TO THE MOTIONS OF
THE PLANETS WITHOUT INVOKING GRAVITY, AS BOTH TYCHO
BRAHE AND KEPLER DID WITH CONSIDERABLE SUCCESS
BEFORE NEWTON PROVIDED A PRINCIPLED EXPLANATION
FOR ELLIPTICAL ORBITS. AN OBVIOUS LIMITATION OF THE
PURELY STATISTICAL MODEL IS THAT IT DOES NOT SUGGEST
UNIFYING MECHANISMS. HENCE, EACH ORBIT HAS ITS OWN
INDEPENDENT DESCRIPTION.

....

fingo. This is because Newton was unable to provide a mechanical underpinning for the inverse square law.

When we turn to ahistorical theories, their primary character is to provide explanations for features of the AP that make
limited use of inherited, or temporally sequential, processes with
long memories. In the natural sciences, rapid dynamics and
boundary conditions are sufficient to guarantee the uniqueness
of an AP when the initial conditions of the system are minimally
predictive of the final state. Thus a process that has a single possible solution, or attractor state, regardless of what initial state
the system inhabited, bears no trace of its origin. This is a very
common feature of economic theory, such as game theory [12].
Economic theory is largely concerned with the optimal solution to
conflicts of interest among two or more parties. Costs and benefits of coordinated behavior (such as a competition) are provided,
and an optimal, stable, ahistorical strategy derived. It should be
emphasized that this is a feature of a subset of economic theory
and not of economics—an area of endeavor which certainly possesses significant historical regularities. So if we should ask why
gold is favored over iron as a currency, we will find no answer
to this question within an ahistorical economic theory. To begin

to answer this question seriously, we will need ecological economics, to include substantial elements of economic history.

Darwinian Selection as an Ahistorical Mechanism

Perhaps counterintuitively, evolution by natural selection (in principle if not in practice) provides a fairly good example for an ahistorical process in biological history. When interpreting correlations among organismal characters and environmental features, analogous traits are those that manifest similar correlations for reasons other than history (where history here is thought of as common descent). The cause of these correlations is selection, which leads certain traits and their genetic complement to be perpetuated in accordance with their "fit" to the environment. Hence, worms and snakes have morphologically converged from very disparate starting positions and through independent, historical processes. For this reason, natural selection is one of the major nuisance factors when trying to reconstruct an evolutionary history, or phylogeny. Natural selection tends to diminish the historical signal present in comparative-trait data, as regardless of where a trait starts, it tends to finish up in the same position. The creation of the neutral theory [17] — evolution by mutation and sampling drift rather than selection — was one of the major technical innovations that allowed for the reconstruction of biological history. This is because neutrality is permissive of historical changes that are selectively equivalent — mutations that generate phenotypes that are selectively indistinguishable. We might say that largely ahistorical selection mechanisms can erase historical patterns in evolution. The same intuition applies to language change. Language is a strong indicator of human history — patterns of migration — as long as independent language groups do not converge or acquire the same language through selective benefits, like conformity or economic opportunity — which lead populations to speak the same language when they have very different histories.

Complexity

The way we set about explaining regularity and randomness relates directly to the concept of complexity. The only time series without regular sequences, and thus requiring an interpolation (event-by-event description), is a random sequence. There is no trend in random data, and all new observations require a new description. By contrast, perfectly regular sequences permit a very short (compressed) description in terms of simple functions and processes.

These compressed descriptions of data can be either mechanical explanations (along the lines of Newton's laws) or somewhat arbitrary, statistical explanations in terms of convenient data structures like decision trees. The natural sciences have been drawn traditionally to phenomena that have little randomness and permit highly parsimonious (elegant) representations of their regularities in mathematical or algorithmic languages: Einstein's field equations, Darwin's theory of evolution by iterated natural selection, Mendel's laws of segregation. The social sciences have been drawn to elaborate theoretical frameworks that seek to capture regularities at many scales of space and time with little explicit mention of random processes: dialectical materialism, institutional economics, political sociology, and so forth. When we turn to history proper we identify the chronicle — largely lists of sequential events positioned on a reliable calendar — and the historical narrative. The historical narrative is a very complex representation of sequential events that seeks to fit detailed descriptions of people and places within a series of nested regular processes — from psychology to ecology.

We can measure the complexity of a time series in terms of both its regular and random components. Complex time series traditionally have properties of both. This leads to two contrasting views of complexity, one emphasizing the random (Kolmogorov complexity) and the other, the regular (effective complexity) [13]. We might think of the complexity of a process as a function of the minimum number, of maximally compressed sequences of events, required to produce the observed pattern in the arbitrary present. A related problem has been approached formerly by attempting to calculate the "logical depth" of an object or process—the time required by a standard universal Turing machine to generate an output from an input that is algorithmically random [1].

Random events in a historical time series will tend to inflate the complexity estimate, as, by definition, they have no structure. Thus we can either choose to filter out the random, incompressible events, leaving only regular structure, or leave both in the data. A very useful approach is to calculate complexity measures for both, and thereby make a distinction between random events that constitute a legitimate part of the history, and regular mechanisms through which random events are filtered and made consequential. The complexity of history then becomes a function of both of these measures and is best thought about in terms of a two-dimensional space of random and compressed regular contributions (see Figure 2). This provides us with an informal classification of historical time series which provides some insight into traditional, disciplinary preferences.

Critical Events and Critical Systems

I have already explained to you that what is out of the common is usually a guide rather than a hindrance. In solving a problem of this sort, the grand thing is to be able to reason backwards. That is a very useful accomplishment, and a very easy one, but people do not practice it much. In the everyday affairs of life it is more useful to reason forwards, and so the other comes to be neglected. There are 50 who can reason synthetically for one who can reason analytically. . . . Most people, if you describe a train of events to them, will tell you what the result would be. They can put those events together in their minds, and argue from them that something will come to pass. There are few people, however, who, if you told them a result, would be able to evolve from their own inner consciousness what the steps were which led up to that result. This power is what I mean when I talk of reasoning backwards, or analytically.

—Arthur Conan Doyle,
A Study in Scarlet, the conclusion [8]

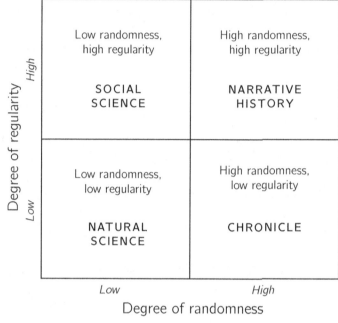

Figure 2. *A classification of* traditional, *disciplinary approaches to dynamics based on the contribution of regular and random processes. Natural science, and physical science especially, has tended to consider systems with fairly clear-cut regularities and little in the way of randomness. The orbits of the planets, the mass of solids, the freezing temperature of liquids, the colors of the rainbow, etc. As a result, simple law-like expressions are capable of explaining much of the variability in the observations. This approach differs from the chronicle which focuses only on sequences, treated as random events, with little or no attempt to provide an explanation for the sequence. The social sciences tend to provide elaborate, theoretical frameworks for events, neglecting random processes in data that lie outside of the purview of "theory." This is in part because data has made a small contribution to the formation of these fields, although this is rapidly changing. Narrative history attempts to provide various kinds of overarching theory to explain, or at least frame, a large quantity of particularist data. These are merely patterns of scholarship, and any comprehensive theory for a sufficiently complex phenomenon will converge towards the upper right quadrant.*

When we learn the "cause" of World War I, we are told that this can be traced to June 28, 1914, and the assassination of Archduke Franz Ferdinand, heir to the Austro-Hungarian throne, by Gavrilo Princip, a Bosnian Serb citizen of Austria-Hungary and a member of the Black Hand. The retaliation by Austria-Hungary against Serbia initiated a chain reaction of war declarations. Within a month, much of Europe was in a state of war. Historians explaining this event adopt either what Holmes describes as the *synthetic mode of detection*, where the outcome follows from the special properties of a sequence of events, or the *analytic mode of detection*, where the cause can be identified uniquely based on a careful examination of the outcome. The analytic mode relies on what we might call a critical event. A critical event is a perturbation of a system which preserves in the final outcome properties of the perturbation. Hence the system supports a long memory for an initial triggering intervention. Alternatively, the system itself might be critical, in which case a larger number of unrelated events could all trigger a similar or identical outcome, and no unambiguous trace of the initial intervention would be preserved. The system loses its memory of the perturbation. The success of Holmes and his method of detection relies on the fact that all of his cases (at least those reported by Watson) involve critical events and not critical systems.

Thus, on the one hand we stress the singular, random event, and on the other, the systemic properties that amplify events. The important task is to discriminate between critical events and critical systems in order to assign to each its relative causal contribution to history. In order to clarify this line of reasoning, let me expand a little on the distinction between systems and perturbations.

1.   **System.** There are a variety of related interpretations of a critical system. One possibility is that a system—a relatively densely connected network of variables—is positioned at, or tuned to, a threshold or phase transition. Beyond this point, the system will switch into a different state when perturbed regardless of the magnitude of the

perturbation—the variables will adopt very different values. Alternatively, the system contains a contagion or chain-reaction mechanism which allows small perturbations to be amplified far from the critical point. An example for tuning to a critical point is a system with a property of self-organized criticality, whereas a good example for chain reactions is infectious diseases.

2. **Perturbation.** Most systems have a finite range of operation, and if a change in the value of a variable or change in the coupling of variables—perturbation—is sufficiently large, the system can be compromised. We can make an analogy with the elastic limit of a material—the point of deformation beyond which the material ceases to behave elastically and fails. For a given system we can characterize the distribution of perturbation magnitudes and frequencies: for example, the frequency of mutations in a lineage through generational time and the number of sites (magnitude) that are modified by the mutation. We can monitor the perturbations without considering their consequence. We can ask how well the perturbations, when considered alone, correlate with the distribution of salient variables in the system. When these two distributions are strongly aligned, then additional system dynamics can be ruled out.

3. **Mixed Cause.** Most interesting examples from history have both properties. Infection with the right mutant form of a pathogen allows for exponential growth of a pathogen. Infection with a pathogen to which the host is resistant, does not lead to proliferation. Contagion requires a mechanism of complementation (recognition or non-recognition by the immune system and binding to a substrate, generated by random mutation events), and a mechanism for amplification based on a regular/predictable dynamical process. Many disagreements in the study of complex systems turn on the relative contribution of extrinsic perturbations versus intrinsic dynamics.

The history of a system requires that we attempt to isolate random perturbations from their filters or amplifiers through an appropriate, regular system dynamics. This is logically an elementary insight, but it is very difficult practically without first having established a method for making this distinction possible, and even then it might not be tractable. I suspect that not recognizing, or at least not treating, this problem has contributed to fanning the flames of the interminable debate in academic history between "laws" spoken of in terms of the generalities of system properties versus contingencies that would seem to require a "deep-description" of a system's particulars.

Competing theories for the transformation of Mayan society are illustrative of this tension. Ecological theories tend to emphasize common mechanisms of decline such as resource depletion and sustained drought. Intrinsic theories include social upheavals such as peasant revolt. The ecological theory presents itself as a rather general process capable of explaining a large number of unrelated collapses, potentially in a large range of circumstances. The social theory involves a larger number of historical contingencies peculiar to Mayan society. In all likelihood, these factors have interacted in multiple ways to accelerate the collapse, making a Holmesian elucidation of one guilty party rather difficult. Whatever the case may be, as Vilar wrote in defense of systematic attempts to "explain" history: "Today, too many theories in flight before history make the history of thought into a discontinuous series of singular totalities" [28]. Our efforts are directed at discerning generalities and singularities.[3]

Coarse-Graining Causal Variables

When we attempt to account for features of the AP, we naturally need to choose some best scale, or set of scales, for the causal explanation. It is rare that we use the most fine-grained data (individual psychology, for example), largely because this

---

[3] The protagonist of Poe's short story "The Angel of the Odd" complains along similar lines: "These fellows, knowing the extravagant gullibility of the age, set their wits to work in the imagination of improbable possibilities — of *odd accidents* as they term them. . . . For my own part, I intend to believe nothing henceforward that has anything of the singular about it."

is not available to us, or more interestingly, because it does not possess the strongest explanatory power. Aggregating or averaging over finer scales to generate average scales is called coarse-graining, and this procedure typically yields greater regularity in the averages. For an analysis of the value of the opposite procedure — the decomposition of events — see, for example, Krakauer [19], where I explain how the problem of uniqueness can be mitigated by recognizing common constituents of independent, aggregate events.

A familiar example is temperature, an average over the microscopic motions of single particles. Technically, it is an average over the degrees of freedom of the particles (say, translational and rotational motion) and is measured at a local equilibrium (we require this in order to calculate an average that applies globally).

Rather than think about multiple individual particles in motion, we can think of a single quantity heat — the internal energy of a system, with transfer properties we think of as conduction, convection, and radiation. These are all concepts constructed at the scale of an "effective" variable. Fourier's law of heat conduction can predict how temperature is transferred from hot to cold material without describing individual particles. This represents a statistical law or regularity, expressed through an equation which predicts the average behavior of a system — an effective degree of freedom — without attending to the microscopic degrees of freedom of the system [20]. A more or less direct application of the heat equation formalism has proven to be of some utility in the economics of the market, where the heat equation is called the Black-Scholes equation. Rather than heat, one considers the diffusion of price. This model does not consider individuals moving the price, because at sufficiently large scales, these processes often appear random, like the particles constituting heat in thermodynamics. It all depends on the level you are interested in.

Whereas this is an example of the direct application of formal concepts of effective variables to social phenomena, informal notions of causal aggregates pervade historical writing.

Here is Edward Gibbon in chapter 9 of *The History of the Decline and Fall of the Roman Empire*:

> *The comparative view of the powers of the magistrates, in two remarkable instances, is alone sufficient to represent the whole system of German manners. The disposal of the landed property within their district was absolutely vested in their hands, and they distributed it every year according to a new division. At the same time, they were not authorized to punish with death, to imprison, or even to strike, a private citizen. A people thus jealous of their persons, and careless of their possessions, must have been totally destitute of industry and the arts, but animated with a high sense of honor and independence.* [14]

~133~

And Lewis Namier, in *In the Margin of History*:

> *Most nations are extremely touchy. "National Honor" and "National Prestige" were a fetish in this country in the eighteenth century, and are still, on the European continent; and the less honor nations observe in practice, the more sensitive are they to anything which might seem to question what amount of it they possess.* [22]

Both Namier and Gibbon ascribe psychological motivations to large aggregates, levels at which it is unclear what *honor* or *sensitivity* might mean. Yet as readers, we do not object to, indeed we seem to find coherent, the extrapolation of affective states to aggregates of individuals and institutions. I would like to suggest that there might be ways of increasing the credibility of these remarks that in their current form perform as suggestive metaphors. It would seem to be a desirable goal of a metahistory to establish systematic approaches to identifying causal levels where possible.

Intensive and Extensive Historical Dynamics

An important property of temperature is that it is an intensive variable (IV), meaning that it does not depend on the system size—the temperature of two rooms can be the same temperature even when they are of very different sizes and hence contain different numbers of particles. This is also true for density and pressure. This is not true for mass, volume, energy, resistance, or entropy—which always grow in the number of components and are described as extensive variables (EV). Whether a variable is an IV or EV can reveal important details about the underlying mechanisms of mixing and sorting of the parts. When we bring together two sub-systems, each in equilibrium with respect to their intensive qualities, we observe flow between the systems measured in terms of variation in their extensive properties—energy in the case of variation in temperature.

If we consider our time series again, we can make partitions of the variables and calculate suitable averages. Many of these will be extensive quantities like the average size or strength of an army, or the purchasing power of a firm. However, there are quantities that can be more intensive in the number of people, like the authority of the Parliament, which need not become more powerful with a larger number of members—a monarch can, nominally, possess total power. When we want to calculate some global property of an aggregate, such as a nation, we need to be mindful of the distinction between intensive and extensive variables, as they will tell us how component properties combine. We do not assume that a history department is twice as interesting because we have two astounding medieval historians in residence rather than one, although the department might be twice as productive. How to assign to historically important events some measure of extensivity is far from trivial. Consider the following quote from John A. Crow's *The Epic of Latin America*:

> *James Truslow Adams, in his* Epic of America, *recalls that John Adams had said that only a third of the people wanted a revolution. A much smaller minority than this carried out the French Revolution of 1789, and the incredibly small minority of approximately fifty thousand "Reds" out of Russia's one hundred and fifty million brought about communism in the Soviet Union.* [4]

The degree of revolutionary force does not seem to scale in a simple way with the number of revolutionaries. Perhaps this potential for revolution, reasoning analogically, is more like pressure which can be measured as a local average and is less like resistance, which always increases with area.

To ground these ideas in my own field, let me turn to evolutionary biology. Perhaps the best-known, intensive variable in biology is adaptedness—some measure of the information-flow, or correlation, between an organism and its environment. Clearly something is not better adapted simply because there is more of it—larger population size or larger body size. The elephant is not better adapted to an environment than a flea. However, knowledge of the adaptive differences between two organisms is assumed to be predictive of flows of genetic information between generations. Hence, better-adapted variants of a species experiencing competition tend to displace worse adapted variants by increasing preferentially the flow of their genomes into the population gene pool. This flow is typically measured as a function of the ratio of lineage biomass over time—a quantity evolutionary biologists refer to as *fitness*. Hence, fitness is a rate of growth of a genome or biomass and scales with the number of genomes replicating in a population. This is an extensive quantity. Knowledge of these fitness gradients is assumed to be predictive of the distribution of adaptive traits into the future.

~135~

The intensive nature of adaptation is the essential idea behind the historical dynamics of invasive species. Whether native or non-native, these are species capable of heavily colonizing a given area by virtue of key traits rather than through force of number. Hence high dispersal, rapid replication, drought tolerance, and plasticity are a few characteristics of a species independent of their number that can promote invasion. The South American cane toad was introduced into Australia in 1935 to control the cane beetle. Its population has grown to an excess of 200 million through prolific rates of breeding. Similar Australian case studies include the red fox, feral cats, and European rabbits. The total Australian biomass under the control of non-indigenous genomes has expanded several orders of magnitude over the course of only a few decades.

To the extent that evolutionary dynamics can provide insights into historical dynamics more generally, we need to be aware of these properties of explanatory variables. An area where these considerations might prove to be important is when cultures making use of different technologies come into contact where technologies, behaviors and rituals provide a considerable competitive advantage in a new habitat. This emphasis on intensive historical variables pervades world history, and is in stark contrast to say national histories, which tend to emphasize extensive variables, such as population size.

~136~

Here is Jared Diamond from *Guns, Germs, and Steel*:

> *Writing marched together with weapons, microbes, and centralized political organizations as modern agents of conquest. The commands of the monarchs and merchants who organized colonizing fleets were conveyed in writing.* [7]

And Hugh Thomas in *The Spanish Civil War*:

> *This XIth International Brigade, however, probably comprised only about 1,900 men. The XIIth International Brigade, which eventually arrived at the Madrid front on about November 12, composed about 1600. This force was too small to have turned the day by numbers alone.* [27]

In the world history of Diamond, there is no need to mention numbers, as these are clearly of second-tier importance next to the "modern agents of conquest." In the Thomas quote, numbers remain critical, even if they are not always simple predictors of outcomes. These are representative of what we might call intensive and extensive histories—histories whose coarse-grained variables are explanatory without recourse to magnitude (Diamond), and histories whose coarse-grained variables are only explanatory in so far as they account for details of relative magnitude between competitors (Thomas). There is in world history a hint of the possibility that history has itself undergone a change—from an extensive ancient world to an intensive modern world—a transformation in patterns of time, aided and abetted by technological innovation. It is as if

....

IN THE WORLD HISTORY OF DIAMOND, THERE IS NO NEED

TO MENTION NUMBERS, AS THESE ARE CLEARLY OF SECOND

TIER IMPORTANCE NEXT TO THE "MODERN AGENTS OF

CONQUEST."

....

technology has promoted a shift to forms of competition and
cooperation that can operate more independently from population size.

~137~

Not all coarse-grainings, whether extensive or intensive,
of observables are equally useful. In physics, a considerably
simpler discipline that human history, the Fourier law of heat
works because temperature is a demonstrably, effective coarse-
graining of the microscopic degrees of freedom of particles in
motion. The test of the utility of a coarse-graining relates to a
fascinating, quantitative property called *statistical sufficiency*. I
shall briefly explain both the idea of a statistic and sufficiency. A
statistic has been described as a well-behaved function of data.
For example, the mean and variance of a Gaussian distribution
of data is uniquely determined and finite. Statistics tell us something important about complicated data sets in a very simple
way, and have the same meaning regardless of the data in question—averages for baseball statistics or stock prices. A sufficient statistic takes the statistical idea further. It is a function
that is just as informative about a statistical parameter or variable as the complete data set. Put differently, it is as predictive
of a variable or parameter as the complete data set. This implies
that knowledge of this variable allows you to bypass tedious,
microscopic scrutiny of data. Heat in the Fourier law, or price
in the Black-Scholes equation, are treated as sufficient statistics
in restricted domains of thermodynamics and economics

For the metahistorical sciences, finding sufficient statistics is a very challenging problem. However, this framework
is often implicit in national comparisons based on mean levels
of education, gross national product and related statistics, as

these are meant to connote something of future states. It would be of great interest, and perhaps importance, to determine how legitimate these approaches are. As an example, in evolutionary biology, the attempt to identify statistically sufficient aggregates has a long and contentious history. The debate typically centers around the concept of the "levels of selection."

The Levels of Selection

Coarse-graining in evolutionary biology seeks to explain the individual in terms of levels of selection [16]. An individual is an aggregate of many microscopic degrees of freedom (molecules, cells, tissues etc), which nevertheless possesses average properties that remain informative. And perhaps most importantly, other organisms and the environment are capable of detecting these average properties, and this detection contributes to the survival the entire aggregate. Hence, predators are not conspicuous to their prey by virtue of their cells but through gross morphological properties comprised of cells. Likewise, prey are capable of escaping mortality through mass coordination of cellular aggregates, generating escape behaviors. The essential idea is that components come to possess a shared fate with selective consequences, and this encourages cooperative behavior which causes components to become statistically "linked," rather than behaving independently as expected in an equilibrium system.

This leads to a perspective in biology that permits multiple, simultaneous levels of description and explanation. Gould called this the "hierarchical theory of selection" [15], even though, strictly speaking, there is as yet no single, accepted theory.

··

THE IMPLICATION OF THE HIERARCHICAL VIEW, JUST LIKE

IN PHYSICS, IS THAT WE CAN CONCEIVE OF EXPLANATORY

THEORIES AT THE LEVEL OF THE EMERGENT, "EFFECTIVE

DEGREES OF FREEDOM."

··

The implication of the hierarchical view, just like in physics, is that we can conceive of explanatory theories at the level of the emergent, "effective degrees of freedom." This endeavor is at the heart of complexity science, which emphasizes that there are fundamental principles of organization at multiple scales, and we do not always have to, nor are we capable of, reducing to the lowest common denominator of matter in order to understand a process. By this logic, historians have been practicing an informal complexity science for as long as there has been a history, switching between alternative coarse grains (individuals and groups) in search of effective explanation:

> *At the King's command, the Thasians tore down their wall and brought all of their ships to Abdera.*
> —Herodotus, *The Histories, Book Six*
> Hellas, fifth century BCE [3]

Herodotus shifts between an individual monarch, a people, and a machine in order to explain a historical sequence of events. Herodotus does not find it necessary to describe each inclusive level by enumerating the individual contributors. Whereas this linguistic and conceptual compression promotes an efficient delivery, it might conceal questionable assumptions. In evolutionary biology, such statements are often met with skepticism, as the statistical sufficiency of each member of the hierarchy has not been demonstrated. Perhaps the best-known example of this level's positivism is Dawkins' concept of the selfish gene [5]:

> *A selfish gene is "striving" to become more numerous in the gene pool. It does this by helping to program the bodies in which it finds itself to survive and to reproduce. Dawkins shifts causality to the lowest level in the statistical hierarchy, and describes bodies as emergent machines, capable of increasing the representation of certain genes in the gene pool. But genes are themselves aggregates of more fundamental chemical elements, which are in turn aggregates of fundamental, physical particles. Each level is "real" to the extent that it can operate as a sufficient predictor of its future state. Prediction however implies a time*

scale—predictions over short or long intervals of time. The source of the debate in evolutionary biology is not whether there are multiple levels of selection, but rather which ones possess long-term predictive potential. The continuous nature of time, and the relative quality of long and short, ensure that the argument continues. A comparable stance in history might be to assert that all true explanations for historical patterns need to be presented in terms of individual, psychological motivations, and that all larger-scale aggregates are merely epiphenomena of individual behavior.

Major Transitions

A natural question to ask is why do new levels, sufficient statistics, or effective degrees of freedom (all descriptions of essentially similar features), come into existence in the first place? Why do complex systems allow us to coarse-grain them into informative and sufficient statistics? Why might we have a history that goes beyond the psychology of individuals to allow for causal contributions from populations and nations? Is there some underlying dynamical process that ensures that this is possible, probable, and perhaps even desirable for a system itself? If the answer to these is positive, then historical explanations become more tractable, as we would have some basis upon which to ignore the multiplicity of detail at the lowest levels of organization and adopt an "emergence" perspective. For metahistorians, this question takes many forms. For the historian of

A COMPARABLE STANCE IN HISTORY MIGHT BE TO ASSERT THAT ALL TRUE EXPLANATIONS FOR HISTORICAL PATTERNS NEED TO BE PRESENTED IN TERMS OF INDIVIDUAL, PSYCHOLOGICAL MOTIVATIONS, AND THAT ALL LARGER SCALE AGGREGATES ARE MERELY EPIPHENOMENA OF INDIVIDUAL BEHAVIOR.

human culture, it entails trying to explain transitions among, for example, nomadic pastoralists and settled urban populations; for the historian of the Earth, the emergence of oxygenetic photosynthesis and all that follows.

Evolutionary biologists answer this question by establishing the conditions promoting transitions from simple replicators to cells, to multicells through to colonies and societies [26]. And anthropologists like to ask similar questions about conditions relating to transitioning from families to local groups, clans, regional polities, and chiefdoms—and through to states. From our perspective, this question can be thought about in terms of those lower-level mechanisms promoting the emergence of higher-level aggregates with novel functions. These emergent levels can then be understood in terms of new effective theories that are level-specific, and are not explanations couched in terms of those levels below, while remaining fully compatible with them.

We might decompose this very difficult issue into a number of nested requirements for emergence: (1) a sophisticated memory mechanism, (2) a mechanism for generating, capturing and freezing accidents (learning, natural selection), (3) a construction mechanism—or a means of creating an aggregate, and finally we should like to (4) identify the dominant pressures, forces, or norms driving the aggregation process. These requirements, I would argue, are very general and equally likely to apply to biological and cultural examples.

1. **Memory.** There is no history without memory. At its most basic, a memory is something like an attractor state of a dynamical system—a configuration towards which dynamical variables converge. Larger memories requires more, stable attractor states. Computer memory, like RAM, stores information in binary, each bit is maintained in a preferred state through the flow of current from a power supply. Without power, the memory effectively volatilizes and disappears. Hard drives offer non-volatile memories using magnetized ferromagnetic material. Brains make use of volatile protein densities to store memories, and humans traditionally make use of inorganic (iron gall or carbon

ink) and organic (cuttlefish sepia) dyes to color surfaces with arbitrary symbols. These are also volatile, as attested to by the decay of over 25 percent of the iron gall ink scores of J. S. Bach. In every case, there is some mechanisms for preserving a combinatorially large number of alternative states.

2. **Freezing accidents.** In order to build aggregates, we need a way of writing symbols into stable memories. Not all events with significant consequences on the future are written into memory. Mass extinction events, which have a huge impact on the AP, do not necessarily get recorded into genetic memory. The KT extinction (around 65.5 million years ago), associated in the popular imagination with the loss of all non-avian dinosaurs, was the likely outcome an asteroid impact. This event left a long lasting trace but was not itself recorded. Contrast this with germ-line mutations. In this case, modest perturbations of a molecule can be "frozen" or fixed in covalent bonds, into sequence of DNA. In the long run, these constitute the basis of new organismal features. It is the frozen accidents recorded in suitable memory materials that play the more important role in adaptive aggregation.

3. **Construction.** It is not enough to store events through time. In adaptive systems, these stored events play an important role in promoting the survival of their carriers—whether organisms, groups, states, or civilizations. Just think of human languages and the memories that languages can preserve, both about humans and about the world. Language is constructed from neural impulses generating regular patterns of motor control, leading to speech or to writing. Without the construction process, the memory is effectively worthless. In biology the construction process is either called development, when describing how the egg-to-embryo transformation makes use of DNA memory in order to build cellular phenotypes, and is referred to as *niche construction*, when focusing on the organism-to-ecosystem,

or social system, construction. The construction process takes the content of memory as a guide to building
statistical aggregates.

With these requirements for emergence in hand, we are
in a better position to discuss the regular processes that might
be sufficient, that by exploiting these requirements, are able
lead to successive aggregation. We should also consider those
neglected processes promoting increasing simplicity without
complete loss of function—when we observe disaggregation in
favor of solitary habits.

Complexity-Driving Processes

Let's consider three plausible, not necessarily orthogonal,
candidates for increasing complexity: the minimization of
energy dissipation, competition, and entropy-driven robustness mechanisms.

1. **Minimization of free energy.** It has been suggested
   that simple biotic agents exist in order to more effectively transduce energy, and thereby alleviate the
   build-up of free energy. Like lightning discharges,
   which arise following charge separation in the upper
   and lower atmosphere and cause a reduction in the
   atmospheric potential difference, organisms might
   be seen to constitute simple, enzymatic channels, in
   a chemical reduction potential. It is still not known
   whether chemically derived free-energy stresses can
   force chemical order into complex biological states

....

IT IS NOT ENOUGH TO STORE EVENTS THROUGH TIME.

IN ADAPTIVE SYSTEMS, THESE STORED EVENTS PLAY AN

IMPORTANT ROLE IN PROMOTING THE SURVIVAL OF THEIR

CARRIERS—WHETHER ORGANISMS, GROUPS, STATES, OR

CIVILIZATIONS.

....

(memory with replication, for example) or stabilize these under chronic perturbations.

Another thermodynamic perspective is that complex delivery networks have evolved in order to more effectively supply large masses with essential energetic resources. The growth of mass and network hierarchy are driven by selection for more efficient metabolism. These energy transport theories can not in themselves explain the origins of very complex adaptive structures, but they can help us to explain why there might be a historical trend towards more efficient systems.

Both of these energetic, or thermodynamic, perspectives on historical trends towards hierarchy find variant forms in the study of Big History. The growth and fragmentation of cultures or nation-states might be viewed through an appropriate lens of energetic efficiency.

2. **Entropy and robustness.** Once simple adaptive structures come into existence, their improbable configurations make them immediate prey to entropic processes of disordering — there are many more ways to be wrong than right [6].

This creates a strong selection pressure for mechanisms that stabilize these adaptive structures. However, these supporting structures are themselves fragile and require additional mechanisms for support. The sources of instability can be both internal and external. The outcome is the creation of a hierarchy of error-correcting mechanisms, many of which do not serve the primary functional values but are second- and third-order stabilizing mechanisms. This is a theory of telescoping bureaucracy.

3. **Competition.** Competition is a special form of dissipation resulting from the removal of energy for growth and maintenance following the depletion of scarce resources by other forms of life. Competition can lead to the exclusion of rivals, promoting a reduction

of population diversity with an increase in individual complexity. Competition can also, under certain conditions, select for niche construction. In this scenario, competition promotes more effective mechanisms for harvesting and protecting scarce resources. There is an ongoing effort to identify useful proxies for competitive superiority, including social power.

Simplicity-Driving Processes

Not all historical processes lead to increases in hierarchical complexity. Many, if not the majority, lead to greater simplicity. I consider two.

1. **Mutation-selection ratios.** When rates of change are significantly greater than rates of repair, or of freezing (fixation), there is no possibility of memory being preserved, and consequently no prospect for interesting structures to be built. The clearest exposition of this risk is the error threshold in genetics, which states that beyond a threshold rate of mutation (equal to the reciprocal of the coding genome size), all adaptive information will be lost. The same will be true of many cultural objects. If cathedrals are razed as frequently as they are built, there will be no enduring monuments to faith.

2. **Coevolution, autonomy, and minimality.** When networks of mutual dependencies have been established (food webs) and resources are shared by co-evolving lineages, then individual simplicity is very likely to evolve. The preservation of a regular history in the form of a genome, for example, is not required if that history is preserved elsewhere. This is the essence of parasitism, which is the purposeful exploitation of the history of a competing lineage. Biological parasites do not need to encode proteins that are provided with high probability by their hosts. Cultural parasites do not need to work to generate an income that they can easily steal. This leads to minimality in the life or production cycle, as formerly essential proteins or products that served

to increase the survival probability of the organism in uncertain environments, are dispatched. When uncertainty is great, then autonomy is favored, taking the form of a larger genome capable of generating a more secure number of input-output functions and returning us to those scenarios of increasing complexity.

The major transitions are thereby associated with the factors: memory, frozen accidents, and processes of construction. These factors, when considered alongside energy minimization, competition, and robustness, may be able to promote the emergence of levels amenable to historical explanation. When rates of change are too high or resources inadequately monopolized, then historical signals are expected to disappear, or least become highly simplistic and biased toward descriptions of sequences of events at microscopic levels. In this way, metahistory seeks not only to provide some formalisms for historical analysis, but to establish the conditions upon which an "interesting" history is expected to exist.

Conclusion

In this chapter, I have identified shared elements of historical explanations. Coming from a background in a historical, natural science, I have sought to describe a few key concepts that might prove of some value in empirically based historical analysis more generally. These include the concepts of regularity, complexity, criticality, coarse-graining, intensivity and extensivity, levels of selection, major transitions, and emergence. These are not in circulation in current historiography, which has tended to steer away from the analysis of large quantitative data sets, but could provide new concepts for organizing phenomena when this tendency is overcome. In discussing these various mechanisms and principles, I have tried to establish the legitimacy of a metahistory—a field of history that encompasses elements of physics, biology, anthropology, archaeology, and more recent human culture. This is distinct from the practice of Big History—seeking to explore grand narratives encompassing both naturalistic and cultural dynamics—and stresses a variety of problems, concepts, and methods that might be applicable to all historical fields. This approach is viewed as both compatible and cooperative with more traditional, textual, narrative history, and might even provide a justification for narrative approaches when regularities are incompressible.[4]

Inevitably, there will be humanists who find all of these ideas distasteful (or euphemistically—*useless*), and would rather not wrestle with the problem of, for example, coarse-graining events, by asserting that only simple-minded, or naive history, deals with events. My hope is that by drawing out explicitly the analogies among histories, we stand to gain from the transfer of ideas formerly sealed into the tombs of disciplinary scholarship:

~147~

They who enter this sacred tomb shall swift be visited by wings of death.

—The curse of Tutankhamun, 1323 BCE 🪽

References

[1] Bennett, C.H. "How to Define Complexity in Physics, and Why." In *Complexity, Entropy, and the Physics of Information*, Edited by W. H. Zurek, 137-148. Redwood City, CA: Addison Wesley, 1990.

[2] Braudel, Fernand. *A History of Civilizations*. New York, NY: Penguin Group, 1995.

[3] Herodotus. *The Histories*. Translated by: Donald Lateiner and G C Macaulay. New York: Barnes & Noble Inc., 2004.

[4] Crow, John A. *The Epic of Latin America*, Fourth Edition. Berkeley, CA: University of California Press, 1992.

---

[4] "The Book of Nature, like a merchant's ledger, might be kept in a double entry style, one column listing phenomena which can be quantified and another listing things which can be qualitatively known" [10].

[5]   Dawkins, R. *The Selfish Gene*. New York, NY: Oxford University Press, 1989.

[6]   de Visser, J.A.G.M., J. Hermisson, G.P. Wagner, L. Ancel Meyers, H. Bagheri-Chaichian, J.L. Blanchard, L. Chao, J.M. Cheverud, S.F. Elena, W. Fontana, G. Gibson, T.F. Hansen, D. Krakauer, R.C. Lewontin, C. Ofria, S.H. Rice, G. von Dassow, A. Wagner, and M.C. Whitlock. "Evolution and Detection of Genetic Robustness." *Evolution* 57 (2003): 1959-1972.

[7]   Diamond, Jared. Guns, Germs, and Steel, First Edition. New York: W. W. Norton, 1997.

[8]   Doyle, Sir Arthur Conan. *A Study in Scarlet*. United Kingdom: Ward Lock & Co., 1887.

[9]   Ferguson, Kitty. *Tycho and Kepler: The Unlikely Partnership that Forever Changed our Understanding of the Heavens*. New York, NY: Walker & Company, 2004.

[10] Fischer, David Hackett. *Historians' Fallacies; Toward a Logic of Historical Thought*. New York: HarperCollins, 1970.

[11] Frank, S.A., and M. Slatkin. "Fisher's Fundamental Theorem of Natural Selection." *Trends in Ecology & Evolution* 7 (1992): 92-95.

[12] Fudenberg, Drew, and Jean Tirole. *Game Theory*. Cambridge, MA: MIT Press, 1991.

[13] Gell-Mann, M., and S. Lloyd. "Information Measures, Effective Complexity, and Total Information." *Complexity* 2(1) (1998): 44-52.

[14] Gibbon, Edward. *The History of the Decline and Fall of the Roman Empire*. Boston, MA: Adamant Media Corp., 2000.

[15] Gould, Stephen Jay. *The Structure of Evolutionary Theory*. New York, NY: Harvard University Press, 2002.

[16] Keller, Laurent. *Levels of Selection in Evolution*. Princeton, NJ: Princeton University Press, 1999.

[17] Kimura, Motoo. *The Neutral Theory of Molecular Evolution*. Cambridge, MA: Cambridge University Press, 1983.

[18] Kirkwood, Burton. *The History of Mexico*. New York: St. Martin's Griffin, 2005.

[19] Krakauer, D. C. "Evolution, Complexity and Metahistoricism." *Nouvelles perspectives en sciences sociales* 4 (2009): 53-67.

[20] Lewis, G. N., and M. Randall. *Thermodynamics*, Second Edition. New York, NY: McGraw-Hill Book Company, 1961.

[21]   Nagel, Ernest. *The Structure of Science: Problems in the Logic of Scientific Explanation.* New York, NY: Harcourt, Brace & World, 1961.

[22]   Namier, Lewis Bernstein. *In the Margin of History.* Manchester, NH: Ayer Publishing, 1967.

[23]   Newton, Isaac. *The Chronology of Ancient Kingdoms Amended* (1728). Whitefish, MT: Kessinger Publishing, 2010.

[24]   Newton, Isaac. *Philosophiae Naturalis Principia Mathematica* (1687). Whitefish, MT: Kessinger Publishing, 2007.

[25]   Prescott, William H. *History of the Conquest of Mexico.* The Modern Library. New York, NY: Random House, 1843, 2001 Edition.

[26]   Smith, J., and E. Szathmáry. *The Major Transitions in Evolution.* New York: Oxford University Press, 1998.

[27]   Thomas, Hugh. *The Spanish Civil War.* New York, NY: Simon & Schuster, 1994.

[28]   Vilar, Pierre. "The Age of Don Quixote." *New Left Review*, I/68, 1971.

℣

HOMOGENEITY, HETEROGENEITY, PIGS & PANDAS IN HUMAN HISTORY

J. R. McNeill, Georgetown University

HISTORIANS ARE CURIOUS CREATURES. We believe nowadays in the uniqueness of events, so much so that notions of regularity, pattern, and system have become inherently suspect. Sometimes efforts to see these in the human past are deemed evidence of some nefarious political inclination toward domination or imperialism. Thus we ordinarily leave the very big picture to others, such as journalists, sociologists, or even biologists, such as Jared Diamond [6]. Their work offers a challenge from which historians usually shrink, although that charge cannot be leveled at David Christian [3], who has recently sought to find regular patterns not only in human history, but throughout the history of the Universe. In this chapter, I offer two different attempts to identify big patterns, regularity, and system in human history. The first concerns a proposed pattern in the evolution of differentiation and integration in human culture, or, as I put it, using terms for the conditions rather than the processes, heterogeneity and homogeneity. The second considers analogies between animal species and human societies.

On Heterogeneity and Homogeneity

In the final pages of *The Human Web* [9], I briefly observed that human history seems to be a progression from simple sameness to heterogeneity to complex sameness. Here is a fuller version of that thought. Whenever it was that *Homo sapiens sapiens* first appeared (let us say 200,000 BP), our cultural diversity was

minimal. Matters of diet, dress, belief, technology, and so forth
were (presumably) very similar because people were very few,
they all lived in East Africa, and faced approximately the same
set of ecological and social challenges. This remained the case
for a long time, perhaps 100,000 years, although it is prudent to
assume (and perhaps there is archaeological evidence for this)
some growing diversity among human groups as they spread
into different parts of Africa.

~152~ With the exodus from Africa beginning roughly 100,000 BP,[1]
the range of environments people inhabited, and adjusted to,
grew faster: from Ice Age Siberia to southernmost Australia.
Tool kits evolved and diverged; some people took to the sea;
intertidal zones and fishing became important in places. Wide
diversity emerged in diet and dress. In belief, too: the emergence of human burials (which probably preceded the exodus
from Africa) implies supernatural belief, and the range of burial
practices (grave goods, body positioning, etc.) suggests wide
diversity. As people spread out over the earth, some of them,
on the edges of the occupied zone, became isolated and more
likely to pursue culturally eccentric practices. The original
Tasmanians, for example, lost contact with all other humans
when sea levels rose at the end of the last Ice Age. More
recently, Easter Islanders apparently became cut off from the
rest of humankind soon after their first arrival (perhaps AD 400)
until Easter Sunday 1722, when a Dutch ship captain happened
upon them.

Here one can draw a loose analogy between cultures and
biological species (something that should be done sparingly and
carefully, of course!). If sufficiently spread out spatially, over
time, species and cultures will both differentiate ("adaptive radiation"). If genuinely isolated from one another, they will do so
faster. The exodus from Africa allowed cultures to spread out
over all of Eurasia in short order, and to differentiate much more
quickly than before within Africa. (To stretch the analogy, what
followed was like a Cambrian explosion in the cultural realm.)

---

[1] Some say 65,000 BP. Probably many groups made the trek at many times,
and we shall never know just when.

The founding populations of Australia, for example, who arrived perhaps 50,000 years ago, diversified so as to speak at least 300 languages as of about AD 1800. The initial occupation of the Americas, similarly, presented another opportunity for rapid differentiation. The first groups to cross Beringia (perhaps 15,000 BP, although all dates for this are controversial) were presumably similar to one another in culture, since they were all residents of eastern Siberia, a particularly challenging environment during the Ice Age that did not reward experimentation. But once in the Americas, these groups soon found a range of ecological niches, ~153~ from tundra to moist tropical forest, and—rather quickly— adapted their ways so as to survive and, often, flourish in them all. Before European contact (AD 1492) Amerindians spoke well over 2,000 different languages [2]. This then amounted to another burst of adaptive radiation in the cultural realm.

The emergence of agriculture (~12,000 BP to 4,000 BP) in the long run may have led to a reduction of cultural diversity, but for several millennia it probably permitted an expansion. First, there were several independent transitions to agriculture—seven at least—on four different continents, all soon involving scores of different plants. Second, with agriculture, human society acquired a new—initially rare and eccentric—way of life: farming. It took millennia before farming became the majority practice, and longer still until it became widespread over the earth; so for many thousands of years small groups of hunters and foragers remained (collectively) demographically dominant and comparatively unmolested except by one another. By the time farming did account for more than half of the human race (it is tough to date this!), a whole new register of cultural diversity had emerged: varying political formats, from tribe to chiefdom to city-state and (perhaps) empire. Furthermore, the elaboration of religions and their rituals, with countless local deities and spirits manifested in particular trees, rocks or, animals, meant that the first several millennia of farming life probably added to, rather than subtracted from, human cultural diversity.

Cultural diversification was sometimes bound up with genetic diversification of the human species. One illustration might help. The emergence of agriculture brought with it the domestication of animals, including, at least in southwest Asia, cattle, sheep, and goats. This opened the door to several new ways of life, such as pastoralism, and various mixes of farming and animal husbandry. At some point, perhaps as early as 9,000 years ago, some small subset of the human race evolved a genetic mutation that linked with a cultural mutation: they became milk drinkers in adulthood. Put another way, they became lactose tolerant, able to digest the most prominent sugar in milk. Most populations in the world cannot do this after early childhood because their bodies cease to produce the required enzymes. This had its metabolic logic in the absence of live-stock: after weaning from mothers' milk, bodies that invested energy in producing the required enzymes wasted resources. But in the presence of livestock, the emergence of lactose tol-erance proved an extraordinary advantage in Middle Eastern and northern European environments especially, and quickly became widespread in those regions. Where cold or aridity lim-ited the prospects of farming but where grazing animals could still prosper—as in northern Europe and much of the Middle East—living off animals opened new opportunities, and living substantially off their milk and other dairy products (rather than killing them to eat their meat) provided abundant regular calories and protein. In northern Europe today some 90 percent of adults can drink milk. A different mutation occurred, some-what later, among pastoralists in East and sahelian Africa, but with similar effect, allowing herder populations to acquire much of their calories and protein from cattle milk. The African ver-sion remains less widespread, meaning it is either more recent, or the selection pressure for this trait has been weaker, or both. These genetic changes, wherever and whenever they occurred, allowed further cultural diversification in diet and in the form of greater reliance in general on cattle [4, 11].

At some point, however, this process of cultural diversi-fication reversed itself. The interconnections among societies and cultures expanded, partly a result of higher population densities, better transport, and communications technologies, and no doubt other things, too. I would guess this turning point came somewhere between 1,000 BC (3,000 BP) and 1 AD. The reverse inaugurated a long, slow process of homogenization, in which farmers took over more and more ecosystems from non-farmers; people with states, formal militaries, and a complex division of labor within society took over peoples without these things; a handful of religions acquired tens and ultimately hundreds of millions of followers, while most religions went extinct; the number of languages spoken began to decline, as forms of Chinese, Latin, Hindi and other "winner" languages absorbed speakers of thousands of now-forgotten tongues. Roughly the same thing happened with other aspects of culture: diet, dress, toolkit, family structures, and a thousand other things. Empire-building was a big part of this process. But bigger still was the less obvious expansion and intensification of networks of commercial, intellectual, ecological (and other) interaction [9].

A fine example of this cultural homogenization process is the long history of China. No one pretends, of course, that modern China is homogenized; it exhibits notable regional variation in diet, dress, religion, family structure, and spoken language. But it exhibits much less such variation than did the peoples occupying the same space 3,500 years ago. That is because of the competitive success of an evolving cultural synthesis that we conveniently term "Chinese." It first took shape in the Bronze Age and was confined to a small region in the Yellow River (Huang He) Valley. It proved successful in at least two senses. First, the bearers of this culture created a series of militarily formidable states, notably the famous Chinese dynasties beginning with Shang (who ruled beginning around 1700 BC) and lasting until the end of the Qing (1911) or until today, if one considers the Communist Party as another dynasty. These states forcefully expanded the sphere of Chinese culture by hundreds of conquests, large and small, the last of which was of Tibet in the 1950s. Tibet now includes far more Chinese speakers, Chinese styles of dress, Chinese food, and so forth than it did in 1950, partly as a result of state policies intended to suppress Tibetan-ness. Simultaneously, however, over the same millennia, millions of people have voluntarily embraced Chinese culture, finding it attractive or advantageous. The precepts of Confucius, the yields of padi rice, and countless other components of Chinese culture held great charm for people whose ancestors may have been Yao or Manchu, but whose descendants are now Chinese. If current trends remain in place, it will soon be true of many Tibetans: they will be Chinese in culture, perhaps partly Chinese in ancestry, but living in Tibet.

~156~

That the Chinese cultural synthesis has evolved and is still evolving so that little of the Shang remained in the Qing—let alone today—is, of course, true, but beside the point: over 3,500 years, the variety of human culture (at least, if one measures this by language and religion) within what is now the Chinese state has drastically declined.[2] The process has been especially rapid in the past 1,000 years, and has intermittently been a component of state policy since at least the latter part of the Tang Dynasty, if not before.

With the names, dates, and other details changed, one could easily offer similar stories of long-term (if, of course, incomplete) cultural homogenization in the Arab world over the past 1,350 years, the Russian or American over the last 350 years, or, on smaller scales, the Germanic realm, the Japanese archipelago, or Turkic Anatolia. All these cases involved military conquests, but also voluntary cultural conversions.

Now, some caveats about this vision of history.

First, a caveat of global chronology. Not all of these things happened on the same schedule. The process of homogenization had scarcely begun in North America before 1650 AD, whereas in China it was by then already well advanced. Moreover, within the broad category of culture, the turning points from heterogenization to homogenization no doubt occurred at different

---

[2] One might dispute this conclusion if one adopted different metrics of cultural variation, for example, the number of types of cloth available, which is probably greater now than 1,000 or 3,500 years ago in China. But I think using language and religion as a shorthand for the broader category of culture is at least as good as any alteRNAtive.

....

LINGUISTS THINK WE HAVE GONE FROM PERHAPS
TEN TO TWELVE THOUSAND LANGUAGES TO THE CURRENT SIX
OR SEVEN THOUSAND, AND WILL LIKELY BE DOWN TO THREE
THOUSAND BY AD 2100. CAN WE GET TO ONE LANGUAGE,
AS THE AUTHOR OF ESPERANTO PRESUMABLY HOPED?

....

moments for religions, languages, and so forth. But I think if looking at the long sweep of time, one can still reduce all of these manifestations of human culture to one curve, for heuristic purposes, at least (see Figure 1).

Second, a caveat of limits. It may be too soon to tell, but I imagine that the process of homogenization, or cultural globalization, has firm limits. Dress, for example, responds to local conditions: people in Scotland and Surinam will never dress just the same; their styles have probably converged as far as they can converge by now. Diet, too, will always have local flavors, except for rich people who can eat food from anywhere. A certain amount of cultural heterogeneity is imposed by geography and climate. Beyond this effect, I wonder whether there is not some additional irreducibility. Linguists think we have gone from perhaps ten to twelve thousand languages to the current six or seven thousand, and will likely be down to three thousand by AD 2100 [5, 8, 10]. Can we get to one language, as the author of Esperanto presumably hoped? Could religious homogenization go much further? It seems at present that the countervailing tendency — new sects, cults, religions hiving off from more established ones — is flourishing. Politically, the number of polities, once (estimated at) over 100,000 is now around 200, but that is more than existed in 1930. Are we as a species wired to prize difference so much that nationalisms, religious chauvinisms, and so forth will always ensure cultural diversity? In other words, Sicilians, Lombards, and Abruzzese can learn to be Italians after 1860 (Italian unification) and could conceivably learn to be Europeans after 1957 (the formation of the European Union's forebear), but cannot learn to be Eurasians (or whatever the next larger grouping could be). Or, in terms of probabilities, perhaps they can, but it remains implausible that everyone at any given time will surrender smaller identities for larger ones (absent threatening Martians to bring us together, of course).

The historical record is full of eddies in the current, counterexamples of expanding cultural diversity in the era that I characterize as one of homogenization. The Russifying Soviet Union broke up, unleashing a dozen nationalisms and expressions of defiantly non-Russian cultural self-assertion. Latin evolved into Rumanian, Italian, French, Spanish, Catalan, and Portuguese (and some smaller languages, or dialects, as some would say, such as Provençal and Galego (Galician)). As long as such countervailing tendencies exist, it would probably require a very improbable political juggernaut to impose any global language or religion, let alone any global cultural synthesis.

Third, a caveat of parochial presentism. Perhaps in the fullness of time, the trends I see, first of heterogenization and then homogenization, will look like swings of a pendulum. Each arrangement contains so many sources of dissatisfaction that it automatically creates pressures to reverse it, in the way that the political scientist Adam Watson [13] saw the history of international society swinging (slowly) between fragmentation and consolidation. When the international system was fragmented, that automatically created opportunities and pressures for consolidations via conquest; and when the international system was highly consolidated in big empires and alliance systems, that condition automatically created opportunities and incentives for fragmentation via rebellions and defections. It seems to me likely that any particular set of arrangements will prove transitory, fleeting in the very long view, and within the very long-term trend of cultural homogenization, one should expect much back-and-forth. But full swings of the pendulum seem unlikely: as long as cheap energy and easy communications remain, no return to the degree of cultural diversity of 1,000 BC or 1 AD seems at all plausible.

Perhaps allowance should be made for shocks, analogous to those seen in biological history, by which the process of and tendency towards speciation is occasionally catastrophically reversed by spasms of extinctions. In the realm of culture, it could be the other way around: the process of homogenization occasionally interrupted by catastrophe that destroys our species's ability (for a while) to communicate and interact. In such moments, with human groups more isolated from one another, cultural speciation—spasms of diversification—would surely result.

~159~

In a slightly more complicated model, such shocks might initially produce a reduction in cultural diversity because, if serious enough, they would wipe out some cultures. But over a longer span their effect would be the reverse, due to isolation and attendant diversification.

Shocks of such magnitude have been vanishingly rare in the past. Perhaps the so-called Toba Catastrophe was one such event. Some 70–75,000 years ago a Sumatran volcano erupted, pulling a dust veil over much of the globe, and subjecting the planet to a "volcanic winter." According to one (not undisputed) view this drastically reduced the number of human beings to something under 20,000, worldwide. The evidence for this brush with extinction is genetic: the observable genetic diversity among humans combined with standard rates of mutation suggests such a small population some 70,000 years ago. If this hypothesis is correct, it surely brought a sharp reduction in human cultural diversity, by wiping out entire groups, as well as the crash in total numbers [1]. But if the surviving humans lived in different parts of the world, their isolation would have been near total, and their tendency toward cultural differentiation thereby maximized. The Toba Catastrophe is hypothetical, and the evidence surrounding it too thin to sustain much in the way of conclusions.

In historical times, the two greatest human catastrophes were the fourteenth-century Black Death and the demographic disaster that befell Amerindians in the wake of Columbus. In the first case, pandemics, probably but not certainly of bubonic plague, killed off perhaps a third of the population of Eurasia in

....

IN HISTORICAL TIMES, THE TWO GREATEST HUMAN
CATASTROPHES WERE THE 14TH-CENTURY BLACK DEATH AND
THE DEMOGRAPHIC DISASTER THAT BEFELL AMERINDIANS
IN THE WAKE OF COLUMBUS.

....

~160~

the century after 1348. Catastrophic as that was, it is impossible
to see any clear increase or decrease in cultural diversity resulting
from it. Within a century, the fabric of communications, trade,
and interaction had been knitted together again, so any increase
in isolation among human groups following upon the pandemics
lasted too briefly to matter in these terms.

The Amerindian population, which probably numbered
something like 40–70 million in 1492, declined by as much as
90 percent over the next 150 years as a result of violence and,
especially, a series of epidemics. Amerindians had no prior
experience of several highly infectious and dangerous diseases
such as smallpox, influenza, whooping cough, mumps, and
measles. Moreover, because they all were descendants of fairly
small "founder" populations, migrants across Beringia at the
end of the last Ice Age, their genetic diversity was (and is) very
restricted. Thus any given infection successful in circumventing
anyone's immune system was likely to circumvent everyone
else's too. Some Amerindian peoples and cultures, especially in
the Caribbean and eastern North America, disappeared altogether. Languages vanished. The reduction in cultural diversity
occasioned by these disasters is not easily disentangled from
subsequent effects of colonizations, expansions, and empire-
building on the part of Spaniards, Portuguese, English, French,
Sioux, and others. In any case, it seems that this particular
shock did genuinely reduce cultural diversity in the Americas
for several centuries.

Such examples, however, are too few to allow a confident assertion that the history of cultural homogeneity and
heterogeneity resembles (or does not resemble) the model of

biological evolution in which extinction spasms periodically prune back diversity, only to see it sprout anew. That idea, happily, remains hypothetical, with luck, never to be properly tested.

Figure 1 sketches the suggested evolution of human cultural heterogeneity over the long haul. It is strictly heuristic. Culture cannot be reduced to a single variable on a y-axis; thus, there are no units. It proposes a slow expansion of cultural heterogeneity, accelerating when humans spread out over Eurasia; it supposes the Toba Catastrophe was real; it proposes a recovery of cultural diversity, slowly at first then faster — consistent with prevailing views about the late Paleolithic — and faster still with the first transitions to agriculture; finally it proposes a sharp reduction in cultural diversity over the past 2,000 or 3,000 years.

~161~

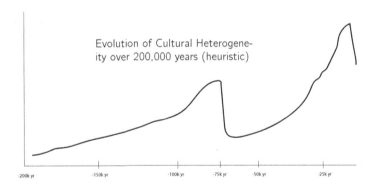

Figure 1. *Evolution of human cultural heterogeneity over the long haul.*

So, from a certain point of view, the long-term cultural evolution of humankind since its inception is one from homogeneity to heterogeneity to partial re-homogenization. But the character of human culture is spectacularly different now from 200,000 years ago: the partial re-homogenization not only is incomplete, and probably destined to remain incomplete, but it is also coalescing around an entirely different equilibrium. This quality I tried to capture at the outset, describing this part of the human cultural epic as an evolution from simple sameness to heterogeneity (of gradually growing complexity) to complex sameness. The homogeneity of human cultures 200,000 and 100,000 years ago consisted mainly in their simplicity. They all had similar technologies because they had so little. Today the convergence (far from full) centers around urban, high-energy, societies with steep social hierarchies and tremendously complex socio-economic structures and technologies.

~162~   Finally, one might also imagine parallel evolutions of heterogenization and homogenizations in the pathogens and parasites that have colonized the human species. At the dawn of human time, these presumably were much the same because humans were few in number and all lived together—and all in the same environment—and thus were exposed to the same microbes, worms, and so forth. But over the millennia, as human population grew, as people moved to new environments and rubbed shoulders with a greater variety of other denizens of the biosphere, the pathogen and parasite load of the human species diversified greatly. Some people carried malarial plasmodia and others did not. Some carried tuberculosis mycobacteria, others not. One of the effects of globalization in recent millennia, and especially in recent centuries, has been the sharing of our collective pathogen load, the (partial) homogenization of it—a brutal experience for billions of people. This process too has shaped our history.

Of Pigs and Pandas

The second issue concerns a broad analogy between societies and species in reference to their adaptability. Some anthropologist whom I read a quarter-century ago [12] once wrote that a pig cannot in a crisis become a giraffe, but societies can (I probably have the specific animals wrong here). They can, and often they do. But sometimes societies cannot reconfigure themselves so as to weather a crisis; they crumble and disappear instead. They fail to adapt to rapidly changing circumstances.

Some animals, pigs, for example, but also rats, humans, cockroaches, are famously versatile, able to flourish in a wide range of circumstances. Others — pandas, koalas, sharks — are very fussy, supremely adapted to one set of conditions and highly successful (in terms of survival and reproduction) while and where those conditions last, but vulnerable should those conditions change (as they are changing for pandas).

Are societies and states like this too?[3] Are some social formats flexible and adaptable to changing conditions, while others are instead supremely adapted to specific conditions? Are the flexible and adaptable (I shall resist the temptation to call them capitalist pigs) at a comparative disadvantage, *vis-à-vis* the pandas, during times of stable conditions? Or perhaps in human affairs, conditions have never been stable enough, and pig-type societies always had an edge, making this moot?

~163~

In addressing these questions, I will begin with what I call a social format. This is not a specific society or state; it is a set of social and political arrangements characteristic of many societies or states. For example, we can detect a panda-type social format, supremely adapted to the circumstances of foraging and hunting societies: the band of 30–80 kin. Other arrangements no doubt were tried now and again during the Paleolithic, but apparently worked less well; like harmful genetic mutations, they did not last. All available evidence suggests that this format evolved early in human history and lasted for some 190,000 years (assuming humans became humans 200,000 years ago). Specific bands came and went; some lasted for generation after generation, due to luck or skill, while others were wiped out by violence, starvation, or some other calamity. Larger social groups tended to fragment, due either to disharmony within a group or localized food shortages, or both. Smaller groups tended to amalgamate (or go extinct), perhaps for reasons of self-defense against rivals, or in order to have enough good hunters to form a team that could

---

[3] I am aware there have been many attempts to draw analogies based on Darwinian precepts that have been intellectually and morally dubious, and contributed to political misfortunes such as Nazi genocidal programs. Perhaps there are babies amid the bathwater, however.

cope with big game. Although these bands no doubt assimilated non-kin frequently, kinship (real or fictive) surely conferred an advantage in the form of group solidarity and willingness to cooperate in the interest of all. Such arrangements lasted so long because they answered the challenges of hunting and foraging in an uncrowded world.

The small-band format did not answer well to the conditions of agrarian life. So with the transitions to agriculture, new social formats arose. Presumably, experimentation, trial, and error selected for the winners. Larger groups became more practical when and where mobility decreased. Defense against rivals, imperative in a sedentary world where fleeing meant loss of almost everything, increasingly favored bigger groups. Tribes emerged, and chiefdoms, too, and probably some other arrangements that left no trace so we have no concept of them. Gradually, agrarian conditions gave rise to a different panda (perhaps we should call it a koala), the sedentary, territorial state, which originated about 5,500 years ago in Mesopotamia. This social format proved supremely adapted to the tasks of survival and reproduction among farming peoples. As farming spread, such states became routine, and hunting-foraging as a way of life was slowly shunted into mountains, deserts, and rain forests, the small-band social format became rare and now is perhaps approaching extinction.

The rise of the sedentary state was surely no accident. It happened in several settings where farming took root. Even if one supposes that it diffused from a single example in the entire Afro-Eurasian landmass (unlikely, in my view), there can be no doubt that it arose in the Americas quite independently. Indeed, it took roughly the same shape in the Americas as in the main population centers of Afro-Eurasia (Egypt, Mesopotamia, north India, and north China). Religious and military specialists shared the topmost rungs of the social order, supported by tax and tribute provided by large peasant majorities. This socio-political order proved very durable. Despite all the upheavals, wars, revolutions, pandemics, droughts, famines, climate swings and so forth, it remained the standard format from ancient times until the twentieth century. The Ottoman Empire, which lasted until 1923, was a perfect example. So was the Romanov state in Russia (which ended in 1917) and the Mughal Empire in India (1858). The Qing Empire in China (which ended in 1911) was a less perfect example, because scholar-bureaucrats shared the top rungs with military specialists, and their authority came only partly from expertise in religious matters. In the pre-Columbian Americas, the Inka and Aztec states, to take the best-documented examples, conformed strongly to this general pattern.

~165~

Naturally, the Ottoman state was not identical to the Romanov, let alone to the Aztec or those of ancient Mesopotamia or Mesoamerica. Indeed, the Ottoman state of 1900 was quite different from that of 1500. Seen close up, in the manner that historians prefer, one is overwhelmed by difference. Seen from afar, all these states, and the societies that underlay them, shared basic features: agrarian production by a toiling peasantry comprising 85–95 percent of the population; modest urban classes but usually some merchant elite; a topmost class clustered around the alliance between military and religious institutions; and a hereditary monarch perched precariously above all else. These arrangements may appear to the modern eye as unjust, exploitative, and immoral, but they seemed to have been the default setting for farming peoples almost everywhere. Nothing else commanded anywhere near the same following in terms of human numbers during the 40 centuries before 1900 AD, although a small minority of farming peoples lived in acephalous or stateless societies, most famously perhaps the precolonial Igbo of West Africa.

The entrenched inequalities characteristic of life in sedentary, territorial states selected for ethical-religious-philosophical systems, such as Buddhism and Christianity, which promise rewards to the meek in the future; such as Confucianism, which emphasizes duty and role; and Islam, which does all of the above. Without these cultural justifications for inequality, it apparently was hard to sustain such a state and society. The sedentary, territorial state, then, was a social format firmly supported by intellectual and ethical edifices, and well calibrated for the conditions of agrarian life.

Those conditions altered suddenly in the nineteenth and especially the twentieth centuries. Fossil fuels and industrial production methods revolutionized economic and demographic systems. The rural village, which had been the habitat for the majority of humans for perhaps 4,000 years, gradually became the minority experience. Cities grew, so that by the end of the twentieth century more than half of humankind lived urban lives. After 1850, the biggest agrarian states crumbled, thanks to the pressures of imperialism undertaken by rapidly industrializing states in northwestern Europe and Japan, and to the forces of internal peasant revolution. The durable cultural systems of ethical justification for inequality quickly lost their legitimacy for millions, who turned elsewhere — Marxism, nationalism, Taiping Christianity[4] — in their efforts to make ethical sense of the world. While much of the world's population still lives in rural villages today, especially in South Asia and in Africa, the urban, electrified, high-energy way of life has spread and continues to spread very quickly and very widely.

~166~

It is still too soon to know whether a new sociopolitical format will succeed in dominating the post-agrarian age. Should socio-economic conditions stabilize around a new way of life, one might expect a new and stable social format. Of late, some have supposed that the more or less democratic nation-state has gained traction and will inexorably sweep the field [7]. Allegedly, an innate human quest for freedom assures the appeal of such polities, and thus to an "end of history." But there is no necessary reason why the future should in this respect resemble the past (pace Thucydides) and societies settle on a preferred social format. The hunting/foraging way of life and the agrarian way of life could well be the only stable patterns in the human

---

[4] In China between 1850 and 1864 a giant rebellion shook the Qing state. The Taipings, as they are called, repudiated existing arrangements, politics, and morality, in favor of a more egalitarian creed based loosely on Christianity, as transmitted by an American missionary to a visionary Chinese, Hong Xiuquan.

career on earth. If the instabilities of the past 150–200 years last indefinitely into the future, we surely should not expect any single social format to endure, unless there is a pig-like one, adaptable to a wide set of circumstances.

So much for social formats. What about specific societies and states? Is it useful to understand them as having pig-like or panda-like qualities? Why has Switzerland proved durable over tumultuous centuries of European history (despite its ethnic and religious divisions) and Yugoslavia or Czechoslovakia not? Is it chance (e.g., not being overrun by invaders) or adaptability? Why has Armenian identity, and Armenian society (and periodically, an Armenian state) survived despite being overrun frequently by invaders and empire-builders, while scores of other peoples, identities, state of eastern Anatolia and the trans-Caucasus were swept into the dustbin of history? Is that chance? Or over the last 2,500 years have Armenians (and Armenian-ness) somehow been more pig-like and less panda-like than their erstwhile neighbors?

Here the time-scales are much briefer. No single state anywhere has lasted more than a dozen centuries, although if one counts successive dynasties in China or Egypt one can extend the time-scale to a few millennia. Most states last far less than that. The variation is tremendous. Some of the difference in durability surely comes down to chance. A battle lost, a string of droughts, a few epidemics — any of these could bring down a state and even put an end to a society. Some (but not much) of the difference in state life expectancy is perhaps explained

....

No single state anywhere has lasted more than a dozen centuries, although if one counts successive dynasties in China or Egypt one can extend the time-scale to a few millennia. Most states last far less than that. The variation is tremendous.

....

by geography. Island states (and societies) such as Iceland or Japan may well be more likely to endure because they are subject to fewer blows from neighbors. But the long history of unstable states and conflict before the formation of a unified Japanese state by the Tokugawa, or the long travails that preceded the creation of a unified Great Britain, and the violent and exciting histories of, say Sri Lanka, Ireland, or Java warn against any strong assertion of an association between island geography and state durability.

While there may well be other variables to consider in explaining the differential durability of states, I think there is a sizeable residual in the form of the internal characteristics of their societies—that is, their adaptability. That characteristic, of course, consists of many parts. One part, for example, is the ability to assimilate, absorb, and tolerate immigrants. To use some contemporary examples, Brazil does this with comparative ease. Japan does not. Japan's longstanding emphasis on Japanese-ness served it well in some circumstances, but in a globalizing world with mass migration it augurs poorly. Moreover, for aging societies likely to suffer labor shortages, trouble absorbing immigrants is a tremendous economic handicap. It may well be that Brazil's comparative success in absorbing newcomers (including several hundred thousand Japanese beginning in 1908) depended and depends on a weak sense of Brazilian-ness, which in some situations could prove a handicap, even a threat to the survival of the state. But to date it has not.

Another part of pig-like adaptability might be flexibility with respect to ideology: if the People's Republic of China outlives the three-score-and-ten lifespan of the Soviet Union, surely one of the key reasons will be its more adaptable version of communism, which by the mid-1980s, let alone by 2009, bore scant resemblance to the Maoism of the 1950s. Chinese communism seems capable of becoming a version of authoritarian state capitalism. But it is too soon to tell: the People's Republic is now only a bit more than 60 years old.

Surely, as among pigs, adaptability among states and societies consists of many, many traits. The collection of traits that make a given society and its state pig-like need not be stable over time. A pig-like society, in a crisis, may change many of its features, and emerge from the crisis quite different but still highly adaptable (a pig becoming a cockroach, if you will). Indeed, if granted decades or centuries of stable conditions, a pig-like society might quietly become panda-like. Indeed, I would expect this to be the norm. Rather less likely, but not impossible, perhaps, a panda-like society could in a crisis reconstitute itself as a pig-like one.

One could extend this elementary Darwinian perspective more broadly to specific facets of human organization and culture. All are subject to "selection" pressures, and some survive; others don't. There is surely some randomness in all this, but perhaps there is some system too. For example, when it comes to languages, there is probably nothing inherent in any of the human languages that changes their probabilities of survival or extinction.[5] Their fates rest entirely on the characteristics — and fates — of the societies which speak them.

~169~

However, when it comes to religions, I would say the opposite is true: some religions are more flexible and adaptable, and more likely to survive changing conditions, than others. A certain vagueness (extending to self-contradiction) allowing a vast range of interpretations is a useful survival trait for religions to have. Those religions too bound up in specific animals, trees, rocks, had (and have) poorer survival chances as their followers might have to move, the animals might go extinct, etc. Other religions, too morally stringent and consistent (Shakers, perhaps), mark themselves for extinction in changing times.[6]

---

[5] Although if it is true, as sometimes reported, that some Amerindian languages of South America either have no words for numbers, or only words for *one*, *two*, and *more than two*, my statement might require modification. If a language's vocabulary genuinely meant an inability to report to one's village the distinction between one canoe of approaching attackers and 20 canoes, this would seem to raise the odds of a language's extinction.

[6] The Shakers, formally the United Society of Believers in Christ's Second Appearing, once numbered several thousand in the US, but their firm commitment to sexual abstinence meant their recruitment relied on voluntary conversion and frequent adoption from orphanages. When US orphanages gradually ceased to provide them with children, the Shakers declined in number and

Conclusion

In any case, thinking about societies and states with a basic model of Darwinian selection in mind opens up new ways of understanding history, especially but not exclusively, political history. It invites new—for historians—sorts of categories based on variables, such as adaptability, that are not often featured in social science and almost never in the work of historians. Historians are, by training, predisposed to prefer understandings of the past not based on any specific models, however informal; by education, usually incapable of entering into dialogue with the natural sciences; and by virtue of their knowledge of misbegotten precedents such as Nazi racial ideology, especially suspicious of concepts imported from biology. So only a few renegade historians are likely to join in the quest to construct understandings of the past and of the dynamics of socio-cultural evolution that involve explicit use of systemic thinking. But, just as historians should no longer shy away from social thought built around concepts from biology, systems thinkers interested in social dynamics should cultivate their appreciation for the unsystemic, particularistic portraits of the past drawn by historians—because history is full of disorder, randomness, and chaos, as well as a goodly quotient of system. 🌿

References

[1]   Ambrose, Stanley H. "Late Pleistocene Human Population Bottlenecks, Volcanic Winter, and Differentiation of Modern Humans." *Journal of Human Evolution* 34 (6) *(1998)*: 623–651.

[2]   Campbell, Lyle. *American Indian languages: The Historical Linguistics of Native America.* New York: Oxford University Press, 1997.

[3]   Christian, David. *Maps of Time.* Berkeley, CA: University of California Press, 2005.

---

today are on the precipice of extinction with a total population of three, in Maine. The Shakers remained true to their principles in a changing world at the cost of self-annihilation.

[4]   Cochran, Gregory, and Henry Harpending. *The 10,000 Year Explosion: How Civilization Accelerated Human Evolution.* New York: Basic Books, 2009.

[5]   Crystal, David. *Language Death.* Cambridge, MA: Cambridge University Press, 2000.

[6]   Diamond, Jared. *Guns, Germs and Steel.* New York: Norton, 1997.

[7]   Fukuyama, Francis. *The End of History and the Last Man.* New York: Free Press, 1992.

[8]   Harrison, K. David. *When Languages Die: The Extinction of the World's Languages and the Erosion of Human Knowledge.* New York and Oxford: Oxford University Press, 2007.

[9]   McNeill, J.R., and William H. McNeill. *The Human Web.* New York: Norton, 2003.

[10]   Nettle, Daniel, and Suzanne Romaine. *Vanishing Voices: The Extinction of the World's Languages.* New York: Oxford University Press, 2002.

[11]   Swaminathan, Nikhil. "African Adaptation to Digesting Milk is 'Strongest Signal of Selection Ever,'" *Scientific American* (2006). http://www.sciam.com/article.cfm?id=african-adaptation-to-dig&sc=I100322

[12]   Radcliffe-Brown, A.R. *Structure and Function in Primitive Society: Essays and Addresses.* New York, The Free Press, 1965.

[13]   Watson, Adam. *The Evolution of International Society.* London: Routledge, 1992.

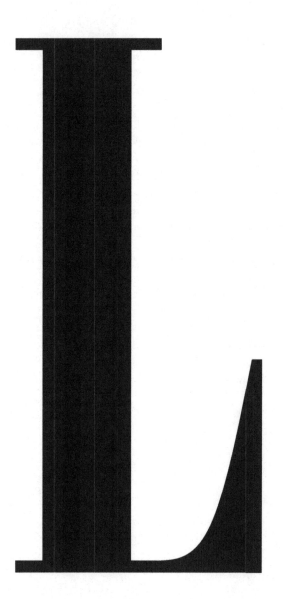

⌥

LABELING & ANALYZING
HISTORICAL PHENOMENA:
SOME PRELIMINARY CHALLENGES

Kenneth Pomeranz, University of Chicago

A SERIOUS OBSTACLE to the search for a more scientific history is that humans label themselves and their actions. These labels can be extremely sticky and often obscure the categories which might be most useful for seeking regularities. Another, related, problem is a focus on dramatic events that seem to be relatively rare and are commonly recognized as landmarks, e.g. political and industrial revolutions. Having formed several of these major events into a class, scientifically-minded historians have then often searched for a very small set of discrete variables that could predict the occurrence or non-occurrence of these very special events. By contrast, I would argue that we are likely to be better off by looking at more general processes that may include but are not limited to these dramatic events, and looking for clusters of variables which interact with each other; the hoped-for result would usually be not to explain the categorical presence or absence of some process (e.g., "economic development") but to group many cases into families, seeking to explain both within-group and between-group variation by means of systematic comparison.

Naming Historical Events and Processes:
Problems of Familiarity

Historians often say that because they study processes in which the participants are consciously trying to affect the results, they cannot be expected to come up with generalizations comparable to those found by people studying, say, microbes or electrons.

But human volition need not be a fatal obstacle to the search for a more scientific history; it does not rule out the possibility that there are regularities to be found in these human responses, at various levels of aggregation.

A bigger problem, I would argue, is that humans label themselves and their actions; these labels can be extremely sticky and often obscure the categories which might be most useful for seeking regularities. Moreover, people interested in a more scientific history cohabit with both professionals and amateurs whose efforts (often in reaction to the emic labels of participants) strongly skew the set of topics in which we are interested and the units we choose for looking at them away from those which might be most promising for developing generalizations.

We already have a few generalizations that are true about the behavior of all human groups, as opposed to all other species, whether or not these take us very far in analyzing history: e.g., all known groups of *Homo sapiens* have made some use of fire, and no other species does. There are also many things that are true of all human groups and of only some other species — and we are reasonably sure, are true to a much greater degree among humans. (The use of language is an obvious example.) There is also a huge range of trends that are discernible in human history over very long periods — though the very fact that they are trends indicates that they have not always characterized all human groups, and they characterize some times and places much more than others. (Increases over the last few centuries in average life expectancy, in carbon dioxide emissions, and in the extent of inter-dependence with humans whom we do not personally know are just a few of many examples.)

It is not clear that grouping humans by their membership in contemporary national states is especially useful for studying most of these particular regularities or trends. Yet those groupings serve other purposes that matter to huge numbers of humans; thus they continue to dominate historians' training, topics of research, and framing of narratives for public consumption (whether in the

~174~

classroom or elsewhere).[1] Those other purposes vary enormously in their moral justifiability, and in their capacity to inspire valuable reflection of other kinds (e.g., artistic and ethical[2]), but that is not the point here; what matters for present purposes is that they are all related to the fact that contemporary people are much more likely to label themselves and others as "Germans" or "Brazilians"—or by somewhat larger or smaller groupings that are linked to these, such as "African-American" or "European"—than as "resident of a tropical/temperate zone society," "resident of an industrial/agricultural/'post-industrial'[3] society," etc.[4] Other regularities based on the past—e.g., "resident of an area that until recently depended on rainfall agriculture and primarily grew tubers," "resident of an area that has practiced irrigated rice agriculture for centuries," "resident of a traditional rainfall-dominated wheat-growing area" are even less likely to be an important part of people's consciousness, though it would not be hard to come up with plausible hypotheses about how they might

---

[1] This is not to deny, of course, that national states, or their closest analogues in earlier times, such as empires, are precisely the right units for looking at other parts of history, which might also prove to exhibit regular patterns.

[2] For an argument by a distinguished contemporary historian that history should be thought of primarily as an aesthetic exercise, see Hunt [1], p. 21. The notion that history should above all provide models for thinking through ethical problems exists in many traditions, but was perhaps strongest in Chinese historical writing before ca. 1895, and especially before ca. 1600. For a variety of examples (with an introductory overview by the editors), see Beasley and Pulleyblank [2].

[3] This is an awful term, since those of us who live in societies where industry makes up a declining share of economic output are still completely dependent on industrial processes for the basics of our lives—but it is the term in common use.

[4] One common emic term that may seem analytical in the way these latter terms are is "modern," but in fact the term has such a variety of meanings that it is usually much more a way of saying "people like us" than anything else. In particular, since the term often slides back and forth between referring to societies with a particular set of technologies, societies that claim to have certain norms (which may be loosely linked to those technologies) or simply societies that are contemporaneous with societies having those characteristics, it does not have the analytic value that I would argue these other terms often have unless it is defined much more carefully for a specific use.

have crucial enduring influences.[5] And it is hardly surprising that historical inquiry aimed primarily at understanding one's own situation and choices often starts by projecting back into time apparently self-evident units that people today take to be crucial to their identities, such as nations, religions, and ethnicities. Inquiry into the history of others is then often structured by analogy. If "American history" is the key to understanding my place in the world—as the nineteenth-century founders of professional history departments, always dominated by historians of the home country (and often composed of state employees), insisted that it

---

[5] Francesca Bray [3] is one interesting attempt to lay out the distinctive ecology and labor requirements of rice paddies, and some possible (though not invariant) implications for population density, property systems, and society, more generally. Kaoru Sugihara [4] and I [5, 47] are two among many scholars who have followed in this tradition in analyzing differences between East Asia and Europe, looking at implications for capital accumulation, the organization of rural industry, principal-agent relationships (which in turn affect property rights and division of labor), etc. More recently, in trying to compare long-term development patterns in the Yangzi Delta and Ganges/Brahmaputra Delta, I have been struck by how much two wet rice societies can diverge on all these points, based (I think) on initial differences in the behavior of the rivers, the density of the human population (which may be partly an effect of the differences in hydrology and geology) and the consequent human adaptations to regular flooding. Meanwhile, James Scott [6], pp 207–8, has developed a very different—but I think ultimately quite compatible—set of oppositions between wet rice and tubers, based in large part on how conducive they are to the building/avoidance of powerful state structures. Wet rice, he argues, stands at one end of a continuum among domesticated crops for the degree of fixed investment it rewards (and thus the degree to which its growers may be reluctant to flee), the extent to which it is best grown in accessible lowlands, the population densities it will support (and the degree to which it rewards increased inputs of labor per acre) and the relatively narrow time window within which it must be harvested (thus making it relatively easy for landlords or tax collectors to seize a large chunk of the crop). Many tubers and root crops, by contrast, will grow in less accessible highlands, can be grown with relatively little labor if one accepts low yields per acre, and will keep well in the ground for very long periods, making it possible to avoid a sharply delineated harvest/surplus extraction season. He does not mean this to be a deterministic scheme—one can, with enough labor, grow wet rice on steep terraced hillsides, or achieve remarkable yields per acre with labor-intensive potato cultivation, for instance—but the affinity of a particular agro-ecology for long-term, large-scale patterns in various realms of life is nonetheless significant.

was[6]—then the key to understanding intriguing or threatening others must also be national histories, be they Japanese, Russian, or Egyptian. Plenty of enlightening work has been, and continues to be, done using those categories—but it is not necessarily the work with the best chance of taking us to a synthetic view of the larger-scale social changes at issue here.

The same is true, I would argue, of a large body of historical scholarship—especially important since the "cultural turn" of the 1980s—that takes as its central task probing the artificiality of categories taken for granted by historical actors at certain moments (and sometimes by many historians as well): work that examines how societies labeled certain people as "black," or certain groups as "tribes," or certain kinds of work as "feminine," with little or no objective basis, and how anomalies were made unthreatening to those categories. Clearly work like this—or about highly subjective shifts in the relative value attached to oral and written testimony, or the moral status of small children—can be very important to anyone seeking to understand how people viewed their world or to make sense of their patterns of behavior. But if we do only this kind of work, it is hard to see how we would ever have much to say about some of the most basic changes in human society (e.g., large changes in life expectancy, energy consumption, or in the status of women) or set any boundaries on the possible variations in social arrangements, ideas, or patterns of change. For those projects, carefully chosen etic categories are indispensable.

~177~

The human groupings most often taken as the subjects of history are not the only relevant units that can be problematic; units that mark off the events/behaviors to be analyzed can also cause difficulties. Here one common problem is a focus on dramatic events that seem to be relatively rare (though on closer examination they may be less so than we think) and are commonly recognized as landmarks: a relative handful of political and industrial revolutions or the outbreaks of major wars come to mind. Having formed several of these major events into a class, scientifically-minded historians have then often

---

[6] See for instance Duara [7] and Tanaka [8].

searched for a very small set of discrete variables that could predict the occurrence or non-occurrence of these very special events. By contrast, I would argue that we are likely to be better off by looking at more general processes that may include, but are not limited to, these dramatic events, and looking for clusters of variables which interact with each other; the hoped-for result would usually be not to explain the categorical presence or absence of some process (e.g., "economic development") but to group many cases into families, seeking to explain both within-group and between-group variation by means of systematic comparison. One short and one lengthy example follow.

First, consider the case of "revolutions." These were once a popular object of comparative analysis (Brinton [9], Moore [10], Skocpol [11], Goldstone [12], et al.), but the results have not been terribly encouraging, in part because there is no consensus on which cases of collective violence leading to a change in government and significant social conflict" (CVCGSC) qualify as "revolutions." The N for the first category is fairly large (instances have occurred in Tunisia and Egypt during just the last 10 days), while the N for "revolutions" is very small, at least according to some historians; and the reasons for categorizing some episodes of CVCGSC as revolutions while excluding others often have more to do with the political uses of historical narratives than with criteria that would be promising for a scientific analysis. Again, my point is not that doing history based on emic categories and political, moral, or dramatic purposes is bad; but it is unlikely to be the most promising route toward identifying important regularities.[7]

---

[7] It is not easy to define what makes for an "important regularity"; I hope it will become clearer as this chapter progresses. But for now, let me suggest two ways of thinking about it. First we want observations that seem likely to have implications for a number of social issues in the societies where we find them. It might well be true that many societies have symbolic color schemes in which red and green are opposed to each other, and united only on special occasions, (such as Christmas in the modern West) [13], 182, 198–203; and this regularity may well tell us something about the way the human visual apparatus works. But its presence or absence in a given society is unlikely to tell us much about whether that society has high literacy rates, lots of inter-personal violence, coerced labor, a long average life expectancy, a

In his 2007 *SFI Bulletin* article, David Krakauer suggests one way around this problem. He makes the point that the "$n = 1$" problem in historical analysis may be partly the result of choosing units that are too big. There has been only one French Revolution, but there were 20 meetings of the Estates General, 15 confiscations of church property, etc.; some of the latter events may be easier to compare, both to each other and to similar events in other times and places.[8] This kind of decomposition could certainly be useful, but there may also be other strategies to create comparable units without always going down in size; and for various reasons, I think it best not to bet exclusively on analyzing any one scale of historical phenomena.

~179~

Charles Tilly long ago suggested one alternative, recommending an initial division between two general types of "revolutions" [14]. One type begins with some cause of instability in a capital, which may be rather narrow or technical (e.g., the fiscal problems of the French state in 1788–89, the dispute between Madero and Diaz over presidential succession

---

static or fluid occupational structure, or peaceful relations with its neighbors. Second, we want the regularity to be at a level of specificity/generality so that it is not initially obvious that it either will or will not be found in many societies. If, for instance, we define the religious group that led a series of uprisings in mid and late imperial China in the narrowest possible terms (as "the White Lotus society") the observation that we do not find it in other parts of the world is relatively trivial; if, at the other extreme, we simply describe it as "a group of dissenters" it is no surprise at all that we find such groups in just about all times and places. It is when we define it at an intermediate level of specificity ("a millenarian group with many adherents that was usually quiescent, but could become rebellious when it thought the times demanded it") that the question of whether groups fitting this category appeared in other times and places, and how they behaved, becomes interesting and capable of illuminating other aspects of the host societies. Both of these criteria, but especially the first, are connected to my preference for examining clusters of variables rather than looking for the presence or absence of a single phenomenon of overriding importance. The second is also connected to David Krakauer's observations about how defining our units properly may help us escape, or at least mitigate the $N=1$ problem.

[8] Ranajit Guha [15] makes a similar move for rather different reasons in his famous *Elementary Aspects of Peasant Insurgency in India*, insisting that rather than focusing on why a nationwide peasant revolution did not occur in India, we look at the dynamics of the hundreds of small peasant uprisings that did occur, and at their cumulative effects.

in Mexico in 1910, or the assassination of Gaitan in Bogota in 1948 — the latter leading to violence which is rarely thought of as a revolution, but which lasted over a decade, fundamentally altered society, and was, in quantitative terms, one of the three largest military conflicts in the history of the Western Hemisphere). This instability at the center temporarily paralyzes or divides the state, allowing the expression of deeper social conflicts which none of the contending elites in the capital initially favored raising. The other type begins with insurgencies among people far from the main centers of power, which benefit at first from being based in inaccessible places, tend to start by mobilizing non-elites, and which generally seize the capital as one of the final acts in the taking of power (e.g., China in both 1368 and 1949, Cuba in 1959).

This kind of grouping, which relies on identifying different ways in which the parts of events can be related to each other, seems a useful way of beginning to create classes of objects we could investigate for both regularities and within-group variations. It is certainly more promising than accepting more everyday categories that depend on one key feature (often chosen by the movement or its opponents at the time) that is said to define the basic significance of the whole event: e.g. "bourgeois," "proletarian," "peasant," "democratic," "radical," etc. (Indeed, much of the turn away from large-scale comparison in recent decades is the result of perfectly justifiable discontent with the ways in which classic social theory often tried to derive prediction from one single defining feature of a group or situation: Marx's strictures on the inevitable nature of "peasant" political behavior[9] is just one example.)

However, it is a significant practical (if not conceptual) obstacle that categories such as "democratic," or "bourgeois" are at least superficially legible to historians' various constituencies in a way that a distinction between "center-out" and "periphery-in" revolutions is not; and for both good and bad reasons, most historians are wary of losing the public relevance

---

9 e.g., *The Eighteenth Brumaire of Louis Napoleon*, pp.123-4 [16]. For accounts of just how varied peasant behavior in precisely that case actually was, see e.g., Merriman [17], Agulhon [18] and Margadant [19].

that comes from addressing units and processes that people recognize as related to their own lives. It is also worth noting that
in investigating these sub-categories of CVCGSC, we might find
some important regularities across all cases, as well as explanations of the variability among the many cases of this general
class of phenomena: while this within-group variability should
be of a smaller order of magnitude than the differences between
examples of this group and examples of other general categories
(e.g., "peaceful transfers of power through elections" or "military coups with no significant participation by civilians"), it may   ~181~
nonetheless be the more interesting phenomenon. Focusing
on this within-group variability would represent a shift away
from the central ambition of many older theories of revolution,
which were centrally concerned with defining the necessary
and sufficient conditions which distinguished "revolutionary
situations" from all other kinds of contentious politics—often
with the further goal of making revolutions predictable.[10] That
older project, if realizable, would have a straightforward kind
of utility that recommends it strongly to some people.

Toward a Typology of Socioeconomic Development Paths: An Example

In the same spirit in which I offered the distinction between "center-out" and "periphery-in" CVCGSC, I would argue that we can go
a long way toward creating comparable cases of "economic development" by separating cases in which agricultural commercialization and early industrialization were accompanied by a large
percentage of cultivators losing secure access to land (or having
never had such rights) from cases where cultivators' access to
land remained secure, or became even more so. The advantage
of choosing this variable is that its differing values have powerful
implications for urbanization, the location of industry (which in
turn probably influences the likelihood of certain kinds of innovation), migration patterns, and so on—which I will turn to
momentarily. How widespread this kind of dispossession is seems

---

[10] For a brief essay arguing for a turn in just the direction I am suggesting
here, see Tilly [20].

to be linked in turn to a cluster of variables: an area's ecology and population density, its main crop and the specific labor require-ments thereof, and the relationships between landed elites and the state. Consequently, the inquiry is not likely to identify a single cause of the development pattern in each case, or to give rise to invariant laws; but I hope it will at least show that this cluster of variables (which are not fully independent of each other) create a limited range of likely outcomes. In other words, this project is also focused on explaining variability within a general phenom-enon, rather than with making future occurrences of a singular kind of event predictable. And, paralleling the case with theo-ries of revolution, such a focus represents a break (already well underway) with older attempts at specifying invariant necessary and sufficient conditions for a "take-off into sustained growth" that (like revolutions in politics) is seen as categorically different from any other instance of economic change.[11]

I have been trying to begin such a typological inquiry in some recent work that compares long-term development in China's Yangzi Delta (and to a lesser extent, other East Asian wet-rice regions) with those in northwestern Europe on the one hand and the Ganges/Brahmaputra Delta on the other [21]. For reasons of length, I will tell only the Chinese version of the story below. The European narrative is more familiar, and some salient points will be mentioned in passing; the South Asian story provides some interesting comparisons, but would take too long to develop here.[12]

---

[11] The term "take-off into sustained growth" comes from Rostow [22], *The Stages of Growth*, but much other work also posits that each society makes a one-time, clearly identifiable break out of a Malthusian world and into a world of essentially limitless growth. See, e.g. R.M. Hartwell's observation that "economic growth is binary: all or nothing, one or zero," discussed in Jones [23]. For historically-based critiques, see Crafts [24], Goldstone [25], and Pomeranz [26]. The idea that a single variable—usually the creation of a proper system of property rights—explains the occurrence or non-occurrence of such a breakthrough is also still very much with us: see e.g. North and Weingast [27]; Acemoglu et. al. [28].

[12] Two points about the Bengal Delta do seem worth making here, however. First, even in areas of Bengal that grew paddy rice, cultivators did not gain the same strong rights to particular pieces of land that they typically gained in

It is convenient that in this case there is a significant overlap between units defined by the variables I am focusing on and more familiar units, since the area strongly influenced by large-scale agricultural commercialization with minimal erosion of secure small-scale cultivation rights roughly corresponds to China, while the places where commercialization went along with the strongest shift in land rights toward undivided power for the owner and extremely weak rights to land for non-owner cultivators, roughly corresponds to modern Great Britain and the Netherlands. This is not just coincidental, of course: national- or imperial-level legal systems and state policy had some significant role in these outcomes. But nor does it show that political units are necessarily the right ones, after all; in many ways, I would argue, the facts that were decisive for the "Chinese" case characterized only a few regions, with nation-wide patterns emerging through the interaction of those regions.

Five facts that were in place by roughly 1500—when there was a significant increase in commercial activity, coinciding with the disappearance of most of the remaining bound labor

---

both China and Japan. This suggests that though wet rice yields respond dramatically to very careful cultivation—making it imperative that the cultivator have strong incentives to maximize yields (as they do under fixed rents and to some extent under share rents, but not if they are slaves or earn a per hour wage), if the landowner wishes to avoid very high monitoring costs—this does not necessarily result in any particular system of property rights. Second, that at least two factors that are themselves probably linked may help explain this difference. First, the Bengal Delta was much less densely populated than the wet-rice parts of Japan and China, until the twentieth century; this meant that maximizing per-acre yields was less important, and that cultivators, still having relatively nearby frontiers to move to, had less incentive to try to attach themselves permanently to a particular plot. Second, the Ganges/Brahmaputra is a much more difficult river to control than the Yangzi; the delta of the latter has barely changed in the last 800 years while that of the former has expanded and shifted by hundreds of miles. Consequently, there was less incentive for elites to try to invest in a particular piece of land, secure it from floods, and try to secure the best possible cultivator for it by offering secure rights to that piece of land; instead the best deals tended to be offered on a short-term basis to attract cultivators to new pieces of land that had just become cultivable due to shifts in the annual flood. Under the circumstances, both cultivation rights and rights to extract surplus were often attached, not to a specific plot, but to a certain amount of land within the area inhabited by a particular group.

in agriculture — combined to decisively shape Chinese economic development over the next few centuries:

1. First, peasant property was relatively widely distributed, at least compared to most other commercialized agrarian societies; and while many of the more commercialized parts of the country had higher tenancy rates, they also had systems in which many tenants managed to gain relatively secure cultivation rights (which themselves eventually became a form of heritable and tradable property). One consequence of this was a very sharp difference in both social and economic status between tenants and agricultural wage laborers (though both might seem "propertyless" in Western eyes). The limited data we have suggests that even a rural laborer who found year-round work (which many did not) earned only 35–40 percent as much as a tenant with an average size plot in the Yangzi Delta of the 1750s; almost 200 years later, when we begin to have far more systematic survey data, the same ratio appears to hold. (The same is true for coastal Fujian, which also had high tenancy rates.)[13] This difference is also significant in that it reconciles estimates of relatively equal living standards for ordinary people in the Yangzi Delta and England ca. 1750 [29] with evidence that a large gap in real wages had emerged by this time [30].

2. Second, since urban unskilled wages did not exceed rural ones by very much — why should they, without strong guilds? — they also lagged far behind the earnings of secure tenants. This meant that most tenants had little reason to try their luck in the city. (By the 1930s, mechanized industry had created some unskilled urban jobs that paid better than being a tenant, but even then not by a wide margin; and by the time the urban/rural gap began to grow rapidly in the 1950s, it was becoming hard to move to take advantage of it.) Instead, it made more sense for most families to stay in the countryside; agricultural surpluses fed spinners, weavers, and other handicraft

---

[13] Calculations in Kenneth Pomeranz [31].

workers, just as they did elsewhere, but they were mostly embedded in families that also participated in agriculture. In the most productive and densely populated areas, the export of handicraft manufactures in return for primary products from elsewhere in China became crucial to the economy. The urbanization rate remained unusually low for a country with China's level of per capita income and productivity in agriculture (which determines the number of non-farmers who can be fed). Even the Yangzi Delta, which probably had a per capita income within 10 percent of England's circa 1750, and agricultural labor productivity within 10 percent of English levels as late as 1820 (along with much higher land productivity) was significantly less urban than England in 1750, and further still behind the Netherlands.[14]

~185~

3. Third, even for those rural poor who did choose to migrate, heading for the cities made less sense than migrating toward the frontier, where average incomes were lower, but the chances of getting secure access to land—and thus obtaining something close to that average income—were reasonably high. This helps make sense of an otherwise puzzling fact: that for centuries, net migration in China was away from the regions with the highest per capita incomes. That, in turn, meant that migration did not contribute to reducing the economic inequalities among regions; if anything, it tended to reinforce them. (For instance, Debin Ma and I have both estimated—using different methods—that per capita income in the Lower Yangzi was about 50 percent

[14] DeVries [32], gives figures of 16.7 percent urban for England and 30.5 percent for the Netherlands, counting only towns of 10,000 or more. For the lower Yangzi, see Skinner [33]; Skinner [34] suggests an upward revision to about 9.3 percent based in both cases on a looser standard including all towns of 2,000 or more. Figures for the Delta alone, instead of the whole Lower Yangzi region would be significantly higher. Xue [35]and Li [36, p. 21; 53, p. 413] provide estimates of 20 percent or more for the early nineteenth century, but their definitions of "urban" places, like Skinner's, would include far more small towns than DeVries'. For the comparison of GDP per capita, see Van Zanden [37, pp. 22-23], and the discussion in Pomeranz [21]. For agricultural productivity, see Allen [29].

higher than the empire-wide average in the mid-eighteenth century, and the gap had widened by the early twentieth century.[15])

4.   China had an enduring shortage of marriageable women, due both to sex-selective infanticide and to a small group of elite men who had both wives and concubines. The imbalance has not been well-measured, and no doubt fluctuated over time, but a good guess is that in most late imperial generations, 10 to 15 percent of men could not marry or reproduce.[16] These were generally the poorest men, who were mostly those without secure cultivation rights; indeed the terms "bare sticks" and "rootless rascals," referring to men who lacked family and village ties, were sometimes used as if they were synonymous with "landless laborers" (see e.g., Zhang Peiguo [42]). Since most wage laborers did not form families—one reason they could survive on 30 to 40 percent of the not-so-princely earnings of a tenant farmer—the size of the proletariat did not grow, even though some people in each generation fell into this class, as one would expect in a competitive economy. It thus makes sense that 1930s surveys estimate that about 15 percent of farm work was done in exchange for wages—about the same as we think this percentage had been 200 years earlier.[17]

5.   State concerns about stability focused primarily on heading off rural uprisings; it was relatively rare for collective violence to begin in urban centers, at least after 1620 [46]. Efforts were particularly focused on relatively poor and ecologically vulnerable areas, particularly in the North and West, but were mostly paid for by taxes collected in the East and South, and above all in the Yangzi Delta. (The North and West were not only more vulnerable to environmental disaster, but closer to

~186~

---

[15] Debin Ma [38], p. 6. See also Pomeranz [31].

[16] On sex-selective infanticide, see Lee and Wang [39], Lee and Campbell [40]; for an estimate of the rate of concubinage, see Liu [41], 129-30.

[17] Buck [43], 293. For the eighteenth century, see Jing Su and Luo Lun [44] on the North and Li Wenzhi and Jiang Taixin [45], 303, 310, on North China and the Lower Yangzi, respectively.

the steppe which was the traditional source of nomadic invasions. This was an additional reason why stabilizing them had priority.) Thus, for instance, the Yellow River in the North was controlled by the central government in the Qing, at great expense, while Yangzi River communities were expected to pay for their own flood control; subsidies for well-digging were at times available in the semi-arid North and Northwest; people resettling in certain specified frontier areas were subsidized, and so on. The result was a system of inter-locking regions that remained relatively stable for a few hundred years. The relatively prosperous areas were able to commercialize further (which inevitably produces both winners and losers) without accumulating a dispossessed class, in large part because of out-migration, birth control, and uneven sex ratios; they also enjoyed considerable *de facto* autonomy in local affairs, as long as they did not rebel and paid their taxes. Meanwhile, part of the relatively large surplus those regions continued to generate was taxed away to help stabilize areas that had (among other problems) less reliable water supplies and shorter growing seasons.

~187~

But in the nineteenth century, this system fell into crisis, for several reasons. On the one hand, large-scale migration and natural increase in interior regions fueled population growth, which greatly reduced the surpluses of primary products that these areas could sell to coastal regions; the expansion of local markets also led to the development of rural handicraft industries in the interior (often encouraged by local officials in conscious imitation of Lower Yangzi patterns), which reduced demand for imported manufactures. This worsened the terms of trade for "advanced" regions significantly: an average-grade piece of cloth from the Yangzi Delta bought about half as much rice in 1840 as it had in 1750 (Pomeranz [47, pp. 323–326]). Meanwhile the Delta was relatively poorly positioned to move into other kinds of industrial production. On the one hand, the highly dispersed, rural-based nature of much of its industry meant it did not have the strong agglomeration effects that probably helped encourage technical innovation in some other areas.[18] Enterprises set in the countryside—where food, and thus labor, tend to be relatively cheap, and capital relatively expensive—are also that much less likely to favor capital-using, labor-saving, innovations [52]. The Delta was also particularly poorly positioned for the vital transition to much more energy-intensive kinds of production. It had never had much heavy industry, largely because it lacked metallic ores and, above all, energy sources. Wood, coal peat, and even water power (due to flat terrain) were all scarce [47, pp. 63–64, 225–226; 53, pp. 272–342]; there were also significant obstacles to importing large amounts of energy [47, pp. 62–65]. Under the circumstances, the relative price of energy was exceptionally high along the China coast, making it unlikely that people would focus on finding ways to be more productive by using more of it. (One study finds that, in 1704, real wages in Canton were almost at London levels, but charcoal was nonetheless almost 20 times as expensive relative to labor as it was in London.[19]) Moreover, the relative tractability of European rivers and their reliability throughout the year had encouraged the use of water power-driven equipment, and the development of industries and production techniques that could later be further developed with steam power. By contrast, China's major rivers complete most of their drop to the sea even before they enter China proper (90 percent in the case of the Yangzi) and then move quite slowly across the plains during most of the year; they also have a far greater variability in flow over the course of the year than European rivers, because they rely on the

~188~

---

[18] On population concentration and innovation, see West [48]. Northwest European handicrafts were more likely to be clustered in specialized districts and staffed by full-time workers fully detached from agriculture; these conditions encouraged information exchange, as did the journeyman system. See, for instance, Saito Osamu [49]; Markus Cerman and Sheilagh Ogilvie [50]; S.R. Epstein and Maarten Prak [51].

[19] Data from Allen [56], pp.6, 17. The unusually high real wage could be the result of the East India Company (the source of the data) paying above-average prices for the people who serviced their ships while in port; but since there are also some reasons to think that these records understate the in-kind component of wages, we should reserve judgment. At any rate, this would not much affect the point being made here about the extremely high relative cost of fuel.

Himalayan snow melt and (in the south) monsoon rains [54, 55, p. 15]. Under the circumstances, water-driven equipment, though known, was not broadly applicable, and other, more labor-intensive industries and techniques predominated. For these and other reasons, rich areas could not create the sorts of large and sustained productivity increases they would have needed to offset the pressures resulting from changing relations with the interior.

Meanwhile, this same population growth in interior regions created other important pressures. In particular, it exacerbated the ecological problems that had to be managed to stabilize many of these areas. Greatly increased highland settlement, accelerated by the diffusion of American crops that grew well at high altitudes, greatly increased deforestation and raised river beds; water tables decline in semi-arid regions; and people moved closer to the edges of lakes and rivers, increasing the severity of disasters when they did occur. This raised the price of ecological stabilization efforts just as the Delta and other rich regions were finding it harder to pay for them; Yellow River control alone consumed between 10 and 20 percent of all Qing expenditures for 1820–1850 [57, 58]. In a number of cases, increased highland settlement also led to clashes with indigenous populations or problems of social control that resulted in rebellions that were very expensive to suppress. Combined with certain other stresses of the time (particularly the rise of the opium trade and the arrival of Western gunboats) the system reached a crisis point. The height of Chinese emigrants (the only portion of the population for which we have height samples) started to fall with those born about 1840 [59]; and a series of enormous rebellions broke out beginning in 1851 (all of which, significantly, began in "hinterland" areas).

~189~

When those rebellions were finally suppressed, a new political economy, with different fault lines, had taken the place of the old. The Yangzi Delta and other coastal areas no longer subsidized ecological stabilization elsewhere to anything like the previous extent [57]; they also forged stronger ties with hinterlands overseas (especially in Southeast Asia) which served as new outlets for emigration and light manufactures, and new sources of primary products; they also imported new technologies. By the 1890s at the latest, they had recovered from the mid-century crises and — though the data is not what we'd like it to be — at least the Lower Yangzi experienced sustained per capita growth thereafter until World War II [60, 38, 61]. By contrast, interior regions found no new trading partners, continued to grow in population, and lost the subsidies from advanced regions they had once received; with a few exceptions, they suffered from a worsening spiral of environmental, economic, and social decline that lasted until the 1949 revolution. Most indicators of average welfare stagnated or fell in these areas, and the number of disaster victims soared: Xia Mingfang estimates that 12 times as many Chinese starved from 1865 to1937 as from 1644 to1850, with almost all the deaths in the North and Northwest [62, pp. 78-79, 400-402].

Methodological Implications?

Assuming for argument's sake that this sketch is largely accurate empirically, how can we characterize it as an attempt at explanation in a scientific style? Clearly it is not a "natural experiment" of the sort Jared Diamond tries to create in *Guns, Germs, and Steel* [63]; not only is the case not fully independent of others around the world, but there is more than one thing that is different between them. This kind of exercise gives us no way of knowing what would happen if we imagined some coal easily accessible to the Lower Yangzi, but no changes in the property rights or family system. We might instead usefully see it as a story of how a cluster of "frozen accidents"[20] impart to a particular region "laws of motion" that hold for some limited range of time and space shaped by those "accidents." Deriving generalizations of this sort, which held for reasonably large areas of time and space, might allow us to explain diverse outcomes within one particular set of paths, and contrast them with a set of others shaped by different "accidents." That in itself would be a major achievement, though it would be something

---

[20] For "frozen accidents," see Gell-Mann [64].

quite different from finding universal laws of history predictive of individual cases. (Perhaps one could make a loose analogy here to a quantum mechanical world of probabilities rather than one of certainties[21]) But the parallel to natural science suggested by this terminology is inexact, and suggests various further problems.

The term "frozen accident" might raise problems for some historians, since it could suggest a deviation from "normal" development, often associated with Northwestern Europe. It would, however, be equally true (or untrue) to treat this path as "normal" and English development as the result of a cluster of different "frozen accidents": unusually weak tenant rights (even compared to the rest of Western Europe), a religion that forbade polygamy, easily managed rivers (descending from relatively low mountains and fed by year-round precipitation), lots of coal in convenient places, two relatively nearby continents where many of the natives had no resistance to many European diseases, and so on. This point may at first seem unnecessary to natural scientists, or merely a response to an excessively "politically correct" ideological sensitivity. After all, with frozen accidents such as the preponderance of left-handed rather than right-handed amino acids on Earth, it seems fairly clear that either outcome would be equally "accidental" (pending some discovery that shows basic laws should lead us to expect one or the other). But in historical models it is harder—and more important—to maintain that neutrality about the possible values of these accidental variable.

~191~

In part this is because of a second problem with the analogy. While some background factors seem equivalent to frozen accidents from the viewpoint and timescale of human history— the location of coal deposits or the seasonality of rainfall in different areas, for instance—in other cases, the analogy is much looser. That polygamy was legal in China and not in Europe, for instance, had been the case for many centuries at the time that the developments we want to explain begin, and

---

[21] For a physicist advocating quantum mechanics as opposed to Newtonianism as a model for social science, see Stephen G. Brush [65].

was an externally given "accident" from the point of view of the economic dynamics we were interested in. But it was clearly not "frozen" in the same sense as the handedness of our amino acids, having been changed in the twentieth century. The differences in land rights, having been contested at various moments in both places, are even less truly "frozen"; treating them as exogenously given conditions is clearly artificial, though perhaps essential at an early stage of analysis. And since most (though not all) of the convergence in institutions that has taken place in recent centuries has consisted of Chinese institutions moving toward those of a more "successful" Europe, rather than vice versa, it is understandable that some would see the Chinese pattern as a deviation from a European pattern. Indeed the latter was generally treated as "normal" within classical social theory in at least two senses: first, in the sense that its persistence, having produced results that turned out to be preferred at the end of some very long run, would need no explanation, and second, in the sense that it would therefore represent the pattern toward which others should be trying to converge.

~192~

But if we cannot treat some of these factors as "frozen," at least for purposes of a particular exercise, it is hard to see how we would escape from simply saying that everything is influenced by everything else. We might also find ourselves changing which outcome we considered "normal" with embarrassing frequency as our judgments of how "successful" different societies had been changed with contemporary events.[22] There seem, then, to be real advantages to treating certain accidents as if they were truly frozen (while relaxing that assumption in some other study), even though they aren't, and in pursuing what some of us have elsewhere called a strategy of "balanced comparison":

[22] This has happened several times just in the last few decades, as for instance, the "Confucian heritage" of Japan, Taiwan, and Korea went from being considered a serious barrier to individualism, capitalism, and development to being a major contributor to successful "teamwork" and economic success, followed by at least a partial return to the older view in the aftermath of the bursting of the Japanese bubble economy in 1992, and the so-called "Asian financial crisis" of 1997–1998. It would not be surprising if this wheel turns yet again, especially if China continues to weather the Euro-American economic meltdown of 2008 better than most Western economies.

treating two different conditions as each equally odd from the perspective of the other (like different-handed molecules), even if one seems to us to have clearly turned out to be the more successful configuration [47, 66, 67]. To reiterate, what we might hope to get from this is not predictive certainty, but the recognition of different families of development paths, which might help us grasp variability within and between groups.

Concluding Thoughts and Caveats

As the multiple factors employed to frame my example suggest, it seems to me that one thing we would expect from a more scientific history is that it show us patterns that link phenomena in more than one realm of human activity — economic, social, environmental, political, cultural, etc. — at least across a certain range of settings. (The relationship between the size of a polity and its war-making capacity, for instance, is likely to look very different once we enter an era in which the variation in technological ability among societies in contact with each other expands, and once some societies develop institutions that allow their states to spend future revenues now.) After all, without the conviction that changes in many different aspects of life belong in the same story, history — like anthropology or sociology, though *perhaps* unlike economics or psychology — has little justification as a discipline. While claims of simple and deterministic links across these registers are currently very much out of favor, for mostly good reasons, it is hard to imagine how anyone could defend the proposition that there are no such connections. Even people who choose not to practice "economic and social history" still frequently use that phrase to link them together, while referring to "economic and musical history" would strike most people as odd. The intuitions expressed in those ways of speaking could turn out to be wrong, but they give some guidance as to where we should be looking.

It seems likely that most such relationships that we find will not be invariant. Sometimes the reasons for this will be very straightforward and uninteresting for theory-building, though they might be historically important nonetheless. For instance,

~193~

there has been an association found in many case studies between the growth of wage labor opportunities and a lower average age at first marriage; this makes sense, since being able to earn money without owning any tools or land of one's own makes it easier for adolescents to defy their parents' wishes and still have a way to eat [68–70]. But it is hardly surprising that this relationship did not obtain where the age at first marriage was already close to the age of puberty before lots of wage work was available.[23] The thornier problems emerge not when

~194~ there is a simple intervening fact that blocks a relationship from working, as in the case above, but where there are a number of complicated feedback loops. That such relationships might be very complicated, however, doesn't mean we shouldn't try to unravel them, any more than it does in the case of biological evolution. So why is progress so slow?

One difficulty is that the "non-scientific" functions that historical narratives serve, to which I alluded at the beginning of this paper, may encourage us to focus on exceptional cases. Precisely because the reasons why the United States went to war with Mexico in 1846 seem easy to generalize across many cases— US leaders chose a course that offered large potential gains, and relatively little risk of failure—there is not a massive demand, either within or outside the profession, for new research on this question. (At least as narrowly defined: research on American expansionism more generally is another matter.) The Japanese decision to go to war with the US in 1941 attracts much more attention, because it is more interesting and challenging to try to figure out what factors blocked the operation of what would seem like a very powerful rule of behavior: "You are unlikely to go to war if you know that the chance of losing is high and

---

[23] In one such place, the Pearl River Delta in South China, greater availability of wage work actually raised the average age at first marriage, because it gave young women the wherewithal to resist arranged marriages that they were reluctant to enter. One could thus argue that a more generally stated relationship—"the availability of wage work increases the opportunities for young people to make their own marriage decisions" is further confirmed by this example, though the original statement of the relationship turns out to have been too narrowly stated [71].

the consequences of defeat very serious." A very strong interest in cases that seem exceptional, often to the point of asking about whether the participants were somehow abnormal, is not surprising. They may indeed make for better drama, and better examples from which to contemplate moral issues. It is particularly logical that scholars of high politics—where a single decision that seems as if it should have been improbable can have enormous ramifications for millions of people—often focus on just those events, and that people looking for immediate guidance on contemporary issues often feel the same way. But the same intellectual habit may be much less helpful when it leads us to abandon hypotheses in, say, historical demography, as soon as a few villages don't conform, or when it leads us to frame our research largely in terms of emic categories and the questions they suggest. In other words, we may need to think about decomposing the discipline along with some of its objects; we definitely need to think about relabeling many of those objects.

At the same time, it is precisely by combining categories, timescales, and so on which enable us to see patterns that were invisible to historical actors with an attempt to recapture some of the categories that they did see (and therefore tried to act on) that the historical analysis becomes most interesting, and makes its strongest claim for a unique kind of significance. Thus any "decomposition" of the kind I have been recommending can only be partial and provisional. One final contrast may clarify why.

In his presidential address to the American Economics Association, Milton Friedman once suggested that good social science *must* be counter-intuitive, because it aims to greatly simplify an enormously complex reality, constrained only by the need to be predictively accurate. (Not that that is easy.) At one point, he suggests that though expert billiards players do not operate by thoroughly learning Newtonian mechanics and then applying the relevant formulas, they behave *as if* they did; thus assuming that they do so generates good predictions; and thus assuming that they do so can be the basis of a good theory. By contrast, any attempt to discover what they actually do would be extremely difficult; and even if the inquiry was ultimately successful, a model based on the actual process would probably be too complicated to be useful in generating predictions [72].

Almost all historians (myself included) find this quite unsatisfactory as a model for our own discipline; and there are empirically derived descriptions of human activities that seem to uncover the actual heuristics which actors apply, without realizing it themselves, to solve relatively complicated problems. To take an example close to Friedman's—though probably more complex—psychologists have recently produced a convincing account of how experienced baseball players get to the right place to catch fly balls. Not surprisingly this does not involve rapid physics calculations, but a fairly simple heuristic: once the ball reaches something close to its peak height, players move so as to maintain a fixed angle from the horizontal between themselves and the ball. They are not aware of doing this, but it explains both the final result and various steps along the way as seen on film (e.g. sudden accelerations, decelerations, and changes in direction), matches experimental results (e.g. the players were not better than ordinary people at predicting the final destination of simulated batted balls), and is straightforward enough that one can imagine people following it without being aware they are doing so [73]. This is still far short of a full account of relevant processes—it does not, for instance, tell us how some people come to be following this heuristic without consciously learning it, while others do not— and the process it models is presumably far simpler than political revolutions or economic growth. But it does suggest at least the possibility of providing an accurate account of *mechanisms* underlying repeated instances of a complex, voluntary human action without relying on the actors' accounts.

Of course, even when we insist on tracing processes, rather than relying heavily on "as if" models, we also do not produce a one-to-one map of "how things actually happened." The question, then, is what degree of simplification we want, and why. The answers will vary, but one principle that would probably find broad assent is that the mechanisms invoked to explain how circumstances led to an event, and thus to new circumstances, must involve a plausible path by which they would consciously or unconsciously influence human intentions. Thus. it makes sense to argue that rivers with wild seasonal fluctuations and heavy silt loads would inhibit the implementation of known technologies for water mills, even if we cannot find a single document in which somebody says "I'd build a water-powered mill here if only the current were more regular"; and it is a permissible simplification to "explain" a low rate of urbanization at least partly on the basis of wage rates having been lower than tenant earnings, even if most farmers probably did not explicitly frame the problem in those terms.

~197~

On the other hand, the observation that medieval English villagers may have had roughly the same scattering of plots that they would have had if they been consciously maximizing the number of standard deviations by which their average yield was above starvation—a calculation nobody at the time could have done [74]—is an interesting observation, but does not dispense with the need to look at custom, inheritance law, and social conflict to *explain* that fact. Since no individual could have made this calculation and individuals often had very little choice about what plots they worked, anyway, any forces that were somehow guiding the situation toward such an optimal result must have operated through shaping these social institutions. When we are dealing with humans, we will rarely be able to come up with plausible mechanisms without gaining some understanding of the categories through which people saw their world and thus formed intentions—even if the mechanism we then describe involves categories that remained implicit for most people. (The mechanism may also, of course, rest just as much on unintended consequences of their actions as on those they were aiming for, as long as we can show why, given what we know and the actors did not, the unintended consequences follow logically from their actions.) And, at least to some extent, understanding the emic categories of others usually involves some juxtaposition with our own, as when we uncover implicit categories by pointing both to distinctions other people made that we may not use and to some that we make (or at least formulate) and they did not. Thus, as Geoff Eley has suggested in a recent book, it is necessary to take seriously the analysis of historical subjects' mental maps in which "the new cultural history" has specialized, often with the goal of raising questions about our own conceptual categories; but, rather than stopping there, historians needs to also deploy both emic and etic categories to able to address the big questions that would make up a general "history of society" [75].

In sum, an analysis that became completely divorced from our own society's everyday labels for social phenomena (if that were even possible) would probably cease to be recognizable as history, and would certainly lose much of its ability to speak to urgent human questions; but a history that stands at least a bit further from those everyday categories, as it probably must in order to see important regularities, seems to me both possible and desirable.

Acknowledgments

My thanks to Jeffrey Wasserstrom and Vinayak Chaturvedi for their comments on a draft of this essay and to all the participants in the Santa Fe Institute conference of March, 2008, for which the original version was prepared.

References

[1] Hunt, Lynn. "Introduction: History, Culture and Text." In Lynn Hunt, ed., *The New Cultural History*. Berkeley: University of California Press, 1989.

[2] Beasley, W.G., and E.G. Pulleyblank, eds. *Historians of China and Japan*. London: Oxford University Press, 1961.

[3] Bray, Francesca. *The Rice Economies*. Oxford, New York: Blackwell, 1986

[4] Sugihara, Kaoru. "The East Asian Path of Economic Development: A Long-term Perspective," in Giovanni Arrighi, Takeshi Hamashita, and Mark Selden, eds., *The Resurgence of East Asia:* 500, 150 *and* 50 *Year Perspectives* (London: Routledge, 2003), pp.78-123.

[5] Pomeranz, Kenneth. "Chinese Development in Long-run Perspective," *Proceedings of the American Philosophical Society* 152:1 (March, 2008), pp. 83-100.

[6]   Scott, James C. *The Art of Not Being Governed: An Anarchist History of Upland Southeast Asia*. New Haven: Yale University Press, 2009.

[7]   Duara, Prasenjit. *Rescuing History From the Nation: Questioning Narratives of Modern China*. Chicago: University of Chicago Press, 1995.

[8]   Tanaka, Stefan. *Japan's Orient: Rendering Pasts into History*. Berkeley: University of California Press, 1993.

[9]   Brinton, Crane. *The Anatomy of Revolution*. New York: Vintage, 1952.

[10]   Moore, Barrington. *Social Origins of Dictatorship and Democracy: Lord and Peasant in the Making of the Modern World*. Boston: Beacon Press, 1967.

[11]   Skocpol, Theda. *States and Social Revolutions: A Comparative Analysis of France, Russia, and China*. Cambridge: Cambridge University Press, 1979.

[12]   Goldstone, Jack. *Revolution and Rebellion in the Early Modern World*. Berkeley: University of California Press, 1991.

[13]   Sahlins, Marshall. *Culture and Practical Reason*. Chicago: University of Chicago Press, 1976.

[14]   Tilly, Charles. "Town and Country in Revolution." Working Paper #84, Center for Research on Social Organization, 1973.

[15]   Guha, Ranajit. *Elementary Aspects of Peasant Insurgency in India*. Durhan, NC: Duke University Press, 1999.

[16]   Marx, Karl. *The Eighteenth Brumaire of Louis Napoleon*. New York: InterNational Publishers, 1963. (Original edition, 1852).

[17]   Merriman, John. *The Agony of the Republic: The Repression of the Left in Revolutionary France, 1848 – 1851*. New Haven: Yale University Press, 1978.

[18]   Agulhon, Maurice. *La République au village: Les populations du Var de la Révolution au IIe République*. 2nd Edition. Paris: Seuil, 1979.

[19]   Margadant, Ted. *French Peasants in Revolt: The Insurrection of 1851*. Princeton, NJ: Princeton University Press, 1979.

[20]   Tilly, Charles. "To Explain Political Processes," *American Journal of Sociology* 100:6 (May, 1995), pp. 1594-1610.

[21]   Pomeranz, Kenneth. "Chinese Development in Long-run Perspective," *Proceedings of the American Philosophical Society* 152:1 (March, 2008), pp. 83-100.

[22]   Rostow, W.W. *The Stages of Growth: A Non-Communist Manifesto*. Cambridge, MA: Cambridge University Press, 1960.

[23]   Jones, Eric. "Patterns of Growth in History." In *Capitalism in Context: Essays on Economic Development and Cultural Change in*

Honor of R. M. Hartwell, ed. John A. James and Mark Thomas. Chicago: University of Chicago Press, 1994, 15 (attributing this view to R. M. Hartwell).

[24] Crafts, N.F.R. *British Economic Growth During the Industrial Revolution*. Oxford: Clarendon, 1985.

[25] Goldstone, Jack. "Efflorescences and Economic Growth in World History: Rethinking the 'Rise of the West' and the Industrial Revolution," *Journal of World History* 13:2 (2002), pp. 323-389. 2002

[26] Pomeranz, Kenneth. "Le machinisme induit-il une discontinuité historique ? Industrialisation, modernité précoce et formes du changement économique dans l'histoire globale," in Beaujard P., Berger L. and Norel P. (eds), *Histoire globale, mondialisations, capitalisme* (Paris: La découverte, 2009), 335 -373.

[27] North, Douglass, and Barry Weingast, "Constitutions and Commitment: The Evolution of Institutions Governing Public Choice in Seventeenth Century England," *Journal of Economic History* 49:4 (December, 1989), pp. 803-832.

[28] Acemoglu, Daron, Simon Johnson, and James A. Robinson. 2002. "Reversal of Fortune: Geography and Institutions in the Making of the Modern World Income Distribution," *Quarterly Journal of Economics* 117:4 (November): 1231-1294.

[29] Allen, Robert. "Agricultural Productivity and Rural Incomes in England and the Yangtze Delta, ca. 1620-1820," *Economic History Review* 62:3 (August, 2009), pp. 525-550.

[30] Allen, Robert, Jean-Pascal Bassino, Debin Ma, Christine Moll-Murata, and Jan LuitenVan Zanden, "Wages, Prices and Living Standards in China, Japan, and Europe, 1738-1925." http://www.nuff.ox.ac.uk/Users/Allen/unpublished/allen%20et%20all%202007i(7-dp).pdf.

[31] Pomeranz, Kenneth. "Standards of Living in Rural and Urban China: Preliminary Estimates for the Mid 18th and Early twentieth Centuries." Paper for Panel 77 of International Economic History Association Conference, Helsinki, 2006.

[32] DeVries, Jan. *European Urbanization, 1500—1800* (London: Metheun 1984), 39.

[33] Skinner, G. William, "Regional Urbanization in Nineteeenth Century China," in G. William Skinner, ed., *The City in Late Imperial China* (Stanford University Press, 1977), 229 .

[34] Skinner, G. William, "Sichuan's Population in the 19th Century: Lessons From Disaggregated Data," *Late Imperial China* 8:1 (June, 1987) pp. 1-79.

[35] Xue Yong, "Agrarian Urbanization: Social and Economic Changes in Jiangnan from the Eight to the Nineteenth Century" (Yale University Ph. D. dissertation, 2006), pp. 432-470.

[36] Li Bozhong. *Agricultural Development in Jiangnan,* 1620-1850. New York: St. Martin's Press, 1998.

[37] Van Zanden, Jan Luiten, "Estimating Early Modern Economic Growth" (Working Paper, InterNAtional Institute of Social History, University of Utrecht, 2004. Available at http://www. iisg.nl/research/jvz-estimating.pdf, accessed December 17, 2007), pp. 22-23.

[38] Ma, Debin. "Modern Economic Growth in the Lower Yangzi in 1911-1937: A Quantitative, Historical, and Institutional Analysis." Discussion paper 2004-06-002, p. 6. Foundation for Advanced Studies on InterNAtional Development, Tokyo, 2004.

[39] Lee, James, and Wang Feng. *One Quarter of Humanity: Malthusian Mythologies and Chinese Realities.* Cambridge, MA: Harvard University Press, 1999.

[40] Lee, James, and Cameron Campbell. *Fate and Fortune in Rural China: Social Organization and Population Behavior in Liaoning,* 1774-1873. Cambridge: Cambridge University Press, 1997.

[41] Liu Ts'ui-jung. "Demographic Constraint and Family Stucture in Traditional Chinese Lineages." In Stevan Harrell, ed.,*Chinese Historical Microdemography* (Berkeley: University of California Press, 1995), pp. 121-140.

[42] Zhang Peiguo. *Jindai Jiangnan xiangcun diquan de lishi renleixue yanjiu. (Historical Anthropology of Land Rights in Modern Jiangnan Villages.)* Shanghai: shanghai renmin chubanshe, 2002.

[43] Buck, John.L. *Land Utilization in China.* Shanghai: Commercial Press,1937; reprint edition, New York,: Paragon, 1964.

[44] Jing Su and Luo Lun. *Qing dai Shandong jingying dizhu jingnji yanjiu (revised edition of 1958 text). (Economic Research on Managerial Landlords in Qing Dynasty Shandong.)* Jinan: Qilu shushe, 1986.

[45] Li Wenzhi and Jiang Taixin. *Zhongguo dizhu zhidu jingji lun. (An Economic Discourse on China's Landlord System.)* Beijing: Shehui kexue chubanshe, 2005

[46] Yang, C.K. "Some Preliminary Statistical Patterns of Mass Actions in Nineteenth-Century China." In *Conflict and Control in Late Imperial China,* eds. Frederic Wakeman and Carolyn Grant, pp. 186-187. Berkeley, CA: University of California Press, 1975.

~201~

[47]   Pomeranz, Kenneth. *The Great Divergence: China, Europe, and the Making of the Modern World Economy*. Princeton, NJ: Princeton University Press, 2000.

[48]   West, Geoffrey. "Can there be a Quantitative Theory for the History of Life and Society?" *Cliodynamics* 2:1 (2011).

[49]   Osamu, Saito. *Puroto-Kōgyōka no jidai: Seiō to Nihon no hikakushi. (The Age of Proto-Industrialization: A Comparative History of Western Europe and Japan.)* Tokyo: Nihon Hyronsha, 1985.

[50]   Cerman, Markus, and Sheilagh Ogilvie, eds. *European Proto-Industrialization*. Cambridge; Cambridge University Press, 1996.

[51]   Epstein, S.R., and Maarten Prak, eds., *Guilds, Innovation, and the European Economy*, 1400-1800. Cambridge, MA: Cambridge University Press, 2008.

[52]   Rosenthal, Jean Laurent, and R. Bin Wong. *Before and Beyond Divergence*. Cambridge: Harvard University Press, forthcoming, 2011.

[53]   Li Bozhong. *Jiangnan de zaoqi gongyehua. (The Early Industrialization of The Yangzi Delta Region.)* Beijing: shehui kexue wenxian chubanshe, 2000.

[54]   Terje Tvedt, "Why England and not China and India? Water Systems and the History of the Industrial Revolution," *Journal of Global History* 5:1 (March, 2010), pp. 29-50.

[55]   Van Slyke, Lyman. *Yangtze: Nature, History, and the River.* Reading, MA: Addison-Wesley, 1988, p. 15.

[56]   Allen, Robert C. "Mr. Lockyer Meets the Index Number Problem: The Standard of Living in Canton and London in 1704,. Available at http://www. iisg.nl/hpw/papers/allen.pdf, accessed December 7, 2008.

[57]   Pomeranz, Kenneth. *The Making of a Hinterland: State, Society, and Economy, in Inland North China*, 1853—1937. Berkeley: University of California Press 1993.

[58]   Dodgen, Randall. *Controlling the Dragon: Confucian Engineers and the Yellow River in Late Imperial China*. Honolulu: University of Hawaii Press, 2001.

[59]   Morgan, Stephen. "Economic Growth and the Biological Standard of Living in China 1880-1930," *Economic and Human Biology* 2:2 (2004), pp. 197-218.

[60]   Rawski, Thomas G. *Economic Growth in Prewar China*. Berkeley: University of California Press, 1989.

[61]   Ma Junya. *Hunhe yu fazhan: Jiangnan diqu chuantong shehui jingji de xiandai yanbian* (1900-1950). *(Mixture and Development: The*

Modern Evolution of Traditional Society and Economy in the Jiangnan District, 1900-1950.) Beijing: Shehui kexue wenxian chubanshe, 2002.

[62]   Xia Mingfang. *Minguo shiqi ziran hai yu xiangcun shehui. (Natural Disasters and Village Society in the Republican Era)* Beijing: Zhonghua shuju, 2000.

[63]   Diamond, Jared. *Guns, Germs and Steel: The Fates of Human Societies.* New York: W.W. Norton, 1997.

[64]   Gell-Mann, Murray. "Regularities in Human Affairs." *Cliodynamics* 2:1 (2011).

[65]   Brush, Stephen G. "Are the Soft Sciences Too Hard?" *Contentions* 4:2 (1995): 3-12.

[66]   Wong, R.B. *China Transformed: Historical Change and the Limits of European Experience.* Ithaca: Cornell University Press, 1997

[67]   Austin, Gareth. 2007. "Reciprocal Comparison and African History: Tackling Conceptual Eurocentrism in the Study of Africa's Economic Past," *African Studies Review* 50:3 (December), 1-28.

[68]   Levine, David. *Family Formation in an Age of Nascent Capitalism.* New York: Academic Press, 1977.

[69]   Kriedte, Peter, Medick, Hans., and Schlumbohm,Jürgen. *Industrialization Before Industrialization.* Cambridge: Cambridge University Press, 1981.

[70]   Mendels, Frankin F. "Proto-industrialization: the First Phase of Industrialization," 32:1 (1972), pp. 241-261

[71]   Stockard, Janice. *Daughters of the Canton Delta: Marriage Patterns and Economic Strategies in South China,* 1860-1930. Stanford: Stanford University Press, 1989.

[72]   Friedman, Milton. "The Methodology of Positive Economics." In Friedman, *Essays in Positive Economics.* Chicago: University of Chicago Press, 1953.

[73]   Berg, Nathan and Gerd Gigerenzer. "As-If Behavioral Economics: Neoclassical Economics in Disguise?" *History of Economic Ideas* 18 (2010), 133-165.

[74]   McCloskey, Donald. "English Open Fields as Behavior Toward Risk," in P. Uselding, ed., *Research in Economic History* Vol. 1 (Greenwich, CT: JAI Press, 1976), pp. 124-170.

[75]   Eley, Geoff. *The Crooked Line: From Cultural History to the History of Society.* Ann Arbor, MI: University of Michigan Press, 2005.

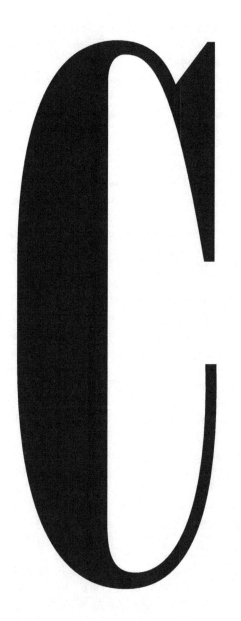

COMPLEXITY IN BIG HISTORY

Fred Spier, University of Amsterdam

Big history can also be summarized as providing an overview of the rise and demise of complexity in all its forms and manifestations ever since the beginning of the Universe. If we want to pursue this approach to Big History, we need a theoretical framework that facilitates us to do so. In this article, I propose such a scheme based on energy flows through matter that are needed for complexity to emerge, and often also to continue to exist, within certain favorable boundaries ("Goldilocks Circumstances").

Introduction

My field of study deals with the very long-range approach to all of history, from the beginning of the Universe until life on Earth today, increasingly known as Big History. This term was coined by one of its modern pioneers, the historian David Christian, who is also a contributor to this book.

Big History can also be summarized as providing an overview of the rise and demise of complexity in all its forms and manifestations ever since the beginning of the Universe. If we want to pursue this approach to Big History, we need a theoretical framework that facilitates us to do so. Over the past 15 years I have been reflecting on how to develop such a general theory of Big History. In 2001, I found great inspiration in the ground-breaking book *Cosmic Evolution: the Rise of Complexity in Nature* by US astrophysicist Eric Chaisson [9]. However, I had a nagging feeling that something was lacking. In 2003, after my wife Gina asked me, "How do you explain all of this?" I saw in a flash what was needed to supplement Chaisson's approach and achieve a new synthesis. In my article "How Big History Works" of 2005 [35], the first contours of this theory were sketched. My book *Big History and the Future of Humanity*, published in 2010 [36], presents a more detailed and improved version of this argument. In this chapter, its key aspects are summarized.

In addition to complexity, my theoretical scheme is based on two familiar physical terms, namely, matter and energy. All forms of complexity in Big History have consisted of matter, while they have all required an energy flow for their emergence. Our solar system, for instance, is thought to have emerged as a result of the energy flow that was released by an exploding star, a supernova, which had reached the end of its stellar life. This cosmic blast would have compressed a large dust cloud, which subsequently contracted under the influence of gravity to form our solar system. Also, the emergence of life must have required an energy source of some sort, perhaps the energy released by undersea volcanoes, while all the forms of complexity that humans have produced could not have been made, either, without energy flows.

After complexity has emerged, it all depends what happens next. Some forms of complexity, such as rocks swinging through space and the general shapes of solar systems and galaxies, do not need any further energy to stay the way they are. Other forms of complexity, by contrast, do need energy to maintain their shapes. If humans, for instance, did not harvest matter and energy from their environment on a regular basis, we would lose our complexity very quickly. And if stars did not release sufficient amounts of energy in their cores, they would collapse under the influence of gravity into neutron stars, if they are little, or black holes, if they are large.

During their lifetime, stars maintain their complexity through a process of self-regulation. This is based on the interplay between the inward-directed force of gravity and the outward-directed radiation pressure resulting from nuclear fusion in its core. Any gravitational contraction produces higher temperatures in the core and thus speeds up the nuclear fusion process. This releases more energy, which makes the star expand. This stellar enlargement, in its turn, cools down the star and thus slows down the nuclear fusion process again. This lowers the star's radiation output, which makes it contract again. As a result of this negative feedback loop, stars are self-regulating steady-state regimes, which maintain their complexity as long as they do not run out of nuclear fuel. Stars begin their lives with a certain amount of nuclear fuel, mostly hydrogen, which is not replenished during their lifetime. As a result, it is fairly straightforward to predict stellar lifetimes as long as these cosmic light bulbs are not disturbed too much by events from elsewhere in the galaxy.

~207~

In contrast to our sun, a planet such as Earth has a rather complex surface. This comes mainly as a result of the interplay between plate tectonics, erosion, and life. Two major energy flows keep our planetary surface complexity going, namely, the energy flow from within, released by nuclear fission processes, and the energy received from outside in the form of solar radiation. Also, Earth can to some extent be considered a self-regulating steady-state regime, although its mechanism is more complex than that of the Sun, not least because its surface complexity depends on two different energy flows.

While stars and lifeless planets may change as a result of outside influences, they cannot adapt to them, because they lack the necessary feedback mechanisms that would allow them to incorporate those changes into their structure. In other words, stars and lifeless planets are unable to learn from their experiences. Since they make up the largest portion of complexity in the known Universe, nature mostly consists of these complex but non-adaptive regimes. Only life, which jointly makes up just a very tiny portion of all the complexity in the Universe, can be considered complex adaptive regimes.

At this point in my argument, a few remarks about academic terminology are in order. In Big History, it is very important to employ technical terms that are understood and accepted within both the natural and social sciences. Unfortunately, there are a good many terms that are understood differently in the various branches of science. The word "system" is one of them. This term is suspect in the social sciences because of its static connotation. This came probably as a result of the social systems approach, advocated by US sociologist Talcott Parsons, which was dominant in the 1950s and 1960s. At the same time, the term "system" is perfectly acceptable within the natural sciences where it has a far more dynamic meaning. As a result of this situation, I prefer to employ the shorthand term "regime" instead of "system." With "regimes," I simply mean "to some extent structured processes." Following this approach, all forms of complexity are regimes of some sort.

All life forms are far from thermodynamic equilibrium. In order to maintain their complexity, they must harvest matter and energy from outside on a continuous basis in order to keep going. At the same time they are able to learn and adapt, thanks to a great many feedback loops based on information. These feedback loops allow life to regulate itself, adapt to changing circumstances, and adapt the environment to its own benefit. Life does so either by Darwin and Wallace's process of natural selection over succeeding generations hardwired in the genome, or by cultural change, which depends on "software" stored in brains and nerve tissues.

The Goldilocks Principle

Now we have reached the point where I can explain what the addition to my emerging theory was that came as a reaction to Gina's question in 2003, namely that all forms of complexity can only emerge and continue to exist within specific boundary conditions. In other words, for complexity to emerge and continue to exist, the situation has to be "just right." If a situation changes beyond the Goldilocks requirements for that particular type of complexity, it will decline or even fall apart completely. Not very originally, I call this the Goldilocks principle.

For those readers who are not familiar with the story of Goldilocks: she is a little girl who happened to wander into a house in a forest where three bears live, papa bear, mama bear and baby bear. The bears are, however, not at home. Goldilocks, hungry and, adventurous as she is, first tries out the porridge bowls on the counter top. She finds that the porridge in the largest bowl is too hot; the middle-sized bowl is too cold, but the little bowl is just right. She then tries out the chairs: the largest one is too hard; the middle-sized chair is too soft; and the little one is just right. And so it goes until the bears come home and do not like what they see. As a result, Goldilocks has to flee.

I am not the first to employ the term *Goldilocks principle.* Over the past ten years increasing numbers of scientists have begun using this term for indicating the circumstances that are required for the emergence and continued existence of complexity. For natural scientists, the Goldilocks principle may, in fact, be totally obvious, because they perform all their analyses from this point of view, at least implicitly. Surprisingly, however, no one appears to have elaborated the Goldilocks principle systematically for all of Big History. My systematic analysis of changing Goldilocks circumstances in combination with the energy flows through matter approach, both leading to the rise and demise of all forms of complexity, from the largest galaxy clusters to the tiniest particles, is what I see as my major theoretical contribution to the understanding of both Big History and complexity theory.

Goldilocks requirements never exist only by themselves. They always depend on the type of complexity under consideration. Humans, for instance, cannot live below or above certain temperatures, while our direct needs also include sufficient air pressure, enough oxygen, food and a regular water supply. The Goldilocks requirements for stars, by contrast, are very different. Stars need enormous amounts of closely packed hydrogen in their cores, while they must be surrounded by cold empty space. If that were not the case, they would suffocate in their own heat and blow up as a result. Under the action of gravity, stars create so much pressure in their interiors that nuclear-fusion processes ignite, converting hydrogen into heavier (and thus more complex) helium nuclei while releasing energy in the form of radiation. These stellar Goldilocks circumstances are very hard to reproduce on Earth, which explains why nuclear fusion has not yet become feasible as a way of generating electricity.

While animals, plants, and even microorganisms have created a great many Goldilocks circumstances that have helped them to survive the vagaries of planetary life, humans can be considered the Goldilocks champions of this planet. Human-created Goldilocks circumstances can have both a social and a material character. Material Goldilocks circumstances include clothing, housing, cars, etc., while an example of social Goldilocks circumstances is represented by traffic rules. These rules are meant to define human behavior in ways that allow members of our species to reach their destination relatively efficiently while seeking to preserve the complexity of all the participants involved. Those who fail to obey the traffic rules usually do so in order to reach their destination more quickly at the risk of compromising safety. Similarly, all other social rules can be seen as social Goldilocks circumstances created by humans that are aimed at preserving certain forms of complexity.

Can We Define Levels of Complexity?

While analyzing the rise and demise of complexity in Big History, a major unresolved issue is the question of how to unambiguously define all these different levels of complexity. It may well be that a good definition of complexity exists, yet I am not aware of it. Here, I present my temporary solution to this problem, which may not be original at all. My approach of defining different levels of complexity is based on a few rather obvious criteria, which include the following. First of all, there is the number of available building blocks. Clearly, with more building blocks, more complicated structures can be built. For instance, a very large number of hydrogen atoms may jointly form a star. In the second place, the level of complexity can rise when the variety of the building blocks increases. In the third and fourth place, the levels of complexity can go up when the connections and other interactions between and among the building blocks become both more numerous and more varied.

There is another important aspect to complexity, namely sequence. Digital computer information, for instance, consists of only two elementary building blocks, ones and zeros. Yet by using enormous amounts of ones and zeros in specific sequences in the form of information, humans have been able to generate a great deal of complexity, namely digital computers, including everything that can be done with these amazing machines that are connected to each other in ever-larger networks. Apparently, the sequence in which these building blocks are organized can produce considerable levels of complexity, while only a slight change in sequence can wreck this complexity entirely. The sequence of building blocks, and thus information, only plays a role in complex adaptive regimes. In life, the genetic information is usually organized in long strands of DNA molecules, in which the sequence of its four major building blocks, namely adenine, thymine, cytosine and guanine, is of overriding importance for determining what happens inside cells. This DNA structure makes possible feedback loops that turn life into a complex adaptive regime. In a similar way, sequence is also very important for all forms of cultural information and communication.

~211~

One may argue that lifeless nature exhibits certain sequences and can thus carry information. Sediments, for instance, may contain layers containing fossils of many different kinds, which are interpreted by scientists as clues to a more or less distant past. Yet there is an important difference between this type of sequence and genetic and cultural information. Whereas sediments do not perform any function for the regime as a whole — they are just there — the information stored in genetic molecules and cultural depots such as brains, books, and hard drives can always be interpreted as having some function for the individuals or societies they are a part of.

By defining complexity in terms of building blocks, connections and sequences, it should, in principle, be possible to determine to what extent the whole is greater than the sum of its parts. Yet in practice this remains very difficult. One wonders which equations would be used, and how the different aspects would be rated. For instance: what would count for more: a greater variety of building blocks, more and more varied connections, or perhaps a longer and more varied sequence? Right now, I find it impossible to rate all these aspects in a way that would allow us to reliably compute all the different levels of complexity. If possible at all, achieving such a goal, even in terms of a first-order approach, could well constitute an entire research agenda. And even if we could achieve this, would this lead to a sufficiently precise characterization of the emergent properties of that particular level of complexity, which are, in the final analysis, its most important characteristic? As a result of all these uncertainties, it seems to me that for the time being we will have to rely on qualitative, rather subjective, statements of how to assess all the different levels of complexity that have existed in Big History. This may be unsatisfactory, yet to my knowledge, it is the best available approach today.

There is another major issue that complicates such calculations. Building blocks at one particular level of complexity may jointly become the building blocks for the next level of complexity. These more complex building blocks are usually linked by different types of connections than those that exist at a lower level of complexity. This makes it even harder to assign values and numbers to building blocks and their connections, and thus achieve a quantitative measurement of complexity in these terms. Quarks, for instance, are thought to be the building blocks of protons and neutrons which, in their turn, can combine to form the nuclei of chemical elements, which may jointly form stars, planets, and black holes. These cosmic objects, in their turn, are the building blocks of galaxies, which, on a greater level of complexity, may be the building blocks of galaxy clusters. Chemical elements may also combine to form molecules, which can link up to become polymers. At a greater level of complexity, a variegated collection of molecules may jointly form cells, which may combine to form individuals which, in their turn, may be the building blocks of society. All these different levels of complexity are relatively autonomous with regard to each other. As a result, such a particular level of complexity exhibits emergent properties that cannot be entirely explained from the properties of a lower level of complexity.

Let's now take a crude qualitative look at the various levels of complexity that can be discerned in Big History. According to many scholars, there are three major types of complexity: physical inanimate nature, life, and culture. In terms of matter, lifeless nature is by far the largest portion of all the complexity known to exist in the Universe. The following example may help to grasp the significance of its sheer size. Let us assume for the sake of simplicity that the entire Earth's mass equals that of an average American car, about 1,000 kilograms. The combined mass of all planetary life would then amount to no more than 17 micrograms. This more or less equals the weight of a tiny sliver of paint falling off that car. Seen from this perspective, the total mass of our solar system would be equivalent to that of an average supertanker. Since the mass of our galaxy is not well known — let alone the mass of the entire known Universe — it is hard to extend this comparison any further. But one major conclusion stands out: Even if life were as abundant in our galaxy, or in the Universe as a whole, as it is within our solar system, its relative total mass would not amount to more than a sliver of paint on a supertanker.

All this cosmic inanimate matter shows varying degrees of complexity ranging from single atoms to entire galaxies. It organizes itself entirely thanks to the fundamental laws of nature. Whereas the resulting structures can be exquisite, inanimate complexity does not make use of any information for its own sustenance. In other words, there are no information centers determining what the physical lifeless world looks like. It does not make any sense, for instance, to wonder where the blueprint of our solar system would be stored that helps to shape Earth or our solar system, because it does not exist.

The second level of complexity is life. As we just saw, in terms of mass, life is a rather marginal phenomenon. Yet the complexity of life is far greater than anything attained by lifeless matter. To maintain these elevated levels of complexity, life organizes itself with the aid of hereditary information, usually stored in DNA molecules. While trying to find out how life works, it does make a great deal of sense to wonder where the information centers are located that help configure it; what this information looks like; how the control mechanisms work that store this information and help to translate it into biological shapes; and what the limitations of these mechanisms are in shaping organisms, given the influences they undergo from the outside world.

The third level of complexity consists of culture: information stored as software in nerve and brain cells or in human records of various kinds, ranging from stone tablets to silicon. The species that has developed this capacity the most is, of course, humankind. In terms of total body mass, our species currently makes up about 0.005 percent of all planetary biomass. If all life combined were just one single sliver of paint, all human beings today would jointly amount to no more than a tiny colony of bacteria sitting on that flake. Yet through their combined efforts, humans have learned to control a considerable portion of the terrestrial biomass, today perhaps as much as 25–40 percent. In other words, thanks to their culture, this tiny colony of microorganisms residing on a sliver of paint has gained control over a considerable portion of that flake. In order to understand how human societies operate, it is therefore not sufficient to look only at their DNA, their molecular mechanisms, and the influences from the outside world. We also need to study the cultural information humans have been using to shape both their own lives and considerable portions of the rest of nature.

In contrast to genes, the building blocks of cultural information cannot be defined unambiguously. It is therefore even more difficult to rigorously define cultural complexity. This is not only caused by the fact that cultural concepts are flexible and apt to change very quickly, but also because they need to be interpreted by people. While within living cells, genetic information needs to be interpreted unambiguously by its cellular machinery in order to function properly; in human societies, such a lack of ambiguity in interpretation is rare, if it ever occurs. Yet although cultural information may often be

ambiguous, it is usually (although certainly not always) sufficiently efficient to allow many animals, including humans, to
successfully wage the struggle for life.

Energy and Complexity

Can we measure and calculate energy flows through matter
during all of history? In his book *Cosmic Evolution,* Eric Chaisson
sought to do so by defining the concept of free energy rate density—indicated with the symbol Φm— as the amount of energy
that flows through a certain amount of mass during a certain
period of time. For human beings, for instance, it is the amount
of energy that we ingest during a certain period of time, let's say
24 hours, divided by our body mass. In principle, this approach
allows us to calculate Φm values for every form of complexity
that has ever existed, ranging from the tiniest particles to galaxy
clusters. This makes it possible to systematically compare all
forms of complexity.

In his analysis, Chaisson showed that there is a clear
correlation between the intuitively defined levels of complexity
observed in the known Universe and the calculated free
energy rate densities. Whereas humans may seem vanishingly
small compared to most other aspects of Big History, we have
generated by far the largest free energy rate densities in the
known Universe. In the following table, Chaisson summarized
some of his findings.

For many people, these results are counterintuitive. One
would expect, for instance, the free energy rate density of the
Sun to be much greater than the Φm value of our brains. Yet
whereas on a daily basis the Sun emits a far greater amount
of energy than the energy used by our brains, the free energy
rate density of the brain is much larger because the brain is so
very little compared to the Sun. More in general, the Φm values
of life are considerably greater than those of lifeless matter.
Apparently, these tiny living regimes generate much greater
free energy rate densities than their lifeless counterparts.

Table 1

Generic Structures	Approximate Age (10^9 years)	Average Φm (10^4 Watt/kg)
galaxies (Milky Way)	12	0.5
stars (Sun)	10	2
planets (Earth)	5	75
plants (biosphere)	3	900
animals (human body)	10^{-2}	20,000
brains (human cranium)	10^{-3}	150,000
society (modern culture)	0	500,000

Before considering these numbers in some more detail, it is important to mention that many other researchers have tried to calculate the amounts of energy that flow through matter, for instance in many living species. In such cases, the term "power density" is often used. Because this term is considerably less cumbersome than "free energy rate density," it has become my preferred term. Yet even though the concept of power density is widely known, it appears that Chaisson has been the first to make a systematic comparison of these values all across nature.

For a good understanding of the numbers provided in this table, we now need to consider Chaisson's calculations in some more detail [9 p. 136-139]. Let's start with the Φm value for galaxies. This is, in fact, the value calculated for our own galaxy, with the assumption that all the dark matter is included in its total mass. Unfortunately, we do not know whether dark matter actually exists, which makes the Φm value for our galaxy less certain. In addition, our galaxy is supposed to harbor a rather heavy "black hole" in its core that would consist of extremely dense matter. This black hole would exhibit very little complexity, if at all. All the energy produced by our galaxy only comes from stars. Since black holes and dark matter do not release any energy, while they may make up a considerable portion of the galaxy's mass, they lower its Φm value, which is therefore smaller than the combined average Φm value for all the stars that make up the galaxy. In fact, Chaisson's value for stars was calculated for our sun, which is an average star.

While the energy flows emitted by stars keep themselves going, they did not create the overall structure of the galaxy: this big swirling cloud of stars with huge arms. The energy flows that once gave rise to the galactic structure are absent in Chaisson's calculations. The reason for this is, or it seems to me, that the structure of the galaxy emerged a long time ago, while today, it no longer needs an energy flow to keep going. However, as soon as galaxies collide, a sudden flow of kinetic energy is released which would reshape them. Also, within galaxies, there is constant change, including contracting gas clouds and exploding stars; these processes release energy flows which reshape these galaxies to some extent. Seen in the long run, however, these energy flows and their effects are probably minute compared to the output of all the combined stars, and, as a result, do not have to be taken into account while computing a first rough estimate of the Φm value of our galaxy.

~217~

In conclusion: Chaisson's Φm value for galaxies characterizes a relatively stable steady-state galactic regime and not a regime in rapid formation or decline. This is actually the case for all of Chaisson's Φm values: they all characterize dynamic steady-state regimes. In other words, in Chaisson's table, the energy flows needed for the emergence of these regimes do not play a role.

Let's now consider Chaisson's Φm value for planets. In actual fact, this value does not reflect the complexity of any known planet as a whole. It was calculated for only a thin slice of the outer shell of Earth by estimating the amount of solar energy that reaches the terrestrial surface during a certain period of time, while using as the total mass the weight of the atmosphere, plus an oceanic layer of 30 meters. According to Chaisson, this is where most of our planet's complexity resides. Since today the heat generated inside Earth reaching the surface is several thousand times smaller than the solar energy received, Chaisson did not include this geothermal energy in his calculation.

The next Φm value in Chaisson's table, the average free energy rate density for plants, is an average value that includes all living matter. The value provided for animals was, in fact, calculated for the energy used by the human body. This Φm value was arrived at by calculating the average food intake per body weight. Yet in reality, as Chaisson pointed out, the power densities of vertebrate animals vary by almost an order of magnitude [9, p.186]. This raises the issue of whether those vertebrate animals that sport the largest free energy rate densities, namely birds, should be considered the most complex. Chaisson thinks so, because birds have to navigate in three dimensions. Chaisson's estimate for human society (modern culture) is based on the current energy use of six billion people with an average body weight of about 50 kg (adults and children). In this case, most of the energy does, of course, not flow through human bodies. If it did, humanity would cease to exist instantaneously.

~218~

The Φm values for human history provided by Chaisson exhibit some further problems. The Dutch scientist Lucas Reijnders, for instance, has pointed out that the number for early humans does not sufficiently include the use of fire. Especially by burning large tracts of land, the early folk might have manipulated enormous energy flows, with the aid of which they created desired forms of complexity such as grasslands, while destroying other forms of complexity, usually woodlands. This fiery action would have created landscapes that attracted large grazers, which could be hunted. By stoking fires, they roasted food, while keeping themselves warm and safe from predators. In doing so, recent Australian aboriginals would have produced power densities between one and two orders of magnitude larger than those of the average US citizen in 1997, thanks mostly to the fact that the aboriginals engaged in extensive land burning. This makes one wonder how large the power densities were that the early folk were able to achieve in Australia and elsewhere, wherever nature could be set on fire on a large scale. If one uses power density as a measure of complexity, as Chaisson suggests, aboriginal society would have been much more complex than modern industrial societies. This seems unsatisfactory to me.

Today, most of the energy employed by humans is not used for keeping their bodies going or for burning the land but for the creation and destruction of what I call forms of constructed complexity. With this term I indicate all the material complexity that has ever been created by humans. These include clothing, tools, housing, engines and machines, means of communication, etc. With the aid of these things humans have transformed both the surrounding natural environment and themselves. To be sure: not only humans but also many animals have produced a great many forms of complexity. Well-known examples include spider webs and beaver dams. Yet it seems fair to say that humans have developed this capacity to a far greater extent than any other living species.

The complexity constructed by humans can be divided into two major categories. The first category consists of things that do not need an energy flow for their intended functioning, such as clothing, houses, etc. As a result of outside effects, all of these things need, of course, some maintenance from time to time for their continued existence, yet they do not need any energy to perform their intended functions. This type of complexity is made by humans as well as by a great many other animals. The second category of constructed complexity consists of things that require continuous energy flow for their intended functioning. I call them forms of powered constructed complexity. This category includes machines driven by wind, water, fossil fuels, or electricity. To my knowledge, only humans have constructed forms of complexity that are driven by external energy sources. In this respect, humans are unique in the known Universe.

Many forms of powered constructed complexity exhibit much higher power densities than the Φm values of human brains (about 15 Watt/kg) or human societies (about 50 Watt/kg). As Chaisson pointed out, jet engines achieve Φm values between 2000 Watt/kg (Boeing 747) and 80,000 Watt/kg (F-117 Nighthawk) [9, p.201]. Relatively high Φm values are not only characteristic of jet planes but also of a great many household appliances. While performing a few calculations at home, my son Louis and I found that even our humble vacuum cleaner exhibited a Φm value of about 180 Watt/kg, thus outperforming our brains more than tenfold. This does not mean that jet engines and vacuum cleaners should be considered more complex than human brains. Unlike forms of complexity that emerged spontaneously, all forms of constructed complexity are not using this energy for the purpose of achieving greater complexity within themselves. They were designed instead to use these considerable amounts of energy for performing certain tasks, such as moving heavy objects through the air or achieving a certain degree of order within our living space.

Whereas on closer inspection a great many complications emerge, as a first-order approach, Chaisson's analysis seems fair enough. In doing so, he has created what US physicist Murray Gell-Mann calls "a crude look at the whole," which is considered perfectly legitimate in the natural sciences. In his approach, Chaisson employed these numbers first of all as a way of measuring different levels of complexity. It was his way of tackling the issue of how to rigorously define and measure different levels of complexity. At the same time, Chaisson used these numbers also as an indication of the energy needed to achieve or maintain certain levels of complexity. In what follows here, I will explicitly not employ the concept of free energy rate density as the yardstick for measuring different levels of complexity. It will solely be used as an indication for the energy that is needed for complexity to emerge and continue to exist.

Complexity in Big History

Let's now examine to what extent the proposed approach of energy flows through matter within certain Goldilocks circumstances leading to the rise and demise of complexity indeed helps us to attain a better understanding of these processes. In doing so, we will very quickly traverse all of history. To be sure, within the context of this chapter any summary of Big History can by necessity touch upon only a few key events. A more detailed discussion can be found in my book, *Big History and the Future of Humanity*.

At the beginning of space and time, the Universe would have emerged with a Big Bang. An infinitely small singularity would have exploded that contained all the still undifferentiated cosmic matter and energy. This Big Bang produced the expansion of the Universe that we can measure today with the aid of redshifted electromagnetic radiation emitted by cosmic objects. Based on these data, it is estimated that the primordial explosion took place around 13.7 billion years ago.

The cosmic expansion led to both a rapid cooling and a decrease of pressure. During a very short period of time, this produced Goldilocks circumstances that made possible the emergence of the basic atomic building blocks, namely, first protons (hydrogen nuclei) and neutrons, and a little later, electrons and neutrinos. After few minutes, however, while the embryonic Universe kept expanding and cooling down, the Goldilocks circumstances that favored this process disappeared and never returned. As a result, these elementary particles only emerged during the very early phase of cosmic history.

Thanks to the continued expansion, favorable circumstances soon emerged that allowed the formation of the nuclei of some heavier chemical elements, most notably helium and deuterium as well as a little lithium. This lasted about 15 minutes. Yet cosmic expansion happened so fast that most matter remained in the form of hydrogen, about 70 percent, while about 27 percent evolved into helium. During this early phase of cosmic evolution, only a few percent of heavier chemical elements emerged. Had the Universe expanded much more slowly, almost all matter would have turned into iron, the most stable chemical element. Because very little complexity can be built with the aid of only iron as building blocks, this would have severely limited the emergence of later forms of complexity. Here we see a very powerful demonstration of the importance of Goldilocks circumstances for the history of the Universe.

It took about 400,000 years of cosmic expansion until the temperature had decreased to about 3,000 K. This provided Goldilocks circumstances for the pairing of the positively and negatively charged particles, which thus canceled out each other's charges. As a result, electromagnetic radiation could suddenly travel through the Universe virtually unimpeded, because it was no longer scattered by all these formerly charged particles. This radiation diluted over time as a result of the ongoing cosmic expansion, thus producing the cosmic background radiation that can be observed today all across the sky.

During the period between about five hundred thousand and two billion years after the Big Bang, Goldilocks circumstances existed that favored the emergence of stars and galaxies out of the primordial matter that had formed earlier, mostly hydrogen and helium. By that time, the Universe had cooled down sufficiently, while the matter density was also just right. Up until about 500,000 years after the Big Bang, the Universe had been homogeneous to a very high degree. Yet after 500,000 years of expansion, under the influence of gravity, spontaneously occurring tiny irregularities began to produce large galactic structures. This led to a differentiation between areas with large matter concentrations (galaxies) and areas with very little matter (intergalactic space). The unrelenting universal expansion accentuated these differences. Also, within galaxies, a differentiation took place between areas with large matter concentrations (stars and black holes) and interstellar space.

This separation into areas with and without matter was extremely important for the rest of cosmic history. Had this not happened, no further complexity could have emerged, not least because there would not have been any empty space where entropy could have been dumped in the form of low-level radiation. This type of entropy is an inevitable by-product of the emergence of greater complexity. Eric Chaisson emphasized that had this growing cosmic dumping ground not existed, no greater complexity would have emerged. After about two billion years, no new galaxies were formed in the known Universe. Apparently, the circumstances were never Goldilockian anymore for this to happen.

Within stars, new Goldilocks circumstances came into being that favored the emergence of the nuclei of heavier chemical elements, all the way up to iron. This was the result of nuclear fusion processes that ignited as a result of the stars' gravitational contraction. These Goldilocks circumstances in stellar cores are very similar to the conditions that reigned during the early Universe. However, there are two major differences. First of all, the early cosmos had been more or less homogenous, while stars and their surroundings are very different indeed. The large matter and energy gradients that had developed between the very dense stars and mostly empty interstellar and intergalactic space allowed stars to get rid of their entropy and keep their complexity going. In the second place, the infant Universe changed so very quickly that there was very little time for nuclear fusion to take place. All stars, by contrast, even the shortest shiners, live a great deal longer. As a result, over the course of time stars became the major cosmic furnaces for forging greater complexity at very small scales, thus producing increasing amounts of heavier chemical elements, thanks to the specific Goldilocks circumstances that reign in their cores.

~223~

When stars that are at least eight times the size of our sun reach the end of their lives, they may detonate. These explosions are called *supernovae* because they appear to be "large new stars" that suddenly shine very brightly for a short period of time. Indeed, some supernovae produce almost as much light as the entire galaxy they form part of. During these explosions, heavier chemical elements are formed all the way up to uranium. Because these processes last for only very short periods of time, heavy chemical elements are rare. These stellar blasts disperse the heavier chemical elements and thus seed their cosmic surroundings with these new elementary building blocks. As a result, over the course of time, galaxies come to contain increasing amounts of more complex chemical elements. When such a galactic dust cloud subsequently contracts to form new stars and planets, the new solar system may contain the building blocks that allow the emergence of forms of greater complexity, such as life and culture. It is thought that our solar system emerged from such a galactic dust cloud around 4.6 billion years ago.

Life may have emerged on our planet as early as 3.8 billion years ago. It is not yet certain whether life emerged spontaneously on Earth or whether it emerged elsewhere in the Universe and was transported to our home planet later. Whatever the case may have been, both the emergence of life and its continued existence must have required very specific Goldilocks circumstances. For instance, scientists have defined a galactic habitable zone in our Milky Way in which the conditions for life (as we know it) are just right. This zone is defined by its distance from the galactic center. Close to this center, a great many stars exist that end their lives with a bang, which would destroy any life that had formed in their vicinity. Yet these supernovae also forge and spread more complex chemical elements that are needed for life. This means that life could not have emerged very close to its core. But it could not have emerged very close to the edge of the galaxy, either, because in such places there were too few supernovae events to accumulate sufficient numbers of heavier chemical elements that are needed for life. As a result, the galactic habitable zone is characterized by sufficient amounts of supernovae that produce the needed heavier chemical elements, while there are not too many star bursts that would flush out life. Calculations show that our galactic habitable zone would have emerged about eight billion years ago as a zone situated between 23,000 and 30,000 light years from the galactic center (the radius of our galaxy is about 50,000 light years). Since astronomers think that, over the course of time, fewer supernovae explosions would have taken place while the amounts of heavy chemical elements increased, over the course of time, the galactic habitable zone has widened towards both the galactic center and its outer edge.

Within our solar system, a similar habitable zone is thought to exist. This Goldilocks region is first of all defined by the amount of radiation our sun produces. The planets that are closest to the sun, Mercury and Venus, are too hot and are thus unable to support life. Not very surprisingly, our planet Earth finds itself in a Goldilocks position, while Mars may just be outside of the planetary habitable zone, because it is too cold while it does not have any other energy sources that could support life. Yet it is thought possible that on some of the moons of Jupiter and Saturn life may exist, sustained by the energy emanating from within or perhaps even by the tidal forces generated as a result of the fact that these moons orbit large planets.

There are more Goldilocks circumstances that needed to be met before life could emerge, most notably liquid water and an atmosphere surrounding a planet that is large enough so that its gravity keeps the water and the atmosphere there for billions of years. Because it is unknown where and how life emerged, scientists are still seeking to define the very specific Goldilocks circumstances within which this would have happened. Yet it is clear that for more than three billion years after life emerged on Earth, our planet has provided Goldilocks circumstances that allowed it to flourish.

~225~

Life is powered by sunlight through photosynthesis or by energy emanating from within the Earth released by, for example, undersea volcanoes. This means that all complex adaptive regimes are powered by complex non-adaptive regimes. It may be that life emerged as a result of energy flows from within the Earth generated by the original accretion heat and later by nuclear fission processes. Yet, over time, as the energy flows from within decreased in intensity, life became more dependent on solar energy from outside, which over the past 4.6 billion years is thought to have increased about 25 percent because of the increasing energy output of the sun.

As James Lovelock has argued with his Gaia hypothesis, it may be that life has created conditions that favor its continued existence. In terms of the process of natural selection or, as some prefer, non-random elimination, this makes perfect sense. Surely, any organism that created and maintained Goldilocks

It may be that life emerged as a result of energy flows from within the Earth generated by the original accretion heat and later by nuclear fission processes. Yet over time, as the energy flows from within decreased in intensity, life became more dependent on solar energy from outside.

circumstances favoring its continued existence (or at least not hampering its survival) had an easier time surviving than life forms which produced circumstances that threatened their survival. To be sure, Goldilocks circumstances for one species may well be unfavorable circumstances for other species, which might be eliminated as a result. Yet the overall effect of this process would have been a biosphere occupied by species that are not diminishing their own chances for survival to the extent that they drive themselves to extinction (at least in the short term), while some of them may actually be improving their living conditions. This is the regime of Gaia as I understand it. As a result of cosmic influences, changing condition of Earth's surface through plate tectonics, and the dynamics of biological evolution interacting with the biosphere, Gaia keeps changing, thus conditioning the circumstances that make possible the rise and demise of complex adaptive regimes. This led to the history of life as we understand it today.

Let's now make a big leap in biological evolution and consider the rise of human beings. The first early humans may have emerged around six million years ago. These were ape-like creatures living in woodlands that may already have begun to acquire stretched legs. Yet it seems clear that around four million years ago, decisive change took place on the emerging East African savannas. This landscape was (and still is) characterized by a rather mild climate. All year round, temperatures would have ranged between 20 and 30 degrees Celsius. This temperature range did not differ a great deal from the average human body temperature, yet it was low enough to allow the early humans to get rid of heir excess heat. As a result, the early hominids who lived there would not have needed any protection against high or low temperatures such as hairy skins. Also, the air pressure on the East African savannas is rather mild, on average about 900 hPa.

Why did these early humans with an upright stride, known as *Australopithecines*, emerge in this habitat? According to the modern scientific view, they owed their emergence to specific Goldilocks circumstances that were only characteristic of East Africa. During this period, for reasons not yet well understood, the African continent was becoming drier and colder. This had profound effects on the African flora and fauna. The tropical forests were receding on both the eastern and western sides of Central Africa and were being replaced by savannas. As a result, all forest-dwelling species found themselves increasingly under pressure to adapt to a new life on the emerging savanna grasslands that were interspersed with trees. Among many larger species, including antelopes, other herbivores and hominids, this led to the innovation of stiffer, stretched, legs. While more elastic legs are better for moving around in forested areas, stiffer legs are superior for living on grasslands, because they allow individuals to run faster and cover longer distances. In other words, stretched legs are more energy efficient in those circumstances. Whereas many species adapted in such ways and underwent adaptive radiations, only among early humans would this have led to clear bipedalism: an upright way of walking. During this period, a whole range of early humans emerged.

~227~

This is not the place to elaborate all of human evolution in great detail. In what follows, I will touch only on certain aspects of human history. Again, a more detailed account can be found in my book, *Big History and the Future of Humanity*. After 2 million years of *Australopithecines* roaming East and Southern Africa, the much brainier *Homo erectus* evolved about 1.8 million years ago, also in East Africa. This considerably smarter human species subsequently spread over large parts of Eurasian continent, in fact to all areas that could be reached by walking and that were not too cold or otherwise uninhabitable. *Homo erectus* made tools and later began to domesticate fire, both of which helped to control more energy resources and shape their environment, even though their bigger brains guzzled up more energy also. Apparently this energy trade-off was sufficiently good to ensure their survival. About two hundred thousand years ago, modern *Homo sapiens* evolved, again in Africa, from where it spread across all the continents with the exception of Antarctica (where it was too cold). As part of this process, over the course of time, the older human forms went extinct while only *Homo sapiens* remained.

Early humans began to create forms of constructed complexity with the aid of culture. Their increasing use and mutual exchange through language of brain software in the form of learned behavior is what has allowed humans to become what they are now and construct all the complexity and artificial Goldilocks circumstances that they have made throughout human history.

~228~

A major distinction between the ways these hominids and other animals constructed complexity was that, perhaps as early as 3.5 million years ago, humans began to use tools for creating complexity (or for destroying it). To be sure, animals also use tools, but they never employ them for making things. Furthermore, over the course of time, only humans have learned to use external energy sources for producing or powering complexity. Their first major external energy source was probably fire control. This allowed humans to expand the range of constructed complexity far beyond anything other animals had achieved, including cooking, heating and providing light during the night. But perhaps even more importantly, humans began to change the complexity of entire landscapes by setting them on fire. Other external energy sources that were harnessed later included animal power as well as wind and water power. It is only very recently that humans began to use fossil and nuclear fuels.

The agrarian revolution, which took off about 10,000 years ago, can be seen as a process of two types of complex adaptive regimes, namely, human beings, on the one hand, and plants and animals, on the other, that mutually adapted to each other under human dominance, with the human aim to harvest increasing amounts of matter and energy from the biosphere. This process is still continuing today. As a result, humans now control between 25 and 40 percent of the energy that flows within the web of life. The first agrarian societies all emerged in subtropical mountainous areas after the last ice age had ended. These were apparently the Goldilocks circumstances that favored the rise of agriculture.

The subsequent process of state formation and development, starting between 6,000 and 5,000 years ago, can be seen as the institutionalization of inequality among humans. Within the emerging states, increasing numbers of humans derived their matter and energy flows no longer from working the land but from other humans. Ever since that time, these matter and energy exchanges have been based on the power and dependency relations prevailing, which were usually unequal. As a result, there have been no states in human history that were based on a more or less equal exchange of matter and energy anywhere close to what is thought to have been the situation among certain groups of gatherers and hunters in the very recent past which, in their turn, may reflect the life ways of the ancient folk before states emerged.

~229~

States could emerge as a result of the fact that by practicing agriculture, humans could in principle produce a surplus. In addition, as humans became tied to the land they worked, this led to population growth. Among agrarian societies, it is profitable to have a considerable number of children, because they are productive at an early age while they hopefully provide your retirement fund. Yet population growth led to a further pressure on the resources, and thus to both migration and more restrictions for those who stayed behind. Furthermore, as Robert Carneiro pointed out, the first states all emerged within very restricted ecological conditions, usually river valleys surrounded by dry areas. All of these were, apparently, the Goldilocks circumstances that were required for early state formation. Within states, humans learned to adapt to each other while living within an often very unequal power structure. These social structures were, of course, never completely uncontested. Also states and their neighbors in whatever form of societal development can be seen as complex adaptive regimes that need to continuously adapt to each other. This ranges from attempts at complete destruction of the neighbors to an almost complete submission to them.

In addition to their own muscle power, humans used energy sources from outside ranging from animal power to wind and water power for constructing complexity for thousands of years. With the onset of the Industrial Revolution, however, steam engines and internal combustion engines driven by fossil fuels allowed humans to expand their constructive and destructive capabilities beyond anything other life forms had achieved. As a result, our species began to adapt nature ever more to its wishes and desires, as long as there was sufficient matter and energy available as well as enough space to get rid of the inevitable entropy. All these human enterprises can be interpreted as efforts to produce Goldilocks circumstances for themselves, while sometimes seeking to destroy the Goldilocks circumstances of others. This has led to unprecedented population growth. Yet right now, we may be approaching the end of the era of cheap fossil fuels, if not their imminent exhaustion. If humans want to keep creating similar amounts of complexity, they will urgently need new energy sources. At this moment, solar energy appears to offer the best option, yet today in many places it is still more expensive than the energy extracted from fossil fuels.

In biological nature as a result of the process of non-random elimination, Gaia has produced a global trash recycling regime that allows life to deal with its entropy problem. Humans are now making some efforts to do so also, yet we still have to find a good solution for this issue. At the same time, both matter (in the form of important natural resources) and energy from fossil fuels will become scarce in the near future. These may be the most important issues humanity faces today. Are we able to adapt ourselves sufficiently to the changing circumstances we have brought about by our collective actions and maintain our complexity with the aid of different matter and energy sources, or will humanity be eliminated by Gaia as a result of a failure to do so? ❦

References

[1] Andel, Tjeerd H. van. *New Views on an Old Planet: A History of Global Change.* Cambridge: Cambridge University Press (1985); 2nd ed. 1994.

[2] Barrow, John D., and Frank J. Tipler. *The Anthropic Cosmological Principle.* Oxford: Oxford University Press, 1986.

[3] Carneiro, Robert L. "A Theory of the Origin of the State." *Science* 169(3947) (1970): 733-738.

[4] Chaisson, Eric J. "The Scenario of Cosmic Evolution." *Harvard Magazine* November-December (1977): 21-33.

[5] Chaisson, Eric J. *Cosmic Dawn: The Origins of Matter and Life.* New York: W. W. Norton, 1981.

[6] Chaisson, Eric J. "The Broadest View of the Biggest Picture: An Essay on Radiation, Matter, Life." *Harvard Magazine* January-February (1982): 21-25.

[7] Chaisson, Eric J. *The Life Era: Cosmic selection and conscious evolution.* New York: Atlantic Monthly Press, 1987.

[8] Chaisson, Eric J. *Universe: An Evolutionary Approach to Astronomy.* Englewood Cliffs, N. J.: Prentice Hall, 1988.

[9] Chaisson, Eric J. *Cosmic Evolution: The Rise of Complexity in Nature.* Cambridge, Mass.: Harvard University Press, 2001.

[10] Chaisson, Eric J. "Complexity: An Energetics Agenda." *Complexity* 9(3) (2004): 14-21.

[11] Chaisson, Eric J. *Epic of Evolution: Seven Ages of the Cosmos.* New York: Columbia University Press, 2005.

[12] Chaisson, Eric J. "Energy rate density as a complexity metric and evolutionary driver." *Complexity* 16(4) (2010): 27-40.

[13] Christian, David. *Maps of Time: An Introduction to Big History.* Berkeley & Los Angeles, Ca.: University of California Press, 2004.

[14] Darwin, Charles. *The Descent of Man: Selection in Relation to Sex* (James Moore & Adrian Desmond Editors & Introduction). Harmondsworth: Penguin Books (1871); new addition 2004.

[15] Davies, Paul. *The Goldilocks Enigma.* London, Allen Lane, 2006.

[16] Daviss, Bennett. "Our Solar Future." *New Scientist* 196(26330) (2007): 32-37.

[17] Gamble, Clive. *Timewalkers: The Prehistory of Global Colonization.* Harmondsworth: Penguin Books (1993); new addition 1995.

[18] Gell-Mann, Murray. *The Quark and the Jaguar: Adventures in the Simple and the Complex.* New York: W.H. Freeman & Co, 1994.

[19] Goudsblom, Johan. *Fire and Civilization*. London: Allen Lane, 1992.

[20] Kasting, James F., Daniel P. Whitmire, and Ray T. Reynolds. "Habitable Zones around Main Sequence Stars." *Icarus* 101 (1993): 108-128.

[21] Lineweaver, Charles H., Yeshe Fenner, and Brad K. Gibson. "The Galactic Habitable Zone and the Age Distribution of Complex Life in the Milky Way." *Science* 303(2) (2004): 59-62.

[22] Lovelock, James E. *Gaia: A New Look at Life on Earth*. Oxford, New York, etc.: Oxford University Press, 1987.

[23] Lunine, Jonathan I. *Earth: Evolution of a Habitable World*. Cambridge: Cambridge University Press, 1999.

[24] Marshall, James. *Goldilocks and the Three Bears: Retold and Illustrated by James Marshall*. New York: Puffin Books, 1998.

[25] McNeill, J. R., and W. H. McNeill. *The Human Web: A Bird's-Eye View of World History*. New York: W. W. Norton & Company, 2003.

[26] McNeill, J. R. *Something New Under the Sun: An Environmental History of the Twentieth Century World*. London: Penguin Books, 2000.

[27] Niele, Frank. *Energy: Engine of Evolution*. Amsterdam: Elsevier, Shell Global Solutions, 2005.

[28] Pyne, Stephen J. *Fire in America: A Cultural History of Wildland and Rural Fire*. Princeton: Princeton University Press, 1982.

[29] Pyne, Stephen J. *Fire: A Brief History*. London: The British Museum Press, 2001.

[30] Reijnders, L. "Is Increased Energy Utilization Linked to Greater Cultural Complexity? Energy Utilization by Australian Aboriginals and Traditional Swidden Agriculturalists." *Environmental Sciences* 3(3) (2006): 207-220.

[31] Smil, Vaclav. *Energy in World History*. Boulder, CO: Westview Press, 1994.

[32] Smil, Vaclav. *The Earth's Biosphere: Evolution, Dynamics, and Change*. Cambridge, MA: The MIT Press, 2002.

[33] Smil, Vaclav. *Energy: A Beginner's Guide*. Oxford: OneWorld Publications, 2006.

[34] Spier, Fred. *The Structure of Big History: From the Big Bang until Today*. Amsterdam: Amsterdam University Press, 1996.

[35] Spier, Fred. "How Big History Works: Energy Flows and Rise and Demise of Complexity." *Social Evolution & History* 4 1 (2005): 87-135. Moscow: 'Uchitel' Publishing House.

[36]   Spier, Fred. *Big History and the Future of Humanity.* Chichester, West Sussex, U.K., Malden, MA, Wiley-Blackwell, 2010.

[37]   Strahan, David. "The Great CoalHole." *New Scientist* 197 (2639) (2008): 38-41.

[38]   Thorpe, S. K. S., R. L. Holder, and R. H. Crompton. "Origin of Human Bipedalism As an Adaptation for Locomotion on Flexible Branches." *Science* 316 5829 (2007): 1328-1331.

[39]   Tudge, Colin. "Taking the Pulse of Evolution: Do We Owe our Existence to Short Periods of Change in the World's Climate?" *New Scientist* 1883 (24) (1993): 32-36.

[40]   Tudge, Colin. *The Day Before Yesterday: Five Million Years of Human History.* London: Random House, 1995; new addition 1996.

[41]   Vrba, E.S., G.H. Denton, T.C. Partridge & L.H. Burckle (eds.). *Paleoclimate and Evolution, with Emphasis on Human Origins.* New Haven & London: Yale University Press, 1995.

[42]   Vrba, Elizabeth S. "Mammal Evolution in the African Neogene and a New Look at the Great American Interchange." In *Biological Relationships between Africa and South America,* edited by Peter Goldblatt, 393-432. New Haven & London: Yale University Press, 1993.

T

℈ ℞

TOWARD CLIODYNAMICS: AN ANALYTICAL, PREDICTIVE SCIENCE OF HISTORY

Peter Turchin, University of Connecticut

THIS ARTICLE RESPONDS to those who think that a science of history is in principle impossible. First, I tackle the issue of prediction and point out that it is not limited to forecasting the future. Scientific prediction is also (an much more usefully) employed in empirical tests of scientific theories. Next, I switch from conceptual to empirical issues, and review evidence for general empirical regularities. I also discuss some recent examples of using scientific prediction in testing theories about historical dynamics. I conclude by pointing out that we now have the right quantitative tools and, even more important, a growing corpus of historical data for testing theories. An analytical, predictive history, or *cliodynamics*, is eminently possible.

Introduction

Philosophers have long debated whether history can be a science in the same sense that physics and biology are sciences. At the heart of the debate are two opposing views of history. Nineteenth century thinkers, such as Leo Tolstoy and Carl von Clausewitz (see Gaddis, this volume, Chapter 3), believed that historical process was governed by some kind of general laws. Many French and English historians of the nineteenth century viewed history as a science [42]. Twentieth-century historians such as Toynbee [31] proposed grand schemes to account for the rise, the flowering, and the decline of civilizations. A less ambitious (but in the long run more influential) effort by

McNeill [17] is another example of an attempt to discern patterns in history.

During the second half of the twentieth century, however, the general opinion among philosophers and historians swung against the possibility of scientific history. For example, Karl Popper [18] argued that there is a qualitative difference between history and natural sciences. Historical processes are too complex and different in nature from physical or biological processes. Most tellingly, people have free will, while atoms do not.

Among the historians, research paradigms that modeled themselves on natural sciences were still popular in the 1960s and 1970s [43]. Perhaps the most influential of such research programs was the French Annales school of history. During these decades the new economic history, or cliometrics, briefly flowered in the United States [44]. However, in the 1980s historians repudiated these approaches. As one reviewer of an early version of this article wrote, "cliometrics went under by the early 1990s; our own quantitative historian was denied tenure in approximately 1996 (by that point, no one really cared about the subject or its application in history)." Instead history experienced its "linguistic turn" or "cultural turn" [44, 45].

The view that history is fundamentally different from natural sciences is the one widely held today by philosophers and the lay public alike. With the exception of a tiny minority (several of whom are represented in this volume) the historical profession has largely abandoned the search for general laws in history. This philosophical stance is very apparent in the views of prominent historians, for example, in "President's Columns," published by *Perspectives on History,* where presidents of the American Historical Association express opinions on a wide variety of general topics confronting the historical profession. During the last decade (the 1999–2008 issues of *Perspectives on History*) there were at least three columns that discussed the role of general laws or theories in history [4, 10, 22]. The following quote appears to be a fair summary of the opinions of the three historians:

> *After a century of grand theory, from Marxism and Social Darwinism to structuralism and postmodernism, most historians have abandoned the belief in general laws. We no longer*

search for grand designs and dialectics. Instead, we concentrate on the particular and sometimes even the microscopic (microstoria, as it is known in Italy) — not because we think we can see the Universe in a grain of sand but because we have developed an increased sensitivity to the complexities that differentiate one society or one subculture from another. Kosovo is very different from the rest of Yugoslavia, to say nothing of Vietnam [4].

In my opinion, historians gave up on general theory too soon. The need for an analytical, predictive history remains acute if we wish to address such problems plaguing humanity as failed states and endemic civil wars [36]. On the other hand, there is no question that the bankrupt paradigms mentioned by Darnton, from Marxism to postmodernism, deserve to be abandoned. However, we now have better theories and approaches, which have profited from recent developments in nonlinear dynamics and complexity science.

It is possible that this new batch of theories will eventually end up on the same trash heap of history as Marxism and Social Darwinism. But I don't think so. My argument has two parts. First, I respond to those who think that a science of history is in principle impossible and discuss a broader notion of prediction that is not limited to forecasting the future. Next, I switch from conceptual to empirical issues, and review evidence for general empirical regularities. I also discuss some recent examples of employing scientific prediction in testing theories about historical dynamics. In the Conclusion I point out that we now have the right quantitative tools and, even more important, a growing corpus of historical data for testing theories. An analytical, predictive history, or cliodynamics, as I propose we call it, is eminently possible.

Is There a Qualitative Difference Between History and Natural Sciences? The Issue of Prediction

As mentioned above, one of the most influential arguments against scientific history was formulated by the philosopher Karl Popper. Popper's main point was that because the future course of human history is critically affected by the development of knowledge, and because future scientific and technological discoveries cannot be predicted, a predictive science of human history is in principle impossible.

There are additional reasons for why accurate forecasts about the future are difficult, or even impossible with real-life social systems. These reasons include such phenomena as the self-defeating prophecy and mathematical chaos (the latter of which was not yet appreciated when Popper wrote *The Poverty of Historicism*). However, the notion of *prediction* in science is not limited to forecasting the future. If it were, whole swaths of science would lose their status as scientific disciplines. The paradigmatic example is the weather, which cannot be forecast more than 7–10 days in the future, even though we perfectly well understand the laws of hydrodynamics underlying weather fluctuations. However, because the dynamical system governing weather is in a chaotic regime and our measurements of initial conditions are not infinitely accurate, long-term prediction of weather is impossible.

In fact, the future is in principle unpredictable. A high-school demonstration of the motion of uniformly accelerated objects, using an inclined plane, may go awry because an earthquake occurs during the experiment. The chance of such an event is rather small, but it is not zero. In social life rare events with huge consequences, the "Black Swans" of Nassim Nicholas Taleb [28], occur with greater frequency than in purely physical applications. The difference, however, is quantitative, not qualitative. Bridges collapse, space shuttles explode, and hurricanes strike from seemingly blue skies. However, we do not decide, on the basis of such prediction failures, that there are no laws of physics.

Prediction is an inherent part of science, but not in the narrow sense of forecasting the future. *Scientific prediction* (to distinguish it from the common usage, which is closer in meaning to "prophecy") is used in empirical tests of scientific theories. Scientific prediction inverses the logic of forecasting: whereas in making forecasts we assume the validity of the underlying theory and want to know what will happen to observables, in a scientific prediction exercise we want to use the degree of match between observables and predictions to infer the validity of the theory (34). Because no theory makes perfect predictions, we typically want to compare the match between predictions and data for two (or more) theories.

Scientific predictions may be, but do not have to be, about the future. In many historical sciences, such as geology and evolutionary biology, making predictions about the future is impractical. Strong predictions should address "out-of-sample" data, that is, data that had not been used to develop the theory that is tested. Thus, it is a perfectly valid exercise to make retrospective predictions, or "retrodictions" [13]. Historical experiments (by an *experiment* I mean a planned comparison between predictions derived from two or more theories and data) may focus on making predictions about the state of a certain variable for a certain past society, which is not known at the time when the predictions are made. For example, Theory #1 says that the variable should be decreasing, while Theory #2 says, no, it should be increasing. We then ask historians to dig through the archives (or, perhaps, archaeologists to literally dig up the data), and determine which of the theories is closer to the truth. As more such experiments are conducted, and if one of the theories consistently yields predictions that are in better agreement with empirical patterns than the other(s), our degree of belief into the better performing theory is consequently enhanced. I will discuss in later section some examples of such experiments in historical applications.

~239~

History and Biology

Karl Popper held strong views about what constituted science. In addition to history, he also criticized evolutionary biology, which, in his view was not a real science, but at best "a metaphysical research program." Ultimately, his rejection of history and evolutionary biology was not due to logic or empirical evidence, but to ideology [2]. His personal experiences (he emigrated from his native Vienna in 1937 just in time to escape the Anschluss) made him into a life-ling opponent of totalitarian ideologies, such as Nazism and Marxism. The real targets of Popper critique were Historical Materialism and Social

Darwinism, but somehow he ended up condemning whole fields of scientific enquiry.

Evolutionary theory, contrary to Popper, is today an established scientific discipline, and, in my opinion, the same will eventually happen to history. Actually, there are some interesting parallels between the state of history now and the state of biology in the nineteenth century, before the scientific triumphs of Charles Darwin and Louis Pasteur. The reigning theory in biology at that time was vitalism, a doctrine that the processes of life were not explicable by the laws of physics and chemistry alone. It was believed that biological entities contained a "vital spark" or "*élan vital*," which could not be studied with the methods of physics and chemistry.

~240~

Vitalism is now thoroughly discredited, but this does not mean that it was a silly theory for its times. Early scientists noted that substances seemingly fell in two general classes. An inorganic substance, such as a lump of gold, could be heated to the point where it changed its state (melted), but on cooling it returned to its original form. Organic substances, when heated, changed irrevocably. The process of heating seemingly expelled the vital force from such substances. The destructive effect of heat on the vital force was the reason why Pasteur had to design the famous "*col de cygne*" (swan neck) bottle to disprove the theory of spontaneous generation—his first experiments were criticized on the grounds that by boiling broth in closed bottles he destroyed the vital force needed for spontaneous generation of life.

Ultimately vitalism was discredited not because of critical experiments, such as that of Pasteur, but as a result of hard, and often mundane, work by myriads of biologists who consistently applied the scientific method to biological questions and eventually found that there was no need of a vital force to explain general regularities in their data. In the process biology transformed itself from the descriptive discipline that it was in the nineteenth century (just as history is today) to an analytical, explanatory, and predictive science of the twentieth century. Are there lessons for those of us who would like to achieve a similar transformation of history?

History and Mathematics

One of the most important lessons is recognizing the key role of mathematics in the transition of biology from the descriptive to explanatory science (see also West, this volume, Chapter 12). It was mathematical reasoning that almost discredited Darwin's theory of evolution in the late nineteenth century. The dominant theory of inheritance in Darwin's time assumed that the off-spring's traits were a blend of its parents' traits. Such blending inheritance destroyed genetic variation that was absolutely necessary for natural selection to work on. No genetic variation meant no evolution. When biologists discovered that the theory of blending inheritance was wrong, it was again mathematical modelers who established the firm logical foundation for the Neo-Darwinist Modern Synthesis during the 1930s.

~241~

One of the most striking examples of the value of mathematical models comes from the field of population dynamics. In 1924 Charles Elton published a paper entitled "Periodic fluctuations in the number of animals: their causes and effects." After reviewing the population data on lemmings, hares, and mice, and considering various hypotheses that might account for periodic changes in their numbers, Elton concluded that these fluctuations must be due to climatic variations. What is remarkable is that Elton never considered the cause that we now know is one of the most common drivers of population cycles — the population interaction between predators and prey [32]. The reason is that it never occurred to him. In *Modeling Nature*, the historian of science Sharon Kingsland [12] relates how two years later Julian Huxley walked into Elton's office and showed him an article by the Italian mathematician Vito Volterra that was just published in *Nature*. The article presented a simple mathematical model of predator-prey interaction, and showed that the outcome is population cycles of both species. Huxley, one of the founders of modern evolutionary biology, and Elton, often considered as the father of animal ecology, were very intelligent people. But it took a paper written by a mathematician who knew nothing about real animals to open their eyes to the possibility of predator-prey cycles.

A common objection to employing mathematical models in the study of historical dynamics is that social systems are so complex that any mathematical model would be a hopeless over-simplification without any chance of telling us interesting things about these systems. This argument gets it exactly wrong—it is because social systems are so complex that we need mathematical models. "Naked" human brain is not a bad tool for extrapolating linear trends, but it fails abysmally when confronted with systems of multiple parts interconnected with nonlinear feedback loops. This is probably why it took a mathematical model to point out that cycles are inherent in the interaction between predators and prey (and this is a very simple system, with just two interacting components). We need mathematical formalism to express our ideas unambiguously, and both analytical methods and fast computers to determine the implications of the assumptions we made.

~242~

Complexity: Social and Biological

It is undeniable that social systems are very complex, and have little resemblance to such paradigmatic success stories in physics as Newton's planetary motions. However, many objects in natural sciences are no less complex than human societies. Consider, for example, a temperate forest ecosystem. There is likely to be at least a dozen species of trees and shrubs and a hundred or more of herbs, forbs, and other smaller plants. There will be innumerable species of insects, mites, lower invertebrates, fungi, protozoa, and bacteria. All this life will be busy doing its thing around you; mice will scurry underfoot and birds will be singing in the branches. It is a horrible mess (or glorious complexity, depending on your point of view). How could it possibly give rise to any laws of nature? Yet it does.

Over the last century ecologists identified many kinds of empirical regularities in forest ecosystems. To continue with population cycles, almost every forest, especially those in boreal and temperate climatic zones, has a particularly voracious species of insect that periodically runs amok denuding trees of their foliage, or even killing them outright. These population cycles can be quite predictable. For example, the populations of the larch budmoth reach a peak in the larch forests of the Swiss

Alps every 8.5 years [32]. The amplitude of these oscillations is remarkable—the population density in the trough is five orders of magnitude (100,000 times) lower than at the peak.

Somehow large-amplitude regular oscillations arise from the mess of nature in ecosystems. Why should the social systems be different? After all a social system consists of only one species. Of course people are not all the same—there are different social classes and professions, different religions and ethnic identities, and so on. Still, when we add together the different kinds of humans in an average historical social system (an agrarian state, for example), I doubt that the total would come anywhere near the number of species in an average ecosystem.

Empirical Regularities

In the Second Afterword to *War and Peace*, Leo Tolstoy argued that in order to find laws of history, we should focus on large masses of people and not on individuals, no matter how important they seem (his example was Napoleon Bonaparte). If from the micro-chaos of molecular motions arise the laws of thermodynamics, and from interactions between individual lynxes and hares arise regular predator-prey cycles, then perhaps there may be general regularities characterizing the dynamics of human societies, even though the behavior of each person is unpredictable. In fact, we have already found a number of empirical regularities in historical social systems. Moreover, certain progress has been made in identifying general principles that may underlie these regularities. At least, it is now possible to point toward successful examples of scientific prediction in historical dynamics. I review three such "success stories" in this section.

A Striking Macrohistorical Pattern: Huge Empires Tend to Rise on Steppe Frontiers

What were the social mechanisms that held together huge historical empires? At present, we do not have a satisfactory theory accounting for the rise of such macrostates, with territories extending across millions of squared kilometers and populations numbering millions (or even tens and hundreds of millions). However, there are certain empirical regularities in the spatial and temporal distribution of "imperiogenesis" hinting that there may be general principles at play.

In a recent publication [38], I collected as many instances, as I could find, of historical "mega-empires" (defined as territorial states that controlled at the peak an area greater than one million square kilometers). I found 65 such polities for the agrarian period of human history (that is, before 1800). Over 90 percent of these empires were situated in, or next to the arid belt that runs through Afroeurasia, from the Sahara in the West to the Gobi in the East (Turchin [34]: figure 1). The exceptions included the only empire in the Americas (Inca), one empire in Southeast Asia (Khmer), and three in Europe (the Roman and Carolingian empires, and perhaps Lithuania-Poland, although the latter expanded during the fourteenth century into steppe lands). Thus, there is a strong statistical association between proximity to steppe and the rise of megaempires.

1. Between the Shang era and the present, China has been unified 14 times (some unifications were partial). All but one of these unifications (the Ming) originated in the North: eight from the Northwest, and three each from the North Central and the Northeast. In other words, with one exception all great unifying dynasties arose in the area right on the Inner Asian frontier of China. The other side of the frontier saw a succession of gigantic imperial confederations of such nomadic peoples as the Xiongnu, the Turks, and the Mongols.

2. Ancient Egypt was unified by native dynasties on four occasions: Early Dynastic (c.3100 BCE), Old Kingdom (2700 BCE), Middle Kingdom (2040 BCE), and New Kingdom (1570 BCE). In all four cases, unifying dynasties arose in Southern Egypt (in Hierakonpolis or Thebes). Furthermore, 5,000 years ago Southern Egypt was surrounded not by a lifeless desert, but by a grassy steppe inhabited by such pastoralist peoples as Nubians and Medjay. Towards the end of the first millennium BCE, the steppe turned into desert, and from that point on Egypt never gave a rise to a native

unifying dynasty, instead being ruled by a succession of foreign invaders. As in East Asia, the southern frontier of Egypt saw a succession of "mirror empires." Starting with the Old Kingdom, and continuing even after Egypt lost its independence, Nubia was repeatedly unified under the empires of Kerma, Napata, Meroë, Nobadia, Makuria (Dongola), and Funj.

3. The Eurasian arid zone intrudes into South Asia from the northwest. Out of nine South Asian unifications (most partial, as they did not include India's far south), five originated in the Northwest, three in the North, and one in the West. Despite the formation of numerous medium- and small-size states in other regions, no megaempires originated in the Northeast, Central, or Southern India. ~245~

In summary, in all these world regions (as well as others, such as Eastern Europe) empires originated on a steppe frontier, and only afterwards expanded into the agrarian hinterland. Thus, steppe frontiers appear to be very special places for imperiogenesis, places where very large territorial states are much more likely to arise than elsewhere. The pattern of association between steppe frontiers and mega-empire occurrence becomes particularly striking in regions that had a steppe frontier on only one side, as in the three cases listed above (and unlike Mesopotamia and Iran, which experienced steppe influences from multiple directions). The connection between steppe frontiers and mega-empires is not deterministic (because there are exceptions), but the statistical correlation is very strong.

Strong macrohistorical regularities suggest that the rise of any particular mega-empire was not a random result of a concatenation of unique events; general social mechanisms must have been at work. Building on the ideas of the fourteenth century thinker Ibn Khaldun [11], as well as contemporary anthropologists [1, 15], I have proposed a "mirror-empire" model as one common route to mega-empire [38]. This model postulates that antagonistic interactions between nomadic pastoralists and settled agriculturalists result in an autocatalytic process, which pressures both nomadic and farming polities to scale up polity size, and thus military power. In many cases, as happened repeatedly in China and Ancient Egypt, the end result of this process is the simultaneous rise of an agrarian empire and a nomadic imperial confederation on their respective sides of the steppe frontier. However, if the agrarian state does not have a deep hinterland to expand into, it may lose the scaling-up race to the nomadic polity, and is conquered by it. This was the typical dynamic in the Maghreb, so admirably described by Ibn Khaldun.

~246~

Secular Cycles: Linked Oscillations in Demographic, Social, and Political Structures of Agrarian Societies

The pattern of population change is strongly affected by the scale at which it is observed. On a very long time scale of millennia, population numbers increase at an accelerating rate, while on the time scale of years, several bad harvests in a row can cause a temporary dip in numbers, which is made up as soon as weather gets better. At the intermediate scale of decades and centuries the dominant pattern appears to be *secular cycles*: roughly century-long periods of sustained population growth followed by a similarly long period of population decline and stagnation [37]. For example, in Western Europe the thirteenth century was a period of vigorous population growth, while during the fourteenth and the first half of the fifteenth centuries population declined. The sixteenth century was another period of rapid growth, followed by the decline and stagnation of the seventeenth.

One possible explanation of this pattern of long-term population oscillations is offered by the demographic-structural theory [8, 31, 39]. First, population growth beyond the means of subsistence leads to declining levels of consumption and popular discontent. Second, and more important, sustained population growth also results in increasing numbers of aspirants for elite positions, leading to intra-elite rivalry and factionalism. A third consequence is persistent inflation, which causes a decline in real state revenues and a developing fiscal crisis of the state. As these trends intensify, the result is state bankruptcy and loss of military control; spiraling conflict among elite factions; and a combination of elite-mobilized and popular uprisings that lead to breakdown of central authority. In turn, political instability (urban riots, peasant uprisings, and full-scale civil war) results in population decline. Eventually, the balance between population numbers and the means of subsistence is restored, and another cycle can begin.

Various assumptions about dynamical feedbacks between key demographic-structural variables, such as population growth, elite overproduction, state strength, and political instability, have been investigated with formal mathematical models (Turchin [31], ch. 7; 35]). A typical dynamical pattern of association between population growth and political instability, predicted by these models, is coupled oscillations of population dynamics and political instability. Both variables cycle with the same period, but are shifted in phase with respect to each other, so that instability peaks during the periods of population decline (Figure 1).

~247~

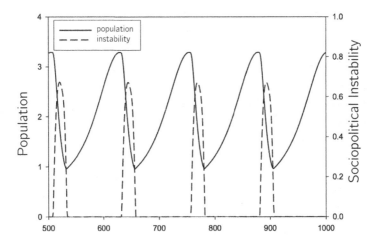

Figure 1. *Linked population-instability oscillations predicted by a demographic-structural model (Turchin and Korotayev [35], eq. 8).*

In real life, we do not expect to see smooth, perfectly periodic cycles. Historical societies are characterized by a much richer, more complex web of dynamical feedbacks than can be portrayed in mathematical models. Multiplicity of nonlinear feedbacks increases the probability that the dynamics will be chaotic, resulting in irregular, noisy-looking oscillations. Furthermore, social systems are affected by exogenous variables, such as climate fluctuations, that also generate erratic dynamics. Events at the microlevel, including acts of individual people, may percolate up and have macro-level consequences. Finally, and most importantly, our data on historical dynamics is often sparse and suffers from large amounts of observation noise. These complications must be taken into account when we look at real data. Yet, despite all these problems, we observe the basic dynamical pattern predicted by theory: linked oscillations with peaks of sociopolitical instability lagging behind population peaks (Figure 2). This observation suggests that the demographic-structural model, indeed, captures an important aspect of the functioning of historical societies.

How can we design a general and quantitative test that goes beyond an eyeball comparison of predictions (Figure 1) to the observed patterns (e.g., Figure 2)? Given the limitations of historical data and the complexity of the dynamical pattern (variability in oscillation periods and phase shifts), we need to employ an appropriately coarse-grained procedure (see also the articles by Murray Gell-Mann and Geoffrey West in this volume). One possible approach works as follows. First, we identify the population growth and decline phases. Although quantitative details of population dynamics for historic societies are rarely known with any precision, there is usually a consensus among demographic historians about when the qualitative pattern of growth changed. Second, we count instability events (peasant uprisings, separatist rebellions, civil wars, etc) that occurred during each phase. Finally, we compare the incidence of instability events per decade between the two phases. Theory predicts that we should have much greater instability during population decline versus growth phases.

First, we apply this procedure to secular cycles in China (Table 1). The test is conducted only for periods when China was unified under one dynasty. The empirical regularity is very strong: in all cases instability is greater during the declining, compared to growth phases (t-test: $P << 0.001$).

Next, we apply the approach to all seven complete cycles examined in Turchin and Nefedov [39] (Table 2). The instability data were taken from such compilations as that of Sorokin [23], Tilly [29], and Stearns [27]. Again, the empirical regularity is strong and statistically highly significant (in all cases instability is greater during the declining, compared to growth phases; t-test: $P << 0.001$).

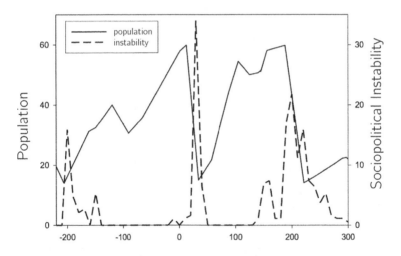

Figure 2. *Population dynamics and sociopolitical instability in China from the Qin unification to the period of Three Kingdoms (220 BCE—300 CE). For data sources, see Turchin ([31], p.164)*

Table 1. *Secular Cycles in Europe and China During the Last Millennium Compared to Global Economy Processes*

European cycles	Chinese cycles	Global economy processes
Ottonian-Salian 920–1150	Northern Song 960–1127	Sung* Breakthrough 930–1190
Capetian 1150–1450	Mongol–Yuan 1200–1368	Nautical/Commercial Revolutions 1190–1430
Valois 1450–1660	Ming 1368–1644	Oceanic Trading System 1430–1640
Bourbon 1660–1870	Qing 1644–1911	Industrial Takeoff 1640–1850

*A variant spelling of Song.

Table 2. *Instability events per decade during the growth and decline phases of the secular cycles surveyed in Turchin and Nefedov [39].*

Secular cycle	Growth phase		Decline phase	
	Years	Instability	Years	Instability
Plantagenet	1151–1315	0.78	1316–1485	2.53
Tudor	1486–1640	0.47	1641–1730	2.44
Capetian	1216–1315	0.80	1316–1450	3.26
Valois	1451–1570	0.75	1571–1660	6.67
Republican	350–130 BCE	0.41	130–30 BCE	4.40
Principate	30 BCE–165 CE	0.61	165–285	3.83
Muscovite	1465–1565	0.60	1565–1615	3.80
Average (±SE)		0.6 (±0.06)		3.8 (±0.5)

In summary, the dynamical pattern predicted by the demographic-structural model is apparent in data ranging across all Eurasia and from the third century BCE to the nineteenth century CE. Furthermore, the same regularity is observed in Egypt from the Hellenistic through the Ottoman periods [14]. In fact, it appears that this empirical pattern holds for all agrarian societies whose dynamics are not unduly influenced by exogenous forces, e.g., large empires (such as the Roman and Chinese ones) or island states (England and Japan).

~251~

The Dynamics of Religious Conversion

The last example concerns testing dynamical theories about religious conversion [31]. Three more-or-less explicit models for religious conversion and ethnic assimilation have been proposed in the literature: the noninteractive, the autocatalytic, and the threshold models. The justification for each of the models does not concern us here (the details are in Turchin [31, section 6:2:1]); what is important is that each model predicts a qualitatively different trajectory (the proportion converted/assimilated as a function of time). This means that we can determine which theory better reflects the reality if we can find data on the temporal course of conversion.

Empirical data on conversion to Islam in Iran and Spain, all strongly supported the autocatalytic model and were nothing like trajectories predicted by the two alternatives (Figure 3a,b). What do we conclude from this result? All models are by definition wrong, because they oversimplify the complex reality, but the autocatalytic model is less wrong than the alternatives. It appears that the assumptions of the conversion process built into the autocatalytic model capture some important aspect of the reality.

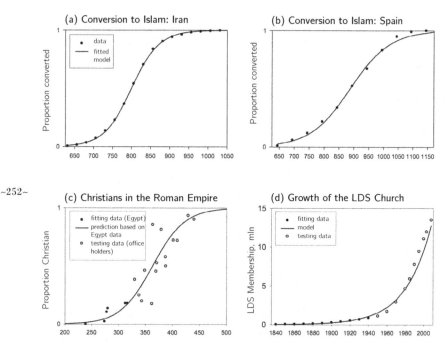

Figure 3. *The dynamics of religious conversion. Trajectories of conversion to Islam in (a) Iran and (b) Spain. The curve is the fitted autocatalytic model (the logistic equation). Out-of-sample predictions: (c) Christians in the Roman Empire and (d) the growth of the Mormon (Latter-Day Saints) Church.*

Note that the three conversion models that I considered were not flexible statistical models, such as splines or neural nets. They were based on specific assumptions about mechanisms underlying conversion, and predicted qualitatively different shapes of trajectories. Thus, the comparison between theoretically predicted shapes and the empirically observed ones was definitely a step forward, because it roundly rejected two of the models in favor of one. Nevertheless, each model had tunable parameters, and it would strengthen the result if one model were capable of successfully predicting out-of-sample data ("in-sample" refers to data used in model fitting, "out-of-sample" data are those that were not used in fitting but were reserved for testing the model; or perhaps were collected after the model was fitted).

There was an element of out-of-sample prediction in the test a third data set, involving conversion to Christianity [31, section 6.3.2]. This case study was based on data in the book by Rodney Stark [24] on the rise of Christianity (see also Hopkins [9], Stark [25]). Stark used a variant of the autocatalytic model to predict how the number of Christians in the Roman Empire grew from the first century on. He estimated (guessed, really) that there were roughly a thousand converts in 40 CE and that their numbers grew at the rate of 40 percent per decade. Several years after he made these estimates, a colleague attracted his attention to the reconstruction by Roger Bagnall of the growth of Christianity in Egypt, based on data in Egyptian papyri. Since Stark was unaware of Bagnall's data at the time when he constructed his prediction, we have here a true test with out-of-sample data.

~253~

This story has a sequel. Two years after I wrote the chapter on conversion in *Historical Dynamics* [31], I happened on a reference to a German dissertation that gave a list of Pagan and Christian office-holders between 324 and 455 [40]. I immediately realized that these data enable us to make another test of the autocatalytic model [34]. The results are shown in Figure 3b. We see that the curve fitted to the Bagnall data (showing the proportions converted before 300 CE, filled circles) does a very good job predicting the course of Christianization in the von Haehling data (after 330 CE, hollow circles). The coefficient of prediction (the proportion of variance of out-of-sample data predicted by the model) is a healthy 0.57.

A similar, although less dramatic, exercise can be performed with the data on the growth of the Mormon (Latter-Day Saints) Church [26]. The model fitted to the data up to the outbreak of World War II does a very good job predicting post-War trajectory (Figure 3d).

Taken together, the results in Figure 3 tell a remarkable story. They suggest that once world religions got going, they generated a kind of momentum that allowed them to expand at approximately constant (per capita) rate. Dramatic events — world wars, imperial collapses, and nomadic invasions — did not derail these massive macrohistorical processes, at least in these particular cases (of course, certain kinds of events, such as the Christian Reconquista in Spain, are capable of reversing the tide of religious conversion).

Conclusion

The empirical studies surveyed above are each based on a powerful macrohistorical regularity cross-cutting across world regions and historical periods. Although Kosovo and Vietnam (to use Robert Darnton's example) differ in many ways, at some deeper level their economic and political dynamics may be driven by similar mechanisms. Certainly, Ancient Rome, Imperial China, Capetian France, and Romanov Russia are as different from each other as Kosovo from Vietnam. Yet these states all arose on metaethnic frontiers and experienced a sequence of secular cycles [33].

History is not "just one damn thing after another." Strong empirical patterns arise because the dynamics of historical societies reflect the action of general social mechanisms. There are laws of history (in the broad sense of the word). Furthermore, successful case studies of scientific prediction, reviewed in this article, show that we are well on the way to identifying some of these laws.

As I noted in the Introduction, attempts to transform history into an analytical, mathematized science have been made before, but were largely unsuccessful. One of the most ambitious efforts is that of Nicholas Rashevsky [21]; a book that, unfortunately, has been largely ignored. How is the situation different today?

Two recent developments, one theoretical and another empirical, have dramatically changed the scientific landscape.

First, the advances in nonlinear dynamics and complexity science have revolutionized how we do theory in science, even (especially) in such difficult fields as history. Our theoretical approaches to complex systems are no longer limited to verbal theories. Dynamical models, such as systems of differential equations, allow us to handle precisely and quantitatively such issues as the importance of contingency and dependence on initial conditions. Such hoary issues as "chance versus necessity" can now be addressed quantitatively by models combining deterministic and stochastic terms [31, pp.6, 14]. Agent-based computer models [5] is another key tool for investigating the effects of stochasticity and the influence of individuals on the historical process. This approach is also custom-made for investigating how macro-level patterns arise from micro-level interactions.

~255~

Second, the recent years saw a qualitative increase in the amount of data available for testing theories about historical dynamics. The key development has been the spread of computer use among the historians and the rise of the Web. As a result, more and more datasets are now easily accessible through the Internet. To illustrate the potential consequences of this shift, consider that invaluable tool of a macrohistorian, the historical atlas. Traditional book atlases are inherently limited. A typical problem is that either the region or the period, in which one is interested, is not in the list of maps collected in the atlas. Furthermore, traditional atlases are ill-equipped to portray dynamical change. What we need is a computer-based dynamical atlas that allows one to zoom in on arbitrary geographic regions and play movies to gain an understanding of temporal changes occurring there. Such a perfect atlas does not exist yet, but I know of several initiatives to create one. It is a matter of years, not decades, before we have one.

I argue that we already have the necessary analytical tools for modeling historical processes and statistically analyzing data. Naturally we need more data, but it is clear how to increase our "empirical capital" — all it takes is more hard work. The greatest challenge that I see is a conceptual one: how do we construct meaningful theory? How do we define and theorize the key variables on which our dynamical models will be based? Some variables are conceptually easy. To study the demographic and economic aspects of historical societies all we need to do is to bring in the concepts already worked out by demographers and economists. That is clearly why demographic history and cliometrics [6, 7] were the first fields of history where the scientific method was systematically applied.

Other variables are much more difficult to wrap one's mind around. As an example, take social cohesion, or the capacity of a group for collective action, for which, I have proposed [31, 33], we could use Ibn Khaldun's term *asabiya*. It is clear that the Romans of the third century BCE, during the Punic Wars, possessed much greater asabiya than the Italians of the fifth century CE, when the Roman Empire in the West was in the process of disintegration. But how do we define and measure this change? (One thing is certain, if we can figure out how to measure asabiya, its units will be called khalduns.) It seems to be a nebulous, hard-to-pin-down quality. Yet recently there has been some progress in measuring it. I am thinking of the concept of social capital as proposed and used by such political scientists as Robert Putnam (and not to be confused with the social capital of Bourdieu [3], Putnam et al., [19], Putnam [20]). As I have argued earlier, social capital is none other than asabiya for modern societies [31, p.43]. Putnam and coworkers proposed a variety of approaches to measuring relative amounts of social capital among different Italian provinces [19], as well as changes over time in the United States [20]. Thus, although at first a concept may appear nebulous, hard work involving theory development and empirical testing may, in the end, lead to precise definitions and ways to obtain quantitative measures. It is important to remember that physics, which appears to us now as a hard science, or biology, had to travel the same route. Such difficult concepts as, for example, entropy, were not obvious right away, and arose as a result of lengthy collective labor by many scientists.

In this essay, I have looked back at the history of natural sciences and argued that, although at present the obstacles to developing a scientific history appear to be formidable, we forget that natural sciences overcame similar challenges during their infancy periods. I am convinced that historical scientists will also solve the problems of how to conceptualize and measure key theoretical variables in cliodynamics, how to build meaningful theory and then test it empirically. It will take time and a lot of work. But what is encouraging is that, as the empirical "success stories" show, we are already well on the way toward a science of analytical, predictive history. ✒

References

[1]   Barfield, T. J. *The Perilous Frontier: Nomadic Empires and China.* Oxford, UK: Blackwell, 1989.

[2]   Beatty, J. "Historical Determinism, Evolution and Totalitarianism in the Works of Hannah Arendt and Karl Popper." In *Thinking about Evolution: Historical, Philosophical and Political Perspectives*, edited by R. Singh, C. Krimbas, D. Paul, and J. Beatty, 62-67. A Festschrift for Richard C. Lewontin. Cambridge, MA: Cambridge University Press, 2001.

[3]   Bourdieu, P. "Le capital social: notes provisoires." *Actes de la Recherches en Sciences Sociales* 3 (1980): 2-3.

[4]   Darnton, R. "President's Column: History Lessons." *Perspectives on History* 37 (6) (1999): 1-3.

[5]   Epstein, J. M., and R. Axtell. *Growing Artificial Societies: Social Science from the Bottom Up.* Washington D C.: Brookings Institution Press, 1996.

[6]   Fogel, R. W., and G. R. Elton. *Which Road to the Past? Two Views of History.* New Haven: Yale University Press, 1983.

[7]   Fogel, R. W. "Economic Growth, Population Theory, and Physiology: The Bearing of Long-Term Processes on the Making of Economic Policy." *American Economic Review* 84 (1994): 369-395.

[8]   Goldstone, J. A. *Revolution and Rebellion in the Early Modern World.* Berkeley, CA: University of California Press, 1991.

[9]   Hopkins, K. "Christian Number and Its Implications." *Journal of Early Christian Studies* 6 (1998): 185-226.

[10]   Hunt, L. "President's Column: Where Have All the Theories Gone?" *Perspectives on History* 40(3) (2002): 1-3.

[11]   Ibn Khaldun. *The Muqaddimah: An Introduction to History.* Translated from the Arabic by Franz Rosenthal. New York, Pantheon Books, 1958.

[12]   Kingsland, S. *Modeling Nature: Episodes in the History of Population Ecology*, 2nd edition. Chicago, IL: University of Chicago Press, 1995.

[13]   Kiser, E., and M. Hechter. "The Role of General Theory is Comparative-Historical Sociology." *American Journal of Sociology* 97 (1991): 1-30.

[14] Korotayev, A., and D. Khaltourina. *Introduction to Social Macrodynamics: Secular Cycles and Millennial Trends in Africa*. URSS, Moscow, 2006.

[15] Kradin, N. N. "Nomads, World-Empires, and Social Evolution." In *Alternative routes to civilization* (in Russian), edited by N. N. Kradin, A. V. Korotayev, D. M. Bondarenko, and V. A. Lynshi, 314-336. Logos, Moscow, 2000.

[16] Lee, J. S. "The Periodic Recurrence of Intrnecine Wars in China." *The China Journal* March-April (1931): 111-163.

[17] McNeill, W. H. *The Rise of the West*. New York: New American Library, 1963.

[18] Popper, K. R. *The Poverty of Historicism*. London: Routledge and Kegan Paul, 1957.

[19] Putnam, R. D., R. Leonardi, and R. Y. Nanetti. *Making Democracy Work: Civic Traditions in Modern Italy*. Princeton, NJ: Princeton University Press, 1993.

[20] Putnam, R. D. *Bowling Alone: The Collapse and Revival of American Community*. New York: Simon and Schuster, 2000.

[21] Rashevsky, N. *Looking at History through Mathematics*. Cambridge, MA: MIT Press, 1968.

[22] Sheehan, J. J. "President's Column: How Do We Learn from History?" *Perspectives on History* 43(1) (2005): 1-3.

[23] Sorokin, P. A. *Social and Cultural Dynamics*. Vol. III. *Fluctuations of Social Relationships, War, and Revolution*. New York: American Book Company, 1937.

[24] Stark, R. *The Rise of Christianity: A Sociologist Reconsiders History*. Princeton, NJ: Princeton University Press, 1996.

[25] Stark, R. "E contrario." *Journal of Early Christian Studies* 6 (1998): 259-267.

[26] Stark, R. *The Rise of the Mormonism*. New York: Columbia University Press, 2005.

[27] Stearns, P. N. *The Encyclopedia of World History*, 6th edition. Boston, MA: Houghton Mifflin, 2001.

[28] Taleb, N. N. *The Black Swan: The Impact of the Highly Improbable*. New York: Random House, 2007.

[29] Tilly, C. *European Revolutions: 1492-1992*. Oxford, UK: Blackwell, 1993.

[30] Toynbee, A. J. *A Study of History*. London: Oxford University Press, 1956.

[31] Turchin, P. *Historical Dynamics: Why States Rise and Fall*. Princeton, NJ: Princeton University Press, 2003a.

[32]   Turchin, P. *Complex Population Dynamics: A Theoretical/Empirical Synthesis*. Princeton, NJ: Princeton University Press, 2003b.

[33]   Turchin, P. *War and Peace and War: The Life Cycles of Imperial Nations*. New York: Pi Press, 2006a.

[34]   Turchin, P. "Scientific Prediction in Historical Sociology: Ibn Khaldun meets Al Saud." In *History and Mathematics: Historical Dynamics and Development of Complex Societies*, edited by P. Turchin, L. Grinin, A. Korotayev, and V. C. de Munck. URSS, Moscow, 2006b.

[35]   Turchin, P., and A. Korotayev. "Population Dynamics and Internal Warfare: A Reconsideration." *Social Science and History* 5(2) (2006): 121-158.

[36]   Turchin, P. "Arise 'cliodynamics'." *Nature* 454 (2008): 34-35.

[37]   Turchin, P. 2009a. "Long-Term Population Cycles in Human Societies." In *The Year in Ecology and Conservation Biology*, edited by R. S. Ostfeld and W. H. Schlesinger, 1-17. 2009. Ann. N. Y. Acad. Sci. 1162.

[38]   Turchin, P. "A Theory for Formation of Large Empires." *Journal of Global History* 4 (2009b): 191-207.

[39]   Turchin, P., and S. Nefedov. *Secular Cycles*. Princeton, NJ: Princeton University Press, 2009.

[40]   von Haehling, R. "Die Religionszugehörigkeit der hohen Amtsträger des Römischen Reiches seit Constantins I. Alleinherrschaft bis zum Ende der Theodosianischen Dynastie." Ph.D. dissertation, Bonn, 1978.

[41]   Zhao, W., and S. Z. Xie. *Zhongguo ren kou shi: China Population History* (in Chinese). Peking: People's Publisher, 1988.

[42]   Carneiro, R. L. 1997. *Human History: A Domain of Competing Perspectives*. Europaea 3:9-32.

[43]   Bonnell, V. E., and L. Hunt. 1999. Introduction. Pages 1-32 in V. E. Bonnell and L. Hunt, editors. *Beyond the Cultural Turn: New Directions in the Study of Society and Culture*. University of California Press, Berkeley.

[44]   Williamson, S. H. 1991. "The history of cliometrics." *Research in Economic History, Supplement* 6:15-31.

[45]   Hunt, L. 1989. *The New Cultural History*. University of California Press, Berkeley.

[46]   Sewell, W. H. 2005. *Logics of History: Social Theory and Social Transformation*. University of Chicago Press, Chicago.

ی ی

A HISTORICAL CONSPIRACY: COMPETITION, OPPORTUNITY, & THE EMERGENCE OF DIRECTION IN HISTORY

Geerat J. Vermeij, University of California, Davis

I DESCRIBE HISTORICAL PATTERNS that I believe would emerge in any system characterized by living things competing for locally scarce resources. I then consider the search for patterns and their explanation in the context of an intellectual climate dominated by anti-adaptationist rhetoric and doubts about the validity of scientific approaches to history. Notwithstanding this hostile environment, I present a summary of the economic principles that in my view not only account for historical patterns but also serve to predict future trends and postdict past ones not yet known. A positive feedback between consumers and resources—a historical conspiracy of sorts—implies the existence of inherent directions in the history of living things, including humans.

Introduction

Alfred Fischer's baritone filled the room when he lectured. I sat transfixed as he painted mental pictures of continents splitting and colliding, the world coming alive with animals at the dawn of the Cambrian period, and relatives of ancient squid swimming about with their long, clumsy, gas-filled shells in an Ordovician sea. He described massive bouts of extinction, subsiding coastal basins in California filling with sediments and leaving a record of stability and change as chronicled by tiny planktonic foraminifers, and the structure of ancient Paleozoic reefs. Here was history writ large, a grand story of life back to its beginnings as revealed by the geological record. Strange

animals and plants from far-away places and remote times wit-
nessed events of unimaginable scale. The narratives Fischer
so evocatively brought to life were every bit as gripping as the
more familiar accounts of human history.

But unlike the written record of human events as interpreted
by traditional historians, the chronology that Fischer sought to
reconstruct was founded on science. Meticulous observations
on ancient rocks and fossils were supplemented with insights
from experimental and comparative biology to establish not
only a temporal framework of life's evolution, but also with
hypotheses of the conditions under which ancient forms of life
existed. The love of seashells I had had since childhood was
rapidly expanding into a love of historical science during my
time at Princeton, where Fischer and others helped shape
my scientific orientation. I wanted not only to describe the
phenomenology of present and past life, but also to look for and
to explain patterns. Without ignoring the welter of fascinating
descriptive details of living and ancient nature, I sought basic
principles; I wanted to become a Bigstoryan.

My approach would be comparative. Relying on
experimental work in living systems, I would use shell
architecture as a guide to the conditions of life that, from the
point of view of the shell-builders themselves, were instrumental
as evolutionary agencies now and in the past. If I were lucky —
that is, if the data revealed a discernible signal — I would be able
to infer how these conditions of life varied in space and changed
through time. Ultimately, I hoped to find a unified explanation
based on first principles for the geography and history of
life, a comprehensive theory that could also encompass the
complexities of the human story.

In this essay, I first describe historical patterns that I
believe would emerge in any system characterized by living
things competing for locally scarce resources. I then consider
the search for patterns and their explanation in the context of
an intellectual climate dominated by anti-adaptationist rhetoric
and doubts about the validity of scientific approaches to history.
Notwithstanding this hostile environment, I present a summary

of the economic principles that in my view not only account for historical patterns but also serve to predict future trends and postdict past ones not yet known. A positive feedback between consumers and resources—a historical conspiracy of sorts—implies the existence of inherent directions in the history of living things, including humans. Contingency—randomness and the enduring effects of particular initial conditions and pathways of change—reigns at the level of the precise times, places, order of events, and participants involved in historical sequences. Finally, I discuss why a scientific approach to history is important. By complementing descriptive accounts of the phenomenology of the past, the approach seeks insights into which courses of change are likely and possible and which ones are not. These insights come not from mere parallels of past events with those of the present, but from laws that govern life as it responds and creates inevitable change in a finite world.

~263~

Patterns in History

When I was exposed for the first time to living snails in the tropical Pacific in 1968, I noticed that many of their shells were difficult to clean. More often than not, the soft parts of the animal had retracted far into the shell, and the aperture was so small or so narrow that fingers or even needles thrust into the openings were unable to extract these tissues. As I began to observe the diverse predators of these snails, it dawned on me that many features of snail shells—small apertures, tightly fitting rigid doors covering the foot when the body was withdrawn into the shell, the sturdy nodes and ribs on the shell's exterior, and even the slippery-smooth surfaces of some species—are adaptations that, though imperfectly effective, often thwarted or slowed attempts by predators to crush, hammer, drill, enter, or swallow the shell. These antipredatory defenses were most spectacularly developed in shallow-water marine snails in the tropics, especially in the western Pacific and Indian Oceans, where the predators likewise seemed to have larger or more potent weapons—claws, jaws, suckers, venomous teeth—than those elsewhere.

Contemplating some fossil shells a few years later, I was suddenly struck with the realization that these ancient snails lacked many of the defenses that are so emblematic of tropical shells in today's seas. Shells with slippery surfaces, long narrow apertures, and apertures lined with thickenings around the rim were wholly absent in fossil faunas living more than two hundred million years ago. Architecturally weak shells, by contrast, seemed to become increasingly common the further back in time I looked. Loosely coiled shells in particular were the norm in tropical faunas of Paleozoic times, whereas today they are found mainly in places where shell-breaking predators are rare. These and other observations led me to propose that an evolutionary arms race—a process of escalation between shell-bearing prey and their predators—was responsible for temporal increases in armament among both victims and perpetrators [63, 64].

Once I began to look at other fossils and at the research of fellow paleontologists, escalation and its consequences turned up everywhere. Sea lilies (crinoids), which lived as permanently attached filter-feeders in Early Paleozoic oceans, became mobile, toxic, and spiny as snails, fish, and other enemies became increasingly abundant [21, 38, 53]. Sand and mud on the sea floor at the dawn of animal evolution were essentially free of burrowing animals, but over time they were colonized by many lineages, perhaps as an evolutionary response to predation at and above the sea floor [14, 15, 68]. Burrowers over time penetrated to greater depths and became faster as escalation proceeded apace below the sea floor and as food there became ever more abundant and accessible [58, 59]. These trends, coupled with the evolution of increasingly powerful and mobile predators, made some modes of life untenable. This was the case, for example, for corals and brachiopods that lived unattached and motionless on the sea floor. When extensive burrowing destabilized their mud substrates, these animals would sink into the soft mud and be unable to escape either from such interment or from mobile enemies above [58, 59].

Plants, too, were caught up in the escalatory frenzy. Seaweeds as well as land plants developed all manner of chemical and mechanical adaptations against grazers, and sometimes even came to depend on their consumers for nourishment and successful reproduction [57, 64, 68]. Plant-eaters, it turns out, were late additions to marine and terrestrial ecosystems, a conclusion so at variance with intuition that we delayed publication of our paper on this topic for a few years until we were quite certain of its validity [73]. A culmination of escalation between plants and their consumers was the Late Cretaceous appearance and mid-Cenozoic expansion of grasses. These plants grow not at the tips, as most plants did and do, but at the base, so that when they are exposed to intense herbivory by grazing mammals (or by lawn mowers), they lose the older, less productive parts of the plant while retaining the ability to grow from less accessible parts of the plant. Grasses and their consumers came to depend on each other [68].

~265~

Parallels with escalation between the superpowers were, of course, glaringly obvious. Reading William McNeill's [34] *The Pursuit of Power,* I could not help but be struck by the rapid increases in the potency of weapons through the ages as successive empires varied for world dominance. Escalation, in turn, coincided with an ever increasing per-capita and collective use of raw materials—food, fuel, fiber, building materials—and increases in productivity of those same resources [8]. I was fascinated by these parallels and patterns. Did they reflect fundamentally similar causes? If so, could the history of life tell us something about how human arms races begin and end? Are there inherent directions in history? Alternatively, are these supposed trends merely illusory? Are we simply more impressed by increases in size and might than by decreases?

History as Science and Theory

It was anything but fashionable to ask these questions or even to search for patterns in history. Karl Popper [43, p.143], for example, held that "history is characterized by its interest in actual, singular, or specific events, rather than in laws or generalizations." In a similar vein, Stephen J. Gould [25, p. 25] doubted the existence of patterns and discouraged the search for them: "The history of life is a story of massive removal followed by differentiation within a few surviving stocks, not the conventional tale of steadily increasing excellence, complexity, and diversity." The intellectual climate of the late 1970s through the 1990s was dominated by the ascendant view that chaos and randomness were the predominant themes of history. Many paleontologists were influenced by Gould and Lewontin's [26] view that adaptation was at most a temporary, ephemeral phenomenon whose effects on the history of life paled into insignificance in the face of periodic mass extinctions and the stranglehold of unique, and therefore unpredictable, initial conditions and coincidences. Perhaps snails and their predators engaged in evolutionary escalation [24], but such patterns and processes could not possibly be the rule in a world dominated by chaos. Even the cherished idea that complexity increased through time—the one pattern of history that still held sway among diverse scientists [1, 4, 6, 37, 56, 61, 80] came under attack as scientists realized that many stocks decreased in complexity and probably outnumbered those that increased in complexity [35, 36].

The atmosphere of the time was aptly captured by Gould's [25] metaphor of the tape of life. Following a similar point made by Simpson [54], Gould held that if the tape of life—the sequences of events comprising life's history—were run twice, the outcomes would be radically different. Initial conditions—ancestral states, the particulars of time and place—put an indelible stamp on subsequent events, participants, and pathways of change. Even if we knew the points of departure, there would be many other chance events and forks in the road along the way, with the result that directions of change would be unpredictable and the search for causal historical patterns would be futile. The only predictable patterns would be inherent in the dynamics of evolving lineages—origin, splitting, and disappearance—that would be independent of time and place. This so-called nomothetic approach [45] led many paleontologists to treat taxonomic and phylogenetic units as abstract entities, which could be counted and modeled without regard to their environments or interactions.

The abstraction of nomothetic paleontology matched in spirit what biologists who were trying to reconstruct ancestor-descendant relationships were doing. For these so-called cladists, the construction of evolutionary trees involved morphological (and later molecular) characters, which were taken as abstract markers of descent from ancestors. Functional aspects of these characters were intentionally ignored or excluded because they were judged to be unreliable indicators of descent.

~267~

The combination of nomothetic paleontology and "tree-thinking" led to the emergence in the 1970s of a macroevolutionary interpretation of the fossil record. Macroevolution is concerned not with the behavior of individual organisms and their interactions, but with the birth, growth, decline, and death of inclusive *taxa* (*genera*, families, orders, etc.) and later of clades. A clade, defined as an ancestor and all of its descendants, has properties—geographic range, number of species, propensity for genetic isolation of populations—that individual organisms do not have. These emergent characteristics, so the thinking goes, differ among clades, and influence the probabilities and rates of species formation and extinction. Phenomena that affect whole populations thus impose a kind of sorting among clades [16, 23, 74-77].

The macroevolutionary world view in its purest form implicitly assumes the null hypothesis that clades are internally homogeneous. Within a given clade, all members are subject to the same adaptive limitations, live in comparable habitats, have comparable modes of life, have similar life histories, and are therefore interchangeable. The clade therefore has time-invariant emergent properties, or at least potentials, throughout its evolutionary history from origin to extinction.

We know, however, that this null hypothesis is false for most clades. The *Rhynchonellata* (the formal name of the clade that contains the vast majority of brachiopods, bivalved suspension-feeding animals commonly known as lamp shells) comprise a hugely diverse group of animals. During the Paleozoic and to a lesser extent the Mesozoic era, they occupied a wide range of marine environments, ranging from shallow tropical reefs and sand-flats to cold waters at high latitudes. Some Late Paleozoic species became large, fast-growing reef-formers whose competitive dominance in those environments derived from the likely presence of photosynthesizing symbionts in their tissues [10]. Today, the few hundred brachiopod species are uniformly slow-growing, low-energy animals confined to cold or cryptic habitats, where they tend to be subordinate to such other suspension-feeders as true bivalves (clams), barnacles, and sponges. Not only has the clade contracted ecologically from mid-Mesozoic times, but much of the heterogeneity of its Paleozoic and Mesozoic members has been lost. By contrast, the Arthropoda (the animal clade including crabs, spiders, and insects) initially consisted of small to medium-sized marine predators, swimming suspension-feeders, and sediment-ingesters. Later it gave rise not only to land animals, including herbivores and social insects (ants, bees, wasps, termites, and bark beetles), but also to my favorite group, the barnacles, sedentary crustaceans whose external mineralized shells converge in their mode of accretionary growth on the shells of molluscs. These clades are internally heterogeneous in every imaginable dimension of morphology, life history, habitat type, geographic range, power, competitive status, adaptive syndrome, and time. A clade is a branch of the tree of life, and nothing more; the characteristics of its founding member have long since been transcended as opportunities arise and as extinction prunes branches and twigs within the clade.

A worldview of human history that would resemble the macroevolutionary perspective on the history of life is an emphasis on the genealogy and replacement of rulers or institutions. For example, we might compare patterns of descent and replacement among the French, English, and Spanish monarchies. Knowing such sequences of the makers of history is indeed essential, but neither the details of genealogy nor an inventory of the wars in which these rulers engaged or the countries these rulers conquered or lost suffice as descriptions or explanations of history.

Neutral theory extends throughout population biology, from genetic mutation to the distribution of individuals and species [29]. Under the null hypothesis of neutrality, outcomes and patterns are determined by chance, with deterministic factors either absent or canceled out. Because the units of interest are effectively interchangeable, their names and roles are superfluous and irrelevant, and their heterogeneity can be ignored. Such a null model may indeed describe the observed behavior of genes, individuals, and species in space and time, and it may be a useful point of reference against which to measure the properties of real systems and their constituents [29]; but it must never be construed as an explanation for the behavior of living things and the structures they produce. Living things are agents of change whose interactions have outcomes that affect their own fates and those of other organisms. Chance and randomness are therefore insufficient agencies for capturing even the fundamentals, let alone the particulars, of living systems.

~269~

If neutral theories and unadorned chronologies of events do not suffice as historical explanation, how do we gain a coherent understanding of history without being overwhelmed and distracted by the details? In my view, we need a theory of history that incorporates the unique, emergent properties of living systems. The theory must explain the causes, effects, feedbacks, and conditions that create the sequences of history. It must predict general patterns of change under all the conceivable circumstances in which metabolizing life is sustainable, but not the times, places, or precise sequences of events. In short, a theory of history must be like the theory of forces in physics in that it circumscribes outcomes when initial conditions are specified and rules of interaction are applied. It must explain variations in the realization of laws in space and time according to circumstances at levels of inclusion ranging from the ephemeral and local to the timeless and global. The interactions must have consequences for the fates of the living entities involved, fates influenced by the environment and by structural properties of those entities. For living things, these interactions and outcomes are economic, with the performance of participants influencing survival and propagation.

This approach is thus a scientifically grounded history of function as influenced by structure rather than a history of structure alone. Patterns and trends must be expressed in terms that are meaningful to the lives, fates, and relationships of living things. I thus prefer the language of adaptation, activity, metabolism, interaction, and performance—all carefully defined, measured, and compared—over the language of diversity, complexity, and information. These latter, more abstract concepts are epiphenomena, manifestations of the more fundamental, function-based properties and capacities that rule organisms' lives. There is, of course, a history of complexity, diversity, and information. In fact, both complexity and diversity appear to have increased over the course of Earth history as well as in the long-run history of humanity. These trends reflect more basic economic changes, which are the product of evolution and the distribution of power in the biosphere.

~270~

But theory, too, was anathema to many historians. Popper [43, p. VII] maintained that "There can be no scientific theory of historical development serving as a basis of historical prediction." For him, "the evolution of life on Earth, or of human society, is an unique historical process" (p. 108). Unique phenomena can be described, and take place in accordance with the laws of physics and economics, but by virtue of their uniqueness are neither available for application of scientific tests nor the basis of a scientific theory. Berlin, too, saw a profound distinction between history and "natural science," by which he mostly meant physics and chemistry, disciplines with timeless laws, forces, and structures. Indeed, he considers a scientific approach to history a fool's errand: "Whereas in ... developed natural science we consider it more rational to put our confidence in general propositions or laws than in specific phenomena ... this rule does not seem to operate successfully in history" [3, p. 111]. In the same vein, "Historical explanation is to a large degree arrangement of the discovered facts in patterns which satisfy us because they accord with life ... as we know it and can imagine it. That is the difference that distinguishes the humane studies—*Geisteswissenschaften*—from those of nature" [3, p. 132]. Berlin ascribes to historians, but not to scientists, "a capacity for integration, for perceiving qualitative similarities and differences, a sense of the unique fashion by which various factors combine in the particular concrete situation ..." [3, p. 140]. In other, more modern words, Berlin saw natural science as reductionist, and history (by which he meant almost always human history) as incorporating synergies and emergence, interactions and organization of parts that create wholes with properties and interactions different from those of component parts. Like Popper, he did not conceive of historical science as real science, reducible to elementary particles and forces.

I believe these distinctions between science and history are far too starkly drawn by these critics. If we applied Popper's and Berlin's logic to the behavior of individual molecules, rocks, continents, stars, or galaxies, we would have to clear away all the particulars to discern the reduced laws of physics and chemistry, yet these laws apply just the same. The behaviors of objects, like the interactions of living things and the conditions in which those interactions take place, are realizations of those laws. General patterns can emerge despite these particulars if certain sequences are more likely than others, and if classes of interaction have predictable outcomes on the basis of measurable properties. The trends are statistical directions, not strictly deterministic; they emerge from simpler components and simpler interactions, much as complex wholes with new properties emerge from interactions among their parts. The fundamental methodology is comparative and systematic [12, 22] rather than strictly experimental, that is, historians must draw inferences from given circumstances rather than from ones they can manipulate. The scientific approach to history entails testing hypotheses with as many independent sources of evidence as possible, set in the framework of a unified explanatory theory. History is at once reductionist and holistic, concerned with elementary principles as well as with the new properties that emerge when circumstances and the things in them work together and effect change.

Although the view of history that I have come to embrace emanates from the world of plants and animals, I believe that this scientific approach is just as powerful in human history. True, studies of human affairs are apt to emphasize motivations and emotions of individuals, attributes that likely do not figure prominently in the lives of most other organisms; but motivations and emotions reflect real circumstances, or at least circumstances as people perceive them, and are therefore as important to understanding human relations as sexual selection and predation are to interaction among, say, butterflies. It is also true that historians value narrative over any kind of theory-laden approach. For them and for like-minded paleontologists, it is the particulars of a situation that are the primary focus of study. But if we are to learn from history, narratives must be placed in a broader context of comparisons among places, among times, among social settings, and so on. I agree with Gordon Wood [78, p. 6] that "History ... may not teach us particular lessons, but it does tell us how we might live in the world." History can do this only if its narratives collectively reveal limitations and possibilities and if they identify pathways of change that are likely and those that are improbable. Comparisons undergirded by a unified scientific theory of history and by hypothesis-driven methods of investigation will, I think, yield the deepest and most useful insights. Studies by Diamond [12, 13], Pomeranz [42], and Clark [7] exemplify the power of this approach well. In short, historians need the principles of interaction that economists and evolutionary biologists have identified, together with systematic methods to construct a chronology of the past.

An Economic Theory of History

History consists of events, conditions, pathways, and participants arranged in temporal sequences. The patterns of history, which we must describe, are linear sequences—one thing following another—that not only branch (or divide), as in a phylogeny (ancestor-descendant relationships), but that interact by exchanging resources, energy, or information. Mathematically, these patterns are best expressed in the language of topology — connectedness in networks, patterns of branching, and transformations of geometrical configurations — and by the use of matrices in which the individual cells represent strengths and signs of interactions. This language accurately reflects the central importance of interactions in creating pattern [66].

But description, even if it is done in precise mathematical language, is not explanation. Essential though it is, description represents only the first step in historical inquiry. History is about causes and effects, about how supply and demand are connected through feedback, about how disruptions affect systems, about how circumstances act together to create or favor new states, and about whether an arrow of time is discernible among the billions of historical sequences that seem so dominated by the particulars of time and place. For living things that depend on resources for survival and propagation, interactions are economic in nature, involving the distribution of a multitude of primary essentials and secondary requirements. Life's metabolism, in other words, implies an explanation of history founded on principles of competition, cooperation, production, consumption, and trade.

Organisms do the work of life — maintenance, growth, reproduction, and adaptation — by harnessing energy and matter through the processes of synthesis and metabolism. Whenever two or more living things attempt to acquire the same resource at the same time and place, the resource will be locally scarce, and the organisms involved will compete for it. The competitive position of living things in the system of which they are a part is determined by the performance of individuals in acquiring or retaining resources. Economic performance is best expressed in units of power (energy, or work, per unit time). Resources are the currency of the system; they can be gained, lost, stored, exchanged, and spent. Success — persistence and the ability to propagate — requires sufficient resources, but does not strictly depend on performance.

A resource like food, shelter, and water (for land organisms) becomes a target of competition among individual living entities when it is locally scarce and when it influences the survival and propagation of competitors. Local scarcity, however, applies only to the competitors themselves, not necessarily to the population to which the competitors belong. For example, animals as a group are not limited by the amount of oxygen in Earth's atmosphere, but oxygen may be in critically short supply for two mammals sharing the same underground burrow. A resource may therefore not limit the size of a population even though at the scale of interaction between individuals it is locally scarce and therefore a target of selection [65, 72]. Evolutionists concerned with selection are therefore apt to view competition and resources differently from ecologists, because the former are concerned with individual interactions whereas the latter deal with phenomena at the population level. Even so, local scarcity and population-related selection occur in the larger context of populations and ecosystems. The availability and accessibility of resources at the population level therefore affect the extent to which individuals can compete for, adapt to, and influence the locally scarce commodity.

A competitive interaction is almost always unequal in its outcome for the participants, with one party gaining more or losing less resource than the other. The winner gains an economic advantage not only in acquiring the contested resource, but also in gaining access to environments where the resource is plentiful and accessible. The loser is economically marginalized or, in extreme forms of competition leading to starvation or predation, eliminated.

Within a system of competitors, the entities with the greatest individual or collective power exert a disproportionately strong influence on the phenotypes, activities, distribution, and resources of the living things with which they interact. Because of intense competition among them, these dominant entities therefore exercise intense selection among subordinates as well as among their fellow dominants. In this view, selection is due largely to enemies, and is a predominantly top-down process whose intensity and effects are proportional to power. The universally observed inequality in performance in competition among individuals and in the distribution of resources thus spreads and amplifies through the entire system [68].

The maximum power available to a dominant competitor increases as resource availability and accessibility at the population or ecosystem scale increase. The scope of adaptation — that is, the range of adaptive possibilities available to an evolving lineage — and the maximum level of performance are higher when the population-level supply of resources is plentiful and predictable, when the system in which the population is embedded is large (enabling a population of rare but metabolically active individuals to sustain itself in the face of chance fluctuations), when temperatures are high (reducing the activation energy required to initiate energy-consuming processes), and when the organism has the chemical and mechanical equipment to locate, acquire, and hold resources [66, 68]. These conditions are satisfied for terrestrial organisms on large, warm, well-watered, productive land masses; and for marine ones in large, warm bodies of water with high inputs of nutrients from the land or from deep-water sources. Power, performance, and the conditions for the enhancement of energy-intensive traits associated with competitive dominance and with escalation are thus most favorable when the economy of life grows, that is, when productivity and temperature — the enabling factors of an economy — rise [67].

~275~

Power, performance, and the scope of adaptation are constrained when resource supply is low and unpredictable. When the economy in which a population operates is small, as on isolated oceanic islands or in island-like habitats such as lakes, very small populations are prone to extinction and cannot persist for long. To maintain a viable population, therefore, individuals in such small habitats must have relatively modest metabolic requirements, because with high per-capita demand the limited available resources can support only a small number of individuals. Power is also limited in organisms that maintain body temperatures similar to those of the environment when conditions are cold, as in today's polar regions and the deep sea. From the dimensionality of power, it is clear that many pathways toward greater competitive performance are available to living things. These include increases in body mass, applied force, velocity, rate of growth, metabolic rate, and cooperation, as well as decreases in the time of exposure to enemies. Still another pathway to greater performance is the ability to interfere behaviorally or structurally with the performance of rivals.

Given that a top competitor has to perform many functions well, it is not surprising that cooperation and other forms of interdependence rank as perhaps the most important means for enhancing the competitive ability of organisms. Most, and perhaps all, organisms are composed of parts that work seamlessly together but which have separate evolutionary origins. Familiar examples are the eukaryotic cell, whose organelles — mitochondria, plastids, and basal bodies, among others — were initially free-living prokaryotes of diverse origin that formed an intimate partnership with another prokaryote bearing what we now recognize as the nucleus; and land plants, which effectively tap nutrients from the soil by virtue of symbiotic fungi in their roots. In such integrated partnerships, the various components perform complementary functions, which collectively enable the emergent individual to perform better as a competitor than any of the components could by themselves. Other forms of cooperation, often associated with division of labor among individuals, lead to colonial animals, insect societies, group-hunting dogs, and human society. Flowering plants have in many cases come to rely on highly mobile pollinators to facilitate sexual reproduction, and therefore need no longer grow close to each other as they do when pollination is by wind or water. Specialized herbivorous insects therefore perceive their hosts as rare, meaning that insect- or bird-pollinated plants can achieve a measure of protection from their enemies and can instead devote more of their budget to rapid growth [28, 30, 31, 47]. The plants themselves, and the ecosystem of which they are a part, therefore achieve higher productivity when they form these intimate partnerships than when they work independently as self-sufficient entities [32]. Interdependencies, in other words, are created by, and in turn further promote, the evolution of competitors.

In the light of these arguments, it should come as no surprise that the most highly escalated species have arisen in the competitively most rigorous situations. Tall, competitively dominant trees are the evolutionary products of continents, not islands. So are weeds—fast-growing plants with prodigious fecundities and short life-spans—and social insects. The most potent and the most heavily armored marine animals evolved in the Indo-West Pacific region, and humans emerged in Africa, not in the much more island-like continents of South America or Australia. In the human realm, civilizations tend to spring up where marine resources are abundant and where equable climates and high diversity have favored the evolution of plants and animals that humans could successfully domesticate [12].

~277~

Competitively subordinate entities vastly outnumber dominants in both individuals and species. Many of them nevertheless evolve toward greater power because of selection due to their enemies. Others succeed in situations where power requirements are low and where resources and enemies are scarce. Such situations include life on or in the bodies of other living things, occupation of cluttered environments, physically hostile habitats such as wave-swept sandy beaches or wind-swept mountaintops, and nutritionally starved environments such as caves or the abyssal plain of the deep sea. Importantly, competitively vigorous species often create situations suitable for subordinates: tall trees cast shade, in which competitively subordinate plants can thrive; fast-growing reef corals, powered by photosynthesizing single-celled algae in their tissues, create numerous crevices and cavities where thousands of small-bodied animals make a living; and the bodies of well-defended plants and animals are inviting targets for vast numbers of parasites and symbionts, which would be highly vulnerable to enemies if they were free-living.

Disruptions affect all systems from time to time. Production, consumption, and escalation are interrupted when catastrophes, often originating outside the sphere of life, disrupt patterns of interdependence. Extreme episodes of disruption in the biosphere are recorded as global mass extinctions, such as those marking the termination of the Paleozoic and Mesozoic eras (the end-Permian and end- Cretaceous extinctions respectively). These episodes may have begun as crashes in production of food by plants and plankton, brought about by collision of Earth with extra-terrestrial bodies and by enormous volcanic eruptions leading to the formation of vast tracts of basalt. The initiation disruption propagated throughout the biosphere, destroying the collective regulation of the resources that remained and creating conditions in which many populations became inviable either because of starvation or overexploitation by consumers [50, 51, 69]. In the realm of recorded human history, climatic change—droughts, volcanically induced cold rainy summers—caused crop failures, which together with a pervasive tendency for technologically sophisticated humans to overexploit natural resources for food and fuel appear to be instrumental in bringing about the collapse of civilizations that, like ecosystems, are built of highly interdependent relationships among individuals [13, 41].

Feedbacks, Cycles, and Trends

Through selection and their own metabolism, living things formulate and test hypotheses of their changing environment, which consists of enemies, allies, resources, and disruptions. They respond (and therefore adapt) to their environment, but they also change their surroundings, and therefore take an active role in creating the circumstances in which they live. The good fit between organism and environment that impresses most naturalists therefore results from a feedback, in which living things and their surroundings influence each other. An organism—its form, activity, physiology, and life cycle—thus represents an integrated system of adaptations reflecting supply, demand, and construction. It is a web of synergy, of interdependence in which resources, metabolism, competition, and structure are inextricably linked through causal feedbacks. Similar statements apply to life at all levels of organization, from the cell to the ecosystem and beyond, as well as to the human realm. The material manifestations of life differ among levels — an ecosystem and a society consist of multiple individuals, whereas organisms and cells are integrated indivisible units — but the feedbacks and interdependencies that make life sustainable are universal [9, 68].

One example will illustrate this point. Hermit crabs are crustaceans that typically inhabit the abandoned shells of snails. Even when shells are abundant, most are occupied by hermit crabs. As a consequence, hermit crabs compete intensely for shells. Because shells deteriorate when occupied by these crustaceans, the hermit-crab population depends on a supply of new shells to remain viable. In some environments, such as freshwater streams, shells become available episodically, especially following floods. Most of the time, therefore, the supply of suitable shells is low, but a few times a year, or perhaps every few years, there is a surplus. This regime of supply is too unpredictable to sustain a population of hermit crabs or other secondary shell-dwellers; and indeed such shell-dwellers are mostly unknown in freshwater ecosystems. In the sea, predators that leave the shells of their snail victims intact are often numerous. Because they must eat year-round, especially in the tropics, they provide the population of hermit crabs with a more or less constant, predictable supply of shells. This regime of supply, regulated by the predators of snails, thus allows animals like hermit crabs to exploit the resource of shells for mobile shelters, a form of specialization that is strongly selected for by abundant predators on and above the sea floor. By effectively lengthening the life-span of shells, the hermit crabs greatly increase the abundance of shell-bearing animals as a potential resource for predators. In so doing, they increase the population and potentially the power of predators, and thus indirectly increase the benefits of occupying well-armored shells.

Neither these feedbacks nor the evolution of high-powered competitors is possible without enabling factors, which comprise resources and the factors that make those resources available, accessible, and predictable to consumers. If the supply of resources were controlled entirely by extrinsic factors—that is, by disruptions or chronic constraints beyond the control of living things—the maximum power achieved by successive dominants and by the system as a whole would fluctuate according to the pattern of supply, but it would not show a generally upward trend. If, however, there were a strong positive feedback between resources and consumers—that is, if high-powered consumers and the system as a whole promote the productivity of resources—and if permissive conditions favoring such feedback are more prevalent than constraining ones, there should on average exist trends toward increasing power among dominants as well as in the systems in which they live. These possibilities prompt a fundamental question in history. Are there trends in performance that transcend the effects of disruption and other conditions beyond life's control, or are disruptions so frequent and so severe that all advances in power, reach, dependency, and regulation are canceled out or even reversed? I believe that long-term trends toward greater power are in fact observable both in human history and in the sequences of nonhuman life, implying a reduction in the effects of extrinsic variation in enabling factors. By establishing a positive feedback between competition and resources, life therefore unintentionally imparts an arrow of time to history.

The repeated occurrence of disruptions has led many historians to view history as a succession of cycles. Following a disturbance, the cycle begins with an episode of renewal and growth, followed by a phase of established maturity, and again terminated by a disruption. Cyclical behavior, often with a very regular periodicity, has been claimed for mass extinctions [46], astronomically forced climate [11, 19, 40, continents coming together and drifting apart [18, 60, 79], diversity [19, 49], empires [5], ocean chemistry [33, 48, 52], flood-basalt volcanic eruptions [44], and prices [25]. Strict periodicity has been disproved for all cycles except astronomically forced climate.

Conditions favorable to the evolution and maintenance of interdependence and powerful competitors should be far more common than disruptions, implying that systems of life should exhibit long-term trends toward greater power and productivity. High-powered competitors are at a disadvantage, and interdependencies break down, only during disruptions, which by definition are infrequent, temporary, and episodic. Competition, on the other hand, is universal and relentless, and tends to favor entities with greater power. The high demand of dominant competitors both requires and promotes high turnover (and therefore high productivity) of resources. Moreover, interdependencies stabilize resource supply and stimulate the biological equivalent of trade. Under permissive conditions of increased extrinsic inputs of accessible material and energy resources, intense competition and interdependence create opportunities for the establishment of energy-intensive innovations, which further stimulate demand and therefore supply. Although permissive conditions are likely to be just as infrequent and episodic as are disruptions, the advantages of power and interdependence apply even when the delivery of resources is constant. Increases in power and productivity are likely to be difficult or impossible under such conditions of resource stability, but the maintenance of high levels of consumption and production is unaffected. Reversals are thus limited to times of disruption, whereas growth and maintenance prevail at all other times [67, 68].

To some authors, the constancy or reduction in power that subordinate entities experience over evolutionary time count as much as do increases in power, and therefore contradict any long-term trend toward increasing power. I maintain, however, that increases have a much greater effect on the selective regime in the larger system than do decreases [71], because a system's productivity and rate of consumption are determined largely by its competitively dominant members. The removal or addition of high-powered producers and consumers has far more dramatic effects on the pattern of selection and on the web of interdependence than does the removal or addition of a low-energy entity. Accordingly, more weight must be given to increases in power than to decreases.

Studies of geochemical cycles of essential inorganic components of life — oxygen, carbon, silicon, calcium, phosphorus, nitrogen, and water — indicate a trend of increasing biological control over these resources through time. These controls are temporarily interrupted during times of mass extinction, but they are quickly re-established during recovery. Increased biological regulation is made possible by dominants with higher metabolic rates, which speed up rates of turnover and therefore productivity of communities. Patterns of trade or subsidy between adjacent systems (land and sea, shallow and deep water, above and below ground) increase as new, faster modes of consumption evolve and as animals become more mobile. Economic dominants owe their competitive success in part to activities and characteristics that "help" entities with which they interact. Cooperation represents a particular effective version of this "help", but consumers also have many indirectly stimulatory effects on the conversion and recycling of resources for use by organisms.

~282~

These long-term trends have persisted despite substantial disruptions. The same is true for the diversity of species in the sea as well as on land [2, 27, 55], per-capita energy use by humans [8], and all escalation-related trends [68]. The available evidence thus indicates that, despite the imposition of cyclical phenomena by disruptions, the history of life is dominated by long-term trends toward increased power, productivity, interdependence, and regulation.

Concluding Remarks

The particulars of history—participants, dates, events, and places—cannot be predicted and remain profoundly contingent, but production and its regulation by consumers conspire to give history a predictable direction of increased power and reach of dominant members of living systems. This directionality is an emergent property of living systems, inherent in the interactions and competitors, consumption, and resources.

The identification of directionality in history has led some authors to postulate the existence of some supernatural driving force. Wright [80, p. 323], for example, argues that biological evolution has "an arrow—the invention of more structurally and informationally complex forms of life" and that "this arrow points toward meaning …" This "isn't, of course, proof of the existence of God. But it's more suggestive of divinity than an alternative world of directional evolution but no consciousness." Conway Morris [39] expressed similar sentiments. I emphatically reject such speculations. Directions and patterns emerge entirely through the interactions of components and circumstances, and need no supernatural force or being.

The ability to reconstruct the past and to explain historical sequences in terms of scientific laws is surely one of the great triumphs of the collective human intellect. The challenge before us now is to use these historical insights to chart the right course for our collective future. ❧

References

[1]   Ayres, R. U. *Information, Entropy, and Progress*. New York: American Institute of Physics, 1994.

[2]   Bambach, R. K. "Species Richness in Marine Benthic Habitats through the Phanerozoic." *Paleobiology* 3 (1977): 152-167.

[3]   Berlin, Isaiah. "The Concept of Scientific History." In *I. Berlin, Concepts and categories: philosophical essays*, 103-142. New York: Viking, 1979.

[4]   Chaisson, E. J. *Cosmic Evolution: The Rise of Complexity in Nature*. Cambridge: Harvard University Press, 2001.

[5]   Chua, A. *Day of Empire: How Hyperpowers Rise to Global Dominance — And Why They Fall*. New York: Doubleday, 2007.

[6]   Cisne, J. L. "Evolution of the World Fauna of Aquatic Free-Living Arthropods." *Evolution* 28 (1974): 337-366.

[7]   Clark, G. *A Farewell to Alms: A Brief Economic History of the World*. Princeton, NJ: Princeton University Press, 2007.

[8]   Cohen, J. E. *How Many People Can the Earth Support?* New York: Norton, 1995.

[9]   Corning, P.A. *Holistic Darwinism: Synergy, Cybernetics, and the Bio-economics of Evolution*. Chicago: University of Chicago Press, 2005.

[10]   Cowen, R. "Algal Symbiosis and Its Recognition in the Fossil Record." In *Biotic interactions in Recent and fossil benthic communities*, 431-478. Eds. M. J. S Tevesz and P. L. McCall. New York: Plenum, 1983.

[11]   Dam, J. A. van, H. A. Aziz, M. A. Álvarez Sierra, F. J. Hilgen, L. W. van den Hoek Ostende, L. J. Lourens, P. Stein, A J. van der Meulen, and P. Pelaez-Campomanes. "Long-Period Astronomical Forcing of Mammal Turnover." *Nature* 443 (2006): 687-691.

[12]   Diamond, J. *Guns, Germs, and Steel: The Fate of Human Societies*. New York: Norton, 1997.

[13]   Diamond, J. *Collapse: How Societies Choose to Fail or Succeed*. New York: Viking, 2005.

[14] Droser, M. L., S. Jensen, and J. G. Gehling. "Trace Fossils and Substrates of the Terminal Proterozoic-Cambrian Transition: Implications for the Record of Early Bilaterians and Sediment Mixing." *PNAS* 99 (2002): 12572-12576.

[15] Dzik, J. "Behavioral and Anatomical Unity of the Earliest Burrowing Animals and the Cause of the 'Cambrian Explosion'." *Paleobiology* 31 (2005): 503-521.

[16] Eldredge, N. *Unfinished Synthesis: Biological Hierarchies and Modern Evolutionary Thought*. New York: Oxford University Press, 1985.

[17] Fischer, A. G. "Climatic Oscillations in the Biosphere." In *Biotic Crises in Ecological and Evolutionary Time*, ed. M. H. Nitecki, 103-131. New York: Academic Press, 1981.

[18] Fischer, A. G. "The Two Phanerozoic Supercycles." In *Catastrophes in Earth History: The New Uniformitarianism*, eds. W. A. Berggren and J. A. Van, 129-150. Princeton, NJ: Princeton University Press, 1985.

[19] Fischer, A. G. and M. A. Arthur. "Secular Variations in Pelagic Realm." In *Deep-Water Carbonate Environments*, eds H. E. Cook and P. Enos, 19-50. SEPM Special Bulletin 25, 1977.

[20] Fischer, D. H. *The Great Wave: Price Revolutions and the Rhythm of History*. New York: Oxford University Press, 1996.

[21] Gahn, F. J. and T. K. Baumiller. "Arm Regeneration in Mississippian Crinoids: Evidence of Intense Predation Pressure in the Paleozoic?" *Paleobiology* 31 (2005): 151-164.

[22] Ghiselin, M. T. "Progress and the Economy of Nature." *Journal of Bioeconomics* 1 (1999): 35-45.

[23] Gould, S. J. "Darwinism and the Expansion of Evolutionary Theory." *Science* 216 (1982): 380-387.

[24] Gould, S. J. "The Paradox of the First Tier: An Agenda for Paleobiology." *Paleobiology* 11 (1985): 2-12.

[25] Gould, S J. *Wonderful Life: The Burgess Shale and the Nature of History*. New York: Norton, 1989.

[26] Gould, S. J., and R. C. Lewontin. "The Spandrels of San Marco and the Panglossian Paradigm: A Critique of the Adaptationist Programme." *Proceedings of the Royal Society of London B* 205 (1979): 581-598.

[27] Kowalewski, M., W. Kiessling, M. Aberhan, F. T. Fürsich, D Scarponi, S. L. Barbour Wood, and A. P. Hoffmeister. "Ecological, Taxonomic, and Taphonomic Components of the Post-Paleozoic Increase in Sample-Level Species Diversity of Marine Benthos." *Paleobiology* 32 (2006): 533-561.

[28] Leigh, E. G. Jr. *Tropical Forest Ecology: A View from Barro Colorado*. New York: Oxford University Press, 1999.

[29] Leigh, E. G. Jr. "Neutral Theory: A Historical Perspective."

Journal of Evolutionary Biology 29 (2007): 2075-2091.

[30] Leigh, E. G. Jr., and T. E. Rowell. "The Evolution of Mutualism and other Forms of Harmony at Various Levels of Biological Organization." *Écologie* 26 (1995): 131-152.

[31] Leigh, E. G. Jr., P. Davidar, C. W. Dick, J.-P. Puyravaud, J. Terborgh, H. ter Steege, and S. J. Wright. "Why do Some Tropical Forests Have So Many Species of Trees?" *Biotropica* 36 (2004): 447-473.

[32] Leigh, E. G. Jr., A. Hladik, C. L. Hladik, and A. Jolly. "The Biogeography of Large Islands, or How Does the Size of the Ecological Theater Affect the Evolutionary Play? *Revue d'Écologie (La Terre et la Vie)* 62 (2007): 105-168.

[33] Lowenstein, T. K., M.N. Timofeeff, S.T. Brennan, L.A. Hardie, and R.V. Demicco. "Oscillations in Phanerozoic Seawater Chemistry: Evidence from Fluid Inclusions." *Science* 294 (2001): 1087-1088.

[34] McNeill, W. H. *The Pursuit of Power: Technology, Armed Force, and Society Since A. D. 1000*. Chicago: University of Chicago Press, 1982.

[35] McShea, D. W. "Metazoan Complexity and Evolution: Is There A Trend?" *Evolution* 50 (1996): 477-492.

[36] McShea, D. W. "A Complexity Drain on Cells in the Evolution of Multicellularity." *Evolution* 56 (2002): 441-452.

[37] McShea, D. W. "The Evolution of Complexity Without Natural Selection: A Possible Large-Scale Trend of the Fourth Kind." *Paleobiology* 31 (2, Supplement) (2005): 146-156.

[38] Meyer, D. L., and D. B. Macurda. "Adaptive Radiation of the Comatulid Crinoids." *Paleobiology* 3 (1977): 74-82.

[39] Morris, Conway S. *Life's Solution: Inevitable Humans in a Lonely Universe*. Cambridge: Cambridge University Press, 2003.

[40] Olsen, P. E., C. L. Remington, B. Cornet, and K. S. Thomson. "Cyclic Change in Late Triassic Lacustrine Communities." *Science* 201 (1978): 729-733.

[41] Perlin, J. *A Forest Journey: The Role of Wood in the Development of Civilization*. Cambridge: Harvard University Press, 1989.

[42] Pomeranz, K. *The Great Divergence: China, Europe, and the Making of the Modern World Economy*. Princeton: Princeton University Press, 2000.

[43] Popper, K. R. *The Poverty of Historicism* (4th edition). New York: Harper and Row, 1964.

[44] Rampino, M. R., and R. B. Stothers. "Flood Basalt Volcanism during the Past 250 Million Years." *Science* 241 (1988): 663-668.

[45] Raup, D. M., and S. J. Gould. "Stochastic Simulation and Evolution of Morphology–Towards a Nomothetic Paleontology." *Systematic Zoology* 23 (1974): 305-322.

[46] Raup, D. M., and J. J. Sepkoski Jr. "Periodicity of Extinctions

in the Geologic past." *PNAS* 81 (1984): 801-805.

[47] Regal, P. J. "Ecology and Evolution of Flowering Plant Dominance." *Science* 196 (1977): 622-629.

[48] Ries, J. B. "Effect of Ambient Mg/Ca ratio on Mg Fractionation in Calcareous Marine Invertebrates: A Record of the Oceanic Mg/Ca Ratio over the Phanerozoic." *Geology* 32 (2004): 981-984.

[49] Rohde, R., and R. A. Muller. "Cycles in Fossil Diversity." *Nature* 434 (2005): 208-210.

[50] Roopnarine, P. D. "Extinction Cascades and Catastrophe in Ancient Foodwebs." *Paleobiology* 32 (2006): 1-19.

[51] Roopnarine, P. D., K. D. Angielczyk, S. C. Wang, and R. Hertog. "Trophic Network Models Explain Instability of Early Triassic Terrestrial Communities." *Proceedings of the Royal Society London B* 274 (2007): 2077-2086.

[52] Sandberg, P. A. "An Oscillating Trend in Phanerozoic Non-Skeletal Carbonate Mineralogy." *Nature* 305 (1983): 29-22.

[53] Signor, P. W. III, and C. E. Brett. "The Mid-Paleozoic Precursor to the Mesozoic Marine Revolution." *Paleobiology* 10 (1984): 229-245.

[54] Simpson, G. G. "The Nonprevalence of Humanoids." *Science* 143 (1964): 769-775.

[55] Stanley, S. M. "Predation Defeats Competition on the Sea floor." *Paleobiology* 34 (2008): 1-21.

[56] Stebbins, G. L. *The Basis of Progressive Evolution.* Chapel Hill: University of North Carolina Press, 1969.

[57] Steneck, R. S. "Escalating Herbivory and Resulting Adaptive Trends in Calcareous Algal Crusts." *Paleobiology* 9 (1983): 44-61.

[58] Thayer, C. W. "Biological Bulldozers and the Evolution of Marine Benthic Communities." *Science* 203 (1979): 458-461.

[59] Thayer, C. W. "Sediment-Mediated Biological Disturbance and the Evolution of Marine Benthos." In *Biotic Interactions in Recent and Fossil Benthic Marine Communities,* eds. M. J. S. Tevesz and P. L. McCall, 479-625. New York: Plenum, 1983.

[60] Veevers, J. J. "Tectonic-Climatic Supercycle in the Billion-Year Plate-Tectonic Eon: Permian Pangean Icehouse Alternates with Cretaceous Dispersed-Continents Greenhouse. *Sedimentary Geology* 68 (1990): 1-16.

[61] Vermeij, G. J. "Gastropod Evolution and Morphological Diversity in Relation to Shell Geometry." *Journal of Zoology London* 163 (1971): 15-23.

[62] Vermeij, G. J. "Biological Versatility and Earth History." *PNAS* 70 (1973): 1936-1938.

[63] Vermeij, G. J. "Evolution and Distribution of Left-Handed and Planispiral Coiling in Snails." *Nature* 254 (1975): 419-420.

[64] Vermeij, G. J. "The Mesozoic Marine Revolution: Evidence from Snails, Predators and Grazers." *Paleobiology* 3 (1977): 245-258.

[65] Vermeij, G. J. *Evolution and Escalation: An Ecological History of Life*. Princeton, NJ: Princeton University Press, 1987.

[66] Vermeij, G. J. "Inequality and the Directionality of History." *American Naturalist* 153 (1999): 243-253.

[67] Vermeij, G. J. "The Geography of Evolutionary Opportunity: Hypothesis and Two Cases in Gastropods." *Integrative and Comparative Biology* 42 (2002): 935-940.

[68] Vermeij, G. J. *Nature: An Economic History*. Princeton, NJ: Princeton University Press, 2004a.

[69] Vermeij, G. J. "Ecological Avalanches and the Two Kinds of Extinction." *Evolutionary Ecology Research* 6 (2004b): 315-337.

[70] Vermeij, G. J. "Historical Contingency and the Purported Uniqueness of Evolutionary Innovations." *PNAS* 103 (2006): 1804-1809.

[71] Vermeij, G. J. "The Ecology of Invasion: Acquisition and Loss of the Siphonal Canal in Gastropods." *Paleobiology* 33 (2007): 469-493.

[72] Vermeij, G. J. "Comparative Economics: Evolution and the Modern Economy." *J. Bioeconomics*. (2008).

[73] Vermeij, G. J. and D. R. Lindberg. "Delayed Herbivory and the Assembly of Marine Benthic Ecosystems." *Paleobiology* 26 (2000): 419-430.

[74] Vrba, E. S. "Evolution, Species and Fossils: How Does Life Evolve?" *South African Journal of Science* 76 (1980): 61-84.

[75] Vrba, E. S. "Macroevolutionary Trends: New Perspectives on the Roles of Adaptation and Incidental Effect." *Science* 221 (1983): 387-389.

[76] Vrba, E. S., and N. Eldredge. "Individuals, Hierarchies and Processes: Towards a More Complete Evolutionary Theory." *Paleobiology* 10 (1984): 146-171.

[77] Vrba, E. S., and S. J. Gould. "The Hierarchical Expansion of Sorting and Selection: Sorting and Selection Cannot be Equated." *Paleobiology* 12 (1986): 217-228.

[78] Wood, G. S. *The Purpose of the Past: Reflections on the Uses of History*. New York: Penguin, 2008.

[79] Worsley, T. R., D. Nance, and J. B. Moody. "Global Tectonics and Eustasy for the Past Two Billion Years." *Marine Geology* 58 (1984): 373-400.

[80] Wright, Robert. *Nonzero: The Logic of Human Destiny*. New York: Pantheon, 2000.

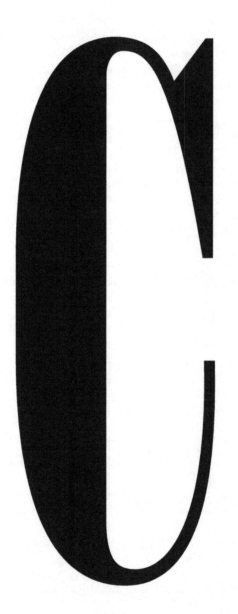

೨6

CAN THERE BE A QUANTITATIVE THEORY FOR THE HISTORY OF LIFE & SOCIETY?

Geoffrey B. West, Santa Fe Institute

MIGHT THERE BE universal laws of society analogous to those of physics and of life? This question can be addressed by identifying coarse-grained, quantitative variables for human phenomena, and placing these within a proven mathematical framework. It is assumed frequently that human intention, coupled to the purposeful human modification of the environment, renders humanity immune to this kind of atemporal, scientific analysis. On the other hand, human collectives struggle with the same basic energetic and informational needs and constraints that we observe at multiple scales of physical and biological organization. These general requirement for life, give us the confidence to attempt to include elements of human history within the framework of a quantitative, natural scientific theory.

To what extent, if any, can History be viewed as a Science? Needless to say, this begs the two fundamental questions: what is History and what is Science? I have neither the qualifications nor expertise to address the first, and, although I have been a practicing "scientist" for more than 40 years, do not feel entirely secure in addressing the second! Nevertheless, having spent much of my career in the field of high energy physics at several distinguished institutions, and now having spent a couple of extraordinary years at the Santa Fe Institute, I have learnt that such inhibitions should not stop one from expressing an opinion. I recognize that I am on dangerous territory here but would like to make some potentially provocative remarks related to these questions.

History is surely more than "just" a record or accounting of a sequence of events deemed of importance to the human experience. Time and sequential relationships play a special role, and presumably the search for a framework for revealing mechanisms and understanding is an integral part of the historical process. To this extent, history can be loosely conceived of as a science. Science implies a search for patterns and regularities that can be assembled into a rational, analytic framework based on a few "fundamental" principles that will ultimately lead to predictions that can be tested against existing data, and more importantly, against new situations typically in the form of proposed experiments. Parsimony of explanation and its relationship to elegance also play a role in what we accept as constituting a deep understanding of a problem. This is hardly the view most of us have of history, although we continually hear the phrase "history teaches us that . . ." as if history were, in some sense, a "science." Although there are presumably patterns in history, almost everything of importance is often viewed as special and dependent upon "accidental" events. History appears to be extraordinarily complex, diverse, contingent and devoid of universals and invariance — or is it? The greatest successes in science have been in areas that are relatively simple, show regularities, patterns, and "universal" behavior and are amenable to logical analyses. Is it at all conceivable that there are significant aspects of history that can be put into such a "scientific" framework?

There is yet another aspect of science that I would like to discuss before launching into how some of my own work can be viewed from this perspective, and that is the central role of mathematics. Such a discussion will expose the cracks in the scientific edifice as we gaze across the spectrum from physics and chemistry to biology and the social "sciences."

Almost 100 years ago, the eminent biologist D'Arcy Thompson began his wonderful book *On Growth and Form* by quoting Kant's observation that "chemistry . . . was a science but not Science . . . for that the criterion of true Science lay in its relation to mathematics." Thompson discussed how there now existed a "mathematical chemistry" (thereby elevating chemistry to Science), but that biology had remained qualitative without mathematical foundations or principles, implying that it was not yet "Science"! The basic question implicit in his challenge remains unanswered: are there "universal laws of life" underlying biological phenomena that can be mathematized so that biology can be formulated as a predictive quantitative Science? Most would argue that it is very unlikely that there are yet-to-be-discovered "Newton's laws of biology" that would lead to detailed calculations of arbitrary biological phenomena to any degree of accuracy, much in the way we are able to calculate the details of planetary or satellite motion to arbitrary accuracy. Indeed, it could be convincingly argued that the very nature of most biological systems precludes such a possibility. Life very likely represents the most complex and diverse phenomenon in the Universe and, even though, and maybe because, it is constrained by natural selection, is contingent on "historical accidents." Each organism, each subsystem, evolved in its own unique environmental niche in interaction with every other system or organism. Furthermore, even the tiniest organism contains an incredible number of variables, constituents and degrees of freedom. Viewed from a "simple" Newtonian viewpoint, it all seems totally mind-boggling.

~291~

I want to ask what might seem to be an even more ambitious question, "might there be universal laws of society analogous to those of physics and of life?" The study of society typically involves the identification of critical events unraveling over the course of time, these events constituting a cumulative, historical account for a pattern we deem interesting. In some fundamental way, history provides a complementary explanation to regular, or law-like processes, as history typically explains patterns in terms of chance events rather than necessary dynamics. Of course, reality represents a complex interweaving of both chance and necessity, and the role of complexity science can be seen to be engaged in the difficult task of isolating each of these factors and weighing their respective contributions to the present.

A critical conjecture in this undertaking is that the generic coarse-grained, or average, behavior of such systems, such as their dynamical structure or organization, obeys quantifiable universal laws that capture their essential features. This view presumes that at every organizational level average idealized systems can be constructed whose properties are "calculable." These provide a "zero'th order" point of departure for quantitatively understanding real systems which can be viewed as variations around idealized norms due to local environmental conditions or historical divergence during evolution as a result of essential contingencies.

~292~

This approach is familiar in physics. For example, classic kinetic theory developed in the nineteenth century is based on the idea that generic features of gases, such as the ideal gas law, can be understood by assuming atoms to be structureless "billiard balls" undergoing elastic collisions. Despite such gross simplifications, the theory captures many essential features of gases and spectacularly predicts many of their coarse-grained properties. Furthermore, this highly simplified theory acted as a starting point for modern sophisticated treatments incorporating structure, inelasticity, quantum mechanics, etc, which allow greater detail to be calculated. Other examples include the quark model of elementary particles and theories describing the evolution of the Universe from the Big Bang. Although the shortcomings of such theories are well-recognized, they quantitatively predict and explain an extraordinary body of data because they do indeed capture much of the essential physics.

When it comes to social phenomena, we would never be so naive as to approximate individuals as billiard balls, but it might be possible as a first working hypothesis in attempting to construct an initial "zeroth order, coarse-grained" theory, to assume that all people are essentially the same. This, of course, is in immediate violation of "traditional" history where the role of special individuals appears paramount. In this context we could imagine asking "coarse-grained" questions like did it actually matter that a specific man named George Washington existed at the end of the eighteenth century in determining how America has evolved into the early twenty-first century, or was there an inevitable dynamic at play and America would actually be pretty much the same. In any case, within this paradigm we can choose levels above the individual—groups, villages, and cities for example, and ask whether at these more inclusive levels, we might not hope to observe some average property that does not depend in crucial ways on the complexities of individual psychology and the accumulation of unpredictable, historical events.

Let me briefly review some ideas in biology that are possibly relevant to this discussion and then extend them to social organizations and the role of growth, decay and innovation. Living organisms span a mass range of over 21 orders of magnitude from the smallest microbe (10^{-13} g) to the largest mammals and plants (> 10^8 g). Overall, the life process covers over 30 orders of magnitude from the molecules of the genetic code and metabolic process up to whales and sequoias. This vast range exceeds that of the Earth's mass relative to the galaxy's (which is "only" 18 orders of magnitude) and is comparable to an electron relative to a cat. Similarly, the metabolic power required to support life over this range spans over 21 orders of magnitude, greater than the Planck (or string) unification scale (10^{19} GeV) relative to the mass-energy of a proton (1GeV). Over this immense spectrum, life uses basically the same chemical constituents and reactions to create an amazing variety of forms, functions, and dynamical behaviors. All life functions by transforming energy from physical or chemical sources into organic molecules that are metabolized to do the work of building, maintaining, and reproducing complex, highly organized systems. Understanding the origins, structures, and dynamics of living systems from molecules to ecosystems is one of the grand challenges of modern science.

Despite its extraordinary complexity and diversity, many of life's most fundamental and complex phenomena scale with size in a surprisingly simple fashion. Typically some trait or physiological variable, Y, scales with mass, M, as a simple power law, $Y = Y_0 M^b$; e.g., metabolic rate scales as $\sim M^{3/4}$ over an astonishing 27 orders of magnitude from complex molecules up to blue whales. Of even greater significance, the exponents, b, invariably approximate simple multiples of ¼ for almost any quantity including metabolic rate, lifespan, growth rate, heart rate, DNA nucleotide substitution rates, lengths of aortas and genomes, heights of trees, cerebral grey matter, mitochondrial densities, RNA concentrations and many others. Thus, in a very real way, a whale is a blown-up elephant, which is a scaled up gorilla which is a scaled up human which is a scaled up rat, despite their obvious superficial differences!

It is compelling to view the ubiquity of these empirical "laws" as reflecting underlying general principles, independent of the specific evolved design, that constrain the function, structure and organization of much of life across all scales and all systems. Working with the biologists James Brown and Brian Enquist, I suggested that these scaling laws are a manifestation of the "universal" geometric, mathematical, physical properties of fractal-like hierarchical branching networks that have evolved by natural selection for solving the problem of efficient distribution of energy, resources and information in multi-level, multi-component complex systems. Some of us have suggested that at all levels of biological organization from the intra-cellular to the multi-cellular life is sustained by optimized, space-filling, hierarchical networks, whose terminal units are invariant. By expressing these general principles in a mathematical language we constructed a general quantitative, predictive theory that captures the essential, coarse-grained, features of many diverse biological systems. The theory was able to address questions like: how many RNA molecules or mitochondria are there, on average, in a cell? Why do we stop growing and what weight do we reach? Why do we live ~100 years, and not a million or a few months, and how is this derived from molecular scales? What are the flow rate, pulse rate, pressure, and dimensions in any vessel of any circulatory system? Why do we sleep eight hours a day and not two, whereas a mouse sleeps 16 and an elephant three? What are the limits on organismal size?

It is natural to attempt to extend these ideas and techniques to analogous situations in other fields where there are obvious similar hierarchical branching network systems. In some areas empirical scaling laws already exist but, in others, data have not been organized in this way. Obvious examples are river systems, where good power law scaling data exist, and urban systems, where they do not. An interesting twist in these systems is that they are two-dimensional rather than three. The main aim here is to determine whether the existence of power law behavior reflects fundamental principles controlling the underlying dynamics and, if so, determine in detail their structure and behavior. An important question is: what are the appropriate quantities to be measured and what are the effective degrees of freedom to be used to construct models? In rivers this may be obvious but in the social context, such as urban systems or corporate structures, this is not so clear so a significant part of the investigation is data analysis to determine the appropriate degrees of freedom.

~295~

In urban systems there has been some investigation of fractal structure and attempts to measure fractal dimensions. In addition, the scaling of the frequency of towns of a given population size as a function of its population ranking, which reveals an approximate Zipf-type power law with an exponent of ~ -1, is well known. We have extended such studies and performed an extensive analysis of urban data to obtain a taxonomy of urban scaling laws. These include transport and communication networks, distributions of various resources and properties among urban residents, demographic growth rates, patent production, and so on, with the view to revealing a common universal behavior and underlying principles of urban evolution. Of particular interest are data on measures of fundamentally social quantities that have no simple analog in biology, such as number of patents and inventors, crime rates, number of hospitals and laundries, etc. Remarkably, we find that, to a large extent, New York is a scaled up Detroit, which is a scaled up Boise, which is a scaled up Santa Fe, and so on; that is, *all* cities are in almost all respects scaled versions of some average idealized city. Thus, despite all the urban planning and the vagaries of history and specific environmental and geographic factors, the time evolution, the "history" of a city or settlement is to a large extent "determined" and "predictable"!

This suggests that generic properties of cities are derivable from underlying principles common to all urban systems. The theory predicts that, in contrast to biology, the pace of social life increases with size and therefore with "historical" time, in quantitative agreement with data (including the speed of walking!), and leads to a growth equation showing how major innovation cycles must be generated at a continually accelerating rate to sustain growth and avoid stagnation or collapse.

The hierarchical networks that distribute resources in settlement systems are of three different kinds, transporting matter, energy, and organizational information. Our idea is that the differences between the spatial configurations and the structures of these three networks determine the precise forms of scaling observed, as well as the aberrations and the dynamics of settlement systems. By crafting the problem in these terms, we anticipate formulating a theory of metropolization, which is threatening to change the geography of the entire world. Can we find other, perhaps more efficient, ways of distributing resources to everyone? It is remarkable that, despite the central role of cities in human development and the rich evidence at our disposal we do not presently understand, in quantitative and predictive terms, the social dynamics that make cities simultaneously the hubs of innovation, the engines of wealth creation, and the sources of much crime, pollution and disease.

The principal theme unifying the study of cities across the social sciences has been their central role in creating social change and organization, ranging from political structures, new artifacts, dynamics in the detailed fabric of human interactions, and how these affect human behavior. From the perspective of social change it is therefore natural, and even compelling, to attempt to integrate these common threads involving human interactions across multiple scales from communities and cities up to urban hierarchies.

This approach aims to build upon a rich empirical tradition of studies of innovation in cities from economics and the social sciences, by integrating it with a novel quantitative perspective inspired by strategies successfully used in physics and biology on how to bridge different levels of organization. The methods, based on scaling analyses, can potentially generate new insights into how social organization is coupled to change in, for example, urban settings. More importantly this reasoning strongly suggests that the evolution of social organizations, their growth and decay, the essential dynamics of innovation, the very pace of life, obey in a coarse-grained fashion definite laws determined by the underlying dynamics inherent in the networks of human interactions. As such the panoply of history plays itself out on a stage subject to very general laws operating over the spatial scale of the planet and the time scales of socialization.

~297~

In summary, our objectives are to identify coarse-grained, quantitative variables for human phenomena, and place these within a proven mathematical framework. We do this in order to generate non-trivial insights and predictions. It is assumed frequently that human intention, coupled to the purposeful human modification of the environment, renders humanity immune to this kind of atemporal, scientific analysis. On the other hand, human collectives struggle with the same basic energetic and informational needs and constraints that we observe at multiple scales of physical and biological organization. These general requirement for life, give us the confidence to attempt to include elements of human history, within the framework of a quantitative, natural scientific theory. ❧

INDEX

A

Acemoglu, Daron 182
Action Committee for the United
    States of Europe 78
actualism 40
Adams, Douglas 4, 63
Adams, Henry 62, 63, 70
Adams, James Truslow 134
Adams, Robert 34
adaptive radiation 152–153, 227
Aeschylus 41
Africa
    early appearance of *Homo sapiens
        sapiens* 152
    early human creativity 27
    exodus from, circa 100,000 BP
        152
    lactose tolerance in herder popu-
        lations 154
    Napoleon in Africa 64
agriculture 33, 164, 185
    domestication of 43
    emergence of 27, 153–154
Agulhon, Maurice 180
Alexander I 60
Allen, Robert 185, 188
Amerindians 153, 169
    decline of population 160
Angel of the Odd, The (Edgar Allen
    Poe) 131
Annales school of history 236
Appleby, Joyce 17
arbitrary present 118–119, 121, 124,
    126, 131, 142
Argon 40 19
Aristotle 41
arrow of biological evolution 282
arrow of time 273, 280
Aryan people 106
    Gobeineau on Aryan creativity 107
    homeland 106
    Renan on differences between
        Aryans and Semites 108
asabiya 256
Australopithecines 226
autonomy 145, 146

B

Bach, J.S. 142
Bacon, Roger 16
Bagnall, Roger 253
Bahn, Paul 13, 19
Barker, Pat 61
Battle of Borodino 57
Becquerel, Henri 18
Bede, Venerable 41
Bellwood, Peter 33
Bengal Delta 182–183
Beringia 153
Berlin, Isaiah 61, 63, 270, 271
    on historical explanation 270
Beyerchen, Alan 63
Big Bang
    dating 21
Big History 40, 43, 47, 101, 103, 146,
        205, 210
    and academic terminology 207
    and the future of humanity 206,
        220, 227
Bigstoryan 6, 262
biological evolution
    arrow of 282
    evolution of human cultural het-
        erogeneity over the long haul
        (figure) 161
    rise of human beings 226
biomarkers 42
Biran, Michael 32
Black Death 81, 159
black holes 216
Black-Scholes equation 132, 137

Boas, Franz 93
Boeckh, P.A. 104, 110
Bonaparte, Napoleon 57, 60, 66, 243
   Tolstoy on 59, 64, 243
Bopp, Franz 106
Borges, Jorge Luis 75
Borodino, Battle of 68
Bowles, Samuel 86
Brahe, Tycho 123–124
Braudel, FeRNAnd 31, 119
Bray, Francesca 176
Brinton, Crane 178
Brodie, BeRNArd 61
Brown, James 294
Brush, Stephen G. 191
Bryan, William Jennings 78
bubonic plague 159
Buck, John L 186
Buffalo Bill 79
Buffon, Comte de (Georges-Louis
   Leclerc) 13–14, 18
Burgess Shale 48

C

Campbell, Cameron 186
Carlyle, Thomas 78
Carneiro, Robert 90, 93, 95, 229
Carroll, Joseph, on the unification of
   science and literature 112
Cerman, Markus 188
Chaisson, Eric. See also Cosmic
   Evolution: The Rise of
   Complexity in Nature 24, 205,
   215–219, 222
chance events 75, 266, 291
   tyranny of the individual chance
   event 79
chaos 63
   microchaos of molecular motions
   243
   as ascendant view in latter twentieth century 266
Chaos Theory 57, 63
China 166–168, 179–180, 183, 186, 191
   cultural diversification in 155
   Population dynamics and sociopolitical instability in China
   from the Qin unification
   to the period of Three
   Kingdoms (figure) 249

Secular Cycles in Europe and
   China During the Last
   Millennium Compared to
   Global Economy Processes
   (figure) 249
shortage of marriagable women 186
unification of 244
Yangzi Delta 182, 184–186
Chinggis Khan 32
Christian, David 7, 11, 151, 205
chronological present, the 118
Chronology of Ancient Kingdoms
   Amended, The (Isaac
   Newton) 117–118
Chronometric Revolution 17–18
   history after 21
Cisne, J.L. 41, 42
clade
   defined 48, 267
   fossil clades 43
Clark, Grahame 15
Clark, Gregory 272
Clausewitz, Carl von 57–58, 60, 62–63,
   66–67, 70, 235
   on battle 58
cliodynamics, defined 235
Cliodynamics: The JouRNAl of
   Quantitative History and
   Cultural Evolution vi, 99
coarse-graining 137, 147
   and neckties 75
   defined 132
   in evolutionary biology 138
   utility of 137
coevolution 145
Cold War 61
collective learning 28, 30, 35
Collingwood, R.G. 16–17, 21, 25, 31
competition 144–145
   competitive dominance 275
   hermit crabs 279
complexity 125, 228
   building blocks 210–212
   candidates for increasing 143–144
   cultural complexity 214
      regression 96
   definition 74, 211
   effective complexity 74
   human-constructed 219, 230
   importance of sequencing 211

~300~

levels of 213–214
originates in the regularities that
are consequences of frozen
accidents 77
regularities 74, 82, 85–86, 126
and human future 86
and individuality 96
discarded by anthropologists 93
in human history 85
scales with size 293
sequencing 211
social complexity 95
types of complexity 213, 214
what gives rise to complexity? 75
complexity science
accelerating human control over
biospheric resources 26
as a uinifying theme for an
expanded view of history 24
engaged with chance and necessity
291
increasing energy flows 25
Confucius 156
Confucian heritage in Japan 192
Copernicus, Nicolaus 4
cornets 39, 47
Cosmic Background Radiation
discovery of 18
*Cosmic Evolution: the Rise of Complexity
in Nature*, (See also Chaisson,
Eric) 205, 215
Crafts, N.F.R. 182
critical events 127, 129, 291
Crow, John A. 134
"crude look at the whole" 5, 86
cultural diversification 154
cultural homogenization 155
Curie, Marie 18
Curie, Pierre 18

D

dark matter 24, 216
Darnton, Robert 254
Darwin, Charles 17, 29, 46, 51, 67, 126,
240–241
Darwinians 14
Darwinism 6
Origin of Species, The 5
Darwinian selection 125, 170
dating techniques

Carbon 14 20
dendrochronology 20
genetic dating techniques 20
Potassium/Argon dating 19
radiometric dating 17
Dawkins, Richard 24, 139
DeCamp, David 87
DeVries, Jan 185
Diamond, Jared 136, 151, 190, 272
Diaz, Porifirio 179
DNA 142
building blocks of 211
discovery of genetic role of 18
domestication of animals 43, 154
Douglass, A.E. 20
Doyle, Arthur Conan 127

E

Earth
first accurate date for the formation
of 20
habitable planet 224, 225
mass relative to the galaxy 293
ecological knowledge
economics
economic theory of history 272
effective degrees of freedom 138–139
Einstein, Albert 126
Eldredge, Niles 47
electron spin resonance 19
*Elementary Aspects of Peasant Insurgency
in India* (Ranajit Guha) 179
Eley, Geoff 197
Elton, Charles 241
emergence of life 206
end-Permian mass extinction 44, 48
Enquist, Brian 294
entailogram 97
entropy 144
Epic of America, The; by James Truslow
Adams 134
Epic of Latin America, The; by John A.
Crow 134
Epstein, S.R. 188
Erwin, Douglas 7, 39
Esperanto 157
"Essay on the Inequality of Races" by
Joseph Arthur de Gobineau 107
estimates of world population 80–81

Euripides 41
evolutionary sequence 93, 98
Evolutionary Synthesis 51
extensive variables (EV) 134

F

Ferdinand, Archduke Franz 129
Ferguson, Niall 77
First InteRNAtional Congress of
   Historians 15
Fischer, Alfred 261–262
Flannery, Tim 27
fossils 42, 44, 49
Fourier's law of heat conduction
   132, 137
free energy rate density 24, 216
French Revolution 14
Friedman, Milton 195–196
frozen accidents 75, 77, 142, 146,
   190–192
Future of Science, The (Ernst Renan)
   103

G

Gaddis, John 7, 57, 235
Gaia hypothesis 225– 226
Gaitan, Jorge Eliécer
   assassination of 180
Galton, Sir Francis 89
Gamble, Clive 30
Garden of Forking Paths, The (Jorge
   Luis Borges) 75
Gaussian distribution 137
Geer, Baron Gerard de 20
Gell-Mann, Murray 5, 7, 73, 190,
   220, 248
*General History of Nature and Theory
   of the Heavens* (Immanuel
   Kant) 15
genetic dating techniques 20
genetic mutations and lactose toler-
   ance in humans 154
Genghis Khan 32
Gibbon, Edward 133
Gilman, S.L. 41
Glaze, F.E. 41
Gliddon, George 108
global marine diversity 43
Gobineau, Arthur de 107–109

Goldilocks principle, the 205,
   208–210, 221–226, 230
Goldstone, Jack 178, 182
Goodfield, June 15
Gorbachev, Mikhail 61
Gould, Stephen Jay 48, 138, 266
Grand Unified Story 35
Grand Unified Theory of History
   35
Great Plague of London 83
Grimm brothers 110
Guha, Ranajit 179
Guns, Germs, and Steel (See also
   Jared Diamond) 136, 190
Guttman, Louis 87
   Guttman scaling 87
Guttman scale 73, 88–89, 93, 95–97
   Guttman's questionnaire 87
   linguistic example 87

H

Han Dynasty 23
Harpham, Geoffrey 7, 101, 111
Hartwell, R.M. 182
Hayles, N. Katherine 63
hedgehogs 63
Hegel, Georg Wilhelm Friedrich 15
Heller, Joseph 61
Herder, Johann Gottfried 15
hermit crabs 279
Herodotus 139
heterogeneity
   evolution of human cultural het-
      erogeneity 161
   Evolution of human cultural het-
      erogeneity 161
hierarchical theory of selection 138
historical accidents 291
Historical Dynamics (jouRNAl) 253
history
   alteRNAtive possible histories 75,
      79
   as model for solving ethical prob-
      lems 175
   capacious definition 3
   different from natural sciences
      236–237
   directionality in 282
   economic theory of 272

explains patterns in terms of
chance events 291
good timelines 12
historians occupy a different
universe 17
historical accident 76
historical sciences
physicists' assertion that
historical sciences are not
predictive 39
narrative history
essence of 122
no history without memory 141
not "just one damn thing after
another" 254
of the universe 75
patterns in 263
time series data 120
viewed as a science 289–290
History of Mexico, The (Burton
Kirkwood) 120
*History of the Decline and Fall of the
Roman Empire, The* (Edward
Gibbon) 133
Hitchhiker's Guide to the Galaxy, The
(Douglas Adams) 4
Holmes, Sherlock 129
Homer 61, 104–105
homogenization
cultural homogeneity 162
limits 157
religious 157
Houssaye, Henri 15–16
Hubble, Edwin 20
Hubble constant 20
Human Relations Area Files 89
Human Web, The (J.R. McNeill) 151
Humboldt brothers 110
Hunt, Lynn 17
Hutton, James 14
Huxley, Julian 241

I

Ice Age 152, 160
*Ideas towards a Philosophy of the History
of Man* (Johann Herder) 15
Iggers, Georg 17
Iliad, The (Homer) 104
Incas 244

Inca quipu, early writing system
33
traits of 90
index of cultural accumulation 95
Indo-European languages 106–107
intensive variable (IV) 133
Introduction to the Study of History
(Charles Victor Langlois and
Charles Seignobos) 16
*Introduction to the Study of History
of 1898* (Langlois and
Seignobos) 16
inverse square law 124
Islam 84, 165

J

Jacob, Margaret 17
Jamaican Creole 87
Jiang Taixin 186
Jing Su 186
Jones, Eric 182

K

Kaiser Wilhelm II 79
Kamminga, Johan 33
Kant, Immanuel 15
on importance of mathematics to
science 290
Kapitsa, Pyotr 80
Kapitsa, Sergei Petrovich 80
Kelvin, Lord, William Thomson 14,
18–19
Kennan, George F. 60–61
Kennedy, Paul 99
Kepler, Johannes 123–124
Keynes, Maynard 32
Khaldun, Ibn 16, 256
Kingsland, Sharon 241
Kirkwood, Burton 120
Kissinger, Henry 61
Kolmogorov, Andrey 126
Krakauer, David 3, 7, 40, 101, 103,
105, 112–113, 117, 132, 179
Kroeber, A.L. 95
Kutuzov, Mikhail 60

L

La Brea tar pits 49

lactose tolerance development in humans 154
Langlois, Charles Victor 16
languages
  linguistic families 107
languages (See also Philology) 157
  Amerindian 169
  Amerindians 153
  Esperanto 157
  Inca quipu, wriitng system 33
  Jamaican Creole 87
  !Kung San 29
  Latin's impact on other languages 158
  Semitic languages 108, 109, 110
  "Turanian" linguistic families 107
  vanishing of 160
larch budmoth 242
Leclerc, Georges-Louis, Comte de Buffon 13, 14, 18
Lectures on the Science of Language (Max Müller) 106
Lee, James 186
Lee, Richard 29, 30
Lewontin, Richard 266
Libby, Willard F. 19, 20
Li, Bozhong 185
Liddell-Hart, B.H. 61
Linnaeus, Carl 46
  Linnean taxonomic hierarchy 44
Liu, Ts'ui-jung 186
Li, Wenzhi 186
logical depth 127
longevity, states 167
longue durée 31
Louis XIV 64
Louis XVIII 65
Lourandos, Harry 33
Lovelock, James 225
Lubbock, John 15
Luo Lun 186

M

macroevolution 267–268
Ma, Debin 186
Madero, Francisco 179
Mahathera, Narada 13
Manhattan Project 19
Mao Zedong 23

Marchetti, Cesare 79–80, 82–84
  clockwork geniuses 84
Margadant, Ted 180
Marx, Karl 15, 180
Massimo, Livi-Bacci 27
mass range of living organisms 293
mathematics
  central role in science 290
  mathematical chemistry 291
  nonlinear mathematics 62
McNeill, John R. 8, 151
McNeill, William H. 18, 236, 265
mega-empires 244–245
Mehta, Ved 16
Mendel, Gregor 126
Merriman, John 180
metahistory 101, 103, 146
  and philology 105, 112
  defined 6
  distinct from Big History 146
  "The Quest for Patterns in Metahistory" (David Krakauer) 101
military conquests
  and the development of culture 156
Mingfang, Xia 190
minimality 145
Modeling Nature (Sharon Kingsland) 241
Modern Synthesis 51
Mommsen, Theodor 110
Monnet, Jean 78
Moore, Barrington 178
Moore, Gordon 81
Moore's Law 81
Morgan, Morgan 93
morphologic similarity 46
Morris, Conway 282
Mozart, Wolfgang Amadeus 84
Mughal Empire 165
Müller, Max 106–109
Mulvaney, John 33
Murdock, George Peter 89
Musil, Robert vii
mutation-selection ratios 145

N

Namier, Lewis 133
Napoléon Bonaparte 57–66, 78, 243

Naroll, Raoul 95
natural selection 125–126
  ahistorical process in biological
    history 125
Net Primary Productivity 26
neutral theory 269
  creation of 125
Newton, Isaac 75, 113, 117–118,
    122–124, 126, 291
  Hypotheses non fingo 123
  law of gravity 69
  modes of historical explanation
    119
North, Douglass 182
Nott, Josiah 108

O

Oakeshott, Michael 113
Oakley, Annie 79
O'Brian, Patrick 61
Odyssey, Homer 104
Ogilvie, Sheilagh 188
On Growth and Form (D'Arcy
    Thompson) 290
On War (Carl von Clausewitz) 57, 61
Opabinia regalis 48
Origin of Species, The (Charles
    Darwin) 5, 46, 50
Osamu, Saito 188
Ottoman Empire 165
*Our Times, the United States 1900-1925:
    The Turn of the Century* (Mark
    Sullivan) 78

P

Paleolithic era 27, 30, 161
Palermo stone 12
Pareto principle 85
Pareto, Vilfredo 85
  Pareto's power law 85
Parsons, Talcott 208
Pasteur, Louis 240
pathogens
  sharing of collective pathogen
    load 162
Patterson, Clair 19
"Perspectives on History" (magazine)
    236

Pevear, Richard 57, 63
Phenomenology 123
philology 103–109, 111–112
  history of 110
  most capacious discipline 105
*Philosophiae Naturalis Principia
    Mathematica* (Isaac Newton)
    118, 122
Planck, Max 102
  Planck unification scale 293
Pliny the Elder 41
Poe, Edgar Allen 131
Poincaré, Henri 62
Polybius 16
Pomeranz, Kenneth 8, 182,–187, 272
Popper, Karl 236–240, 265, 270–271
Positivism 123
Poverty of Historicism, The (Karl
    Popper) 238
power laws 85
  Pareto principle 85
  Zipf-type power law 295
Prak, Maarten 188
prediction 235,–238
  cities 296
  not limited to forecasting the
    future 238
  predictive history
    the need for 237
  scientific 238
predictive science 238, 291
  and religious conversion 251
  biology as a 240
  Linked population-instability
    oscillations predicted by
    a demographic-structural
    model (table) 247
Prehistoric Times (John Lubbock) 15
Prescott, William H. 119, 120
Princip, Gavrilo 129
Prodromus (Nils Steensen) 13
"pull of the recent" 44
Pursuit of Power, The (Wiliam H.
    McNeill) 265
Putnam, Robert 256

Q

Qing Dynasty 23, 156, 165–166, 187, 189
quarks 212

R

radiation
  "adaptive radiation" 152, 227
  and stars 206–207, 209, 220–222
radiocarbon dating 19
radiometric dating 19
randomness 74, 126, 263
  and regularity 63, 70
Ranke, Leopold von 12
rarefaction, defined 45
Rashevsky, Nicholas 254
religion
  Buddhism 165
  Christianity 12, 165, 252– 253
  Christian Reconquista in Spain 254
  divinity and the biological "arrow"
    of evolution 282
  dynamics of religious conversion
    252
  Islam 251, 252
  religious conversion 251–252
  religious homogenization 157
  survival traits 169
Renan, Ernest 103–110
Renfrew and Bahn 13, 19
Renfrew, Colin 13, 19, 31, 34
retrodiction 8, 239
Roberts, Neil 19
Romanov state 165
Rostow, W.W. 182
Russell, Bertrand 118
Rutherford, Ernest 18

S

saber-toothed cats 49
Santa Fe Institute 5, 73–74, 84,
    101–102, 198
scaling laws 294
  and sleep 294
  cities 296–297
Scarre, Chris 27
Schlegel, Friedrich 110

scientific prediction
  defined 238
  relation to the future 239
  retrodiction 239
secular cycles 246
sedentary state, rise of 164
Seignobos, Charles 16
selfish gene 139
Semitic culture 107–109
  Renan's work 109
Sepkoski, J.J., Jr. 44–45
Service, Elman 93
Shakers 169
Shaw, George BeRNArd 78
Simmons, I.G. 26
Simpson, G. G. 266
Skinner, G. William 185
Skocpol, Theda 178
Smail, Dan 12
Smil, Vaclav 26
Smith, William 14
Snow, C.P. 102
solar radiation 207
Solow, Bob 86
Some Estimated Free Energy Rate
    Densities (table) 216
Sophocles 41
Spanish Civil War, The (Hugh
    Thomas) 136
Spengler, Oswald 113
Spier, Fred 8, 205
Stages of Growth, The (W.W. Rostow)
    182
Stalin, Josef 32
Stark, Rodney 253
stars
  development of 206, 209, 222–223
  stellar enlargement 207
states
  immigration and adaptability 168
  longevity of 167
St. Augustine 16
Steensen, Nils 13
  Prodromus 13
Steno 13
steppe frontier 245
Study in Scarlet, A. (Sherlock Holmes)
    127
Suess, Hans 20
Sullivan, Mark 78

Sun-Tzu 61

T

Taleb, Nassim Nicholas 238
telescoping bureaucracy, theory
 of 144
Temkin, I. 47
Thales of Miletus 118
thermoluminescence dating 19
Third Reich 110
Thomas, Hugh 136
Thompson, D'Arcy 290
Thomson, William (Lord Kelvin) 14,
 18, 19
Thucydides 61, 166
Tilly, Charles 179, 181
time series 119–122, 126–127, 134
Toba Catastrophe 159, 161
Tolstoy, Leo 57, 61–64, 67, 69,–70,
 235, 243
 on Borodino 59
 on law 62
 theory of history 63
 thoughts as basis for a science of
 history 69
Tomasello, Michael 28
Toulmin, Stephen 15
Toynbee, Arnold 16, 84, 99, 235
Trevor-Roper, Hugh 16
Turchin, Peter 8, 32, 84, 99, 235
Tutankhamun 147
Tylor, E.B. 89, 93
Types of Mankind (Josiah Nott) 108

U

uniformitarianism 40
universal laws
 of society 291
uranium 19, 32

V

Van Zanden, Jan Luiten 185
varve analysis 20
Verhulst-Pearl logistic equation for
 population growth 41
Vermeij, Geerat 8, 50, 261
Very Big History 4, 5

vitalism, in biology 240
"volcanic" winter 27, 159
Volokhonsky, Larissa 57, 63
Volterra, Vito 241

W

Wang Feng 186
War and Peace (Leo Tolstoy) 57, 61,
 63, 67, 69–70, 243
Washington, George 293
Watson, Adam 158
Weingast, Barry 182
West, Geoffrey 8, 241, 248, 289
What If? I and *II* (Niall Ferguson)
 77
whiskey, study of history second
 only to 16
White, Douglas 89, 97
White Lotus Society, the 179
Wilson, E.O. 22
Wolf, F.A. 105
Wonderful Life (Stephen Jay Gould)
 48
Wood, Gordon 272
World War I
 cause of 129
 Kaiser Wilhelm and Annie Oakley
 79
World War II
 Guttman scaling 87
Wright, Robert 282

X

Xue ,Yong 185

Z

Zhang Peiguo 186
Zipf-type power law 295
Zweite, Wilhelm der 79

DAVID C. KRAKAUER is the President and William H. Miller Professor of Complex Systems at the Santa Fe Institute. An evolutionary biologist by training, he served as the founding director of the Wisconsin Institute for Discovery and currently co-directs the Collective Computation Group.

JOHN LEWIS GADDIS is the Robert A. Lovett Professor of Military and Naval History at Yale University. He is the author of *The Cold War: A New History*, *The Landscape of History*, and *George F. Kennan: An American Life*, which won the Pulitzer Prize.

KENNETH POMERANZ is the University Professor of History at the University of Chicago and the author of *The Great Divergence: China, Europe, and the Making of the Modern World Economy*. He is a former fellow of the Institute for Advanced Studies in Princeton and former president of the American Historical Association.

THE SANTA FE INSTITUTE PRESS

The SFI Press endeavors to communicate the best of complexity science and to capture a sense of the diversity, range, breadth, excitement, and ambition of research at the Santa Fe Institute. To provide a distillation of discussions, debates, and meetings across a range of influential and nascent topics.

To change the way we think.

SEMINAR SERIES

New findings emerging from the Institute's ongoing working groups and research projects, for an audience of interdisciplinary scholars and practitioners.

ARCHIVE SERIES

Fresh editions of classic texts from the complexity canon, spanning the Institute's thirty years advancing the field.

COMPASS SERIES

Provoking, exploratory volumes aiming to build complexity literacy in the humanities, industry, and the curious public.

COLOPHON

Body copy for this book was set in Cochin, a typeface produced in 1912 by Georges Peignot for the Paris foundry G. Peignot et Fils and based on the copperplate engravings of French 17th century artist Nicolas Cochin, for whom the typeface is named.

The SFI Press complexity glyphs used throughout the book were created by Brian Crandall Williams.

SFI PRESS
COMPLEXITY
GLYPHS

ZERO

ONE

TWO

THREE

FOUR

FIVE

SIX

SEVEN

EIGHT

NINE

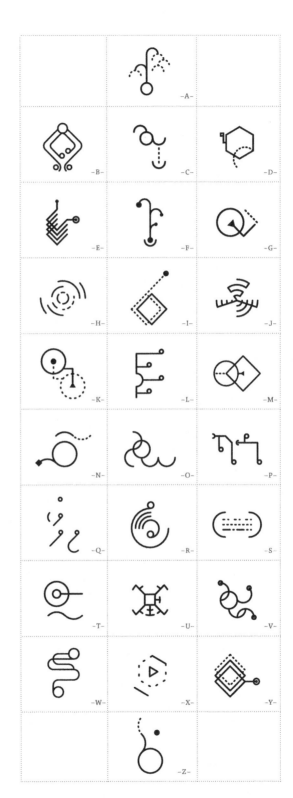

SEMINAR SERIES

Made in the USA
Las Vegas, NV
07 October 2022

56683370R00194